Good Housekeeping

IN ASSOCIATION WITH THE
ROYAL COLLEGE OF GENERAL PRACTITIONERS

eat well
stay well

Good Housekeeping

IN ASSOCIATION WITH THE
ROYAL COLLEGE OF GENERAL PRACTITIONERS

eat well
stay well

ALL YOU NEED TO KNOW ABOUT HEALTHY EATING
WITH OVER 300 RECIPES

A Guide to Nutrition by Christine McFadden

Special Diets; Ailments and Diet by Dr Sarah Brewer MA MB Bchir

Recipes by Joanna Farrow, CJ Jackson, Moyra Fraser, Judy Bastyra, Annie Nichols,

The Good Housekeeping Institute

EBURY PRESS
LONDON

Dietary Notes

High-fibre = 6 grams or more of fibre per serving.
Gluten-free = suitable for those with gluten sensitivity or wheat allergy, but check products (eg mustard, stock cubes) for hidden gluten.
Low-fat = less than 5 grams of fat per serving.
Nut-free = suitable for those with a nut allergy, but check products (eg oils, spreads) for hidden nuts.
Low-cholesterol = suitable for those on a cholesterol-lowering diet.
Low-calorie = main courses under 400 calories per serving, starters under 150 calories per serving, desserts under 200 calories per serving.
Dairy produce-free = suitable for those on a dairy produce-free diet, but check products (eg breads, cereals) for hidden milk powder.
Diabetic = suitable for diabetics.

Nutritional analysis box: the sugar quantity given is the total amount of sugar found in the dish, including both intrinsic and extrinsic sugars.

Cookery Notes

■ Both metric and imperial measures are given for the recipes. Follow either metric or imperial throughout as they are not interchangeable.
■ All spoon measures are level unless otherwise stated. Sets of measuring spoons are available for accurate measurement of quantities.
■ Ovens should be preheated to the specific temperature. Grills should also be preheated. The cooking times given in the recipes assume that this has been done.
■ Where salt is used for seasoning, try to use as little as possible.

This edition published 1999
by BCA by arrangement with
Ebury Press

Text and photography © 1999 Random House UK Limited or the National Magazine Company Limited

CN 6040

Managing editor: Julia Canning
Design: Alison Shackleton
Special photography: Philip Webb
Food stylists: Maxine Clark, Louise Pickford, Moyra Fraser
Other photographs: Jean Cazals, Laurie Evans, David Gill, Christine Hanscombe, Graham Kirk, James Murphy, Philip Webb, Elizabeth Zeschin
Illustrations: Madeleine David

Recipe testing: Catherine Atkinson, Anna-lisa Aldridge, Louise Mackaness
Additional editorial assistance: Donna Wood, Louise Farman, Vicky Robinson, Chris Bernstein

Printed and bound in Slovenia by Delo Tiskarna, d.d. by arrangement with Korotan – Ljubljana, d.o.o

contents

FOREWORD

Nutrition is a fundamental issue in all our lives and the links between diet and health are well recognised. It is a key strand of preventive medicine and doctors are encouraged to advise patients about healthy eating whenever possible. Nowadays few surgeries will fail to offer a healthy eating information sheet or leaflet as part of their drive towards health promotion.

However, conflicting messages from the media and a busy lifestyle mean that this essential facet of our health is all too often overlooked. With increasing pressures in the workplace, new products that supplement or replace the substances occurring naturally in food, and a fast-food culture, our diet can easily be neglected. This book provides reassuring, easy-to-follow advice on what makes a healthy, balanced diet plus over 300 recipes to suit all tastes and all ages.

I believe that *Eat Well, Stay Well* will prove to be an informative and enjoyable guide for all of us involved on a day-to-day basis helping those with diet-related problems. For those who have to follow a special diet for medical reasons, nutritious recipes and menu suggestions are given. The book also provides information on many common ailments and how a change in diet may help prevent or alleviate them.

I am sure you will all enjoy reading this book and preparing the attractive meals that we hope will enable more of us to eat well to stay healthy.

The Royal College of General Practitioners has welcomed the opportunity of working with Good Housekeeping and Ebury Press on this unique project and I am grateful to all those who have contributed to this successful outcome.

Professor Mike Pringle FRCGP
Chairman
Royal College of General Practitioners

INTRODUCTION

Over the last few years *Good Housekeeping* has responded to the demand from people of all ages and lifestyles for healthier, lighter recipes and specific nutritional information. Too much confusing advice has caused the dilemma of what's good for you and what's not.

This ground-breaking book, *Eat Well, Stay Well,* is a guide through the maze of jargon, nutritional myths and diet fads. Clear, independent food facts and inside information are coupled with over 300 of the quickest contemporary recipes from the Good Housekeeping Institute and every one is double-tested and really works.

Many of us are advised by our doctors to follow a specific diet due to a food intolerance or a condition such as diabetes, heart trouble, obesity and food allergies. Knowing exactly what to cook and eat is explained clearly on these pages.

Of course, there's no one diet or eating style that suits everyone. As life becomes more hectic, cooking imaginative, fresh and healthy food is becoming less of a priority. But as you gather knowledge about your dietary requirements and enjoy cooking the recipes from this book, you'll notice that healthy eating has real benefits – you'll have more energy, improved resistance to disease and a greater sense of well-being – as the saying goes, you are what you eat!

A GUIDE TO NUTRITION

Cooking for health isn't only about eating the right kind of food. The way you cook, store and prepare it all have significant effects on the nutritional value. This section contains everyday tips and facts on the benefits of essential nutrients: whether you are on a special diet, coping with stress, pregnancy, feeding babies, children or teenagers, our guidelines show you how to achieve a balanced, healthy diet.

SPECIAL DIETS

Low fat, high fibre, no salt, no sugar…food grows ever more complicated for the millions of people who need to watch what they eat (and for those who have to cook for them). This section tells you what you can eat and what foods to avoid if you need a high-fibre, gluten-free, low-fat, nut-free, low-cholesterol, low-calorie, dairy produce-free or diabetic diet. (All the recipes include a note to tell you which special diet the recipe is suitable for, and there is a diet-by-diet list of recipes on page 383.)

STARTERS

With today's lighter eating style we are more likely to skip the starter and choose nibbles instead to eat with drinks before a meal. Try *Warm Split Pea Dip or Quick Hummus* (page 122), great for people on low-cholesterol diets, dairy produce-free diets and diabetics. Or choose a more substantial starter such as *Tunisian 'Mechouia' Salad* (page 138) which is beneficial to anyone on a gluten-free, low-cholesterol, low-calorie, dairy produce-free or diabetic diet!

SOUPS

More and more people say they could live on soup, and indeed it does seem to be the answer when you're too busy, or don't know what to cook, or simply don't feel like eating very much. This collection of exciting recipes demonstrates that soup, conventionally dismissed as a starter, can be both stylish and a great energy booster. Soups such as *Carrot, Parsnip and Lentil* (page 146) can give you a feeling of well-being which can help lift fatigue, whereas the elegant *Iced Asparagus and Shallot Soup* (page 149) is invigorating and ideal for the weight conscious.

FISH AND SHELLFISH

Ideally, fish should be eaten at least twice a week, especially oily fish as it contains essential omega-3 fatty acids, thought to provide protection against heart disease. Fish is also one of the few dietary sources of vitamin D, vital for calcium absorption, and offers an excellent source of iodine and protein, needed for normal growth. Choose from comforting recipes such as *Salmon Rosti Fishcakes* (page 167) to more adventurous dishes using unusual fish such as *Gremolata Swordfish with Lemon and Mint Bulghar Wheat* (page 169).

MEAT

Meat plays a very important part in our diets, and is a great source of proteins, iron and zinc that can be a great energy boost when carbohydrate and fat stores in the body are low. But keep an eye on your fat intake – animal foods tend to be high in fat. Trim fat from meat and choose lean cuts where possible. Also, try to eat more game meats such as venison and rabbit which are often lower in fat. Eat lighter protein dishes at lunchtime such as *Grilled Lemon and Herb Chicken* (page 188) or *Warm Steak Escalopes and Tomato Salad* (page 216) and a combination of protein with carbohydrates in the evening, as in *Chicken Kebabs with Tabbouleh* (page 187) or *Lamb and Rosemary Ragu* (page 211).

VEGETARIAN

Together with fruit, vegetables play a key role in our diet, as they contain a host of important vitamins and minerals which work together to protect us from disease. With the ever-increasing variety of fresh vegetables, fruit, nuts, seeds, spices and herbs, it is becoming much easier to cook a wide range of tasty, nutritious vegetarian recipes and never get bored! This section includes great main course dishes such as *Moroccan Tagine* (page 224), full on flavour and light and easy on your diet, and *Tuscan Bean Stew* (page 223) which has the advantage of including lots of beans which are incredibly filling but low in fat.

LIGHT MEALS

Light lunches or snacky suppers fit into our time-starved schedules well. But fast food is no excuse for bad eating habits or ready meals. Try *Roasted Tomato Bruschetta* (page 241) as a quick light lunch or *Baked Potatoes with Mackerel and Mustard* (page 244) for a healthy supper.

PASTA, RICE AND GRAINS

Nutritionally, pasta is comparable with other main carbohydrate-rich staples such as rice and potatoes, but has a higher protein and iron content. For a low-fat pasta dish try *Tomato and Basil Sauce with Pasta* (page 262) and if you are on a wheat-free diet, avoid pasta and try rice noodles, corn, maize, potatoes or rice dishes such as *Mixed Rice and Almond Pilaff* (page 269). In this section you will also find other grain recipes such as *Millet and Pepper Salad* (page 275) which is ideal for gluten-free, nut-free, low-cholesterol, low-calorie, dairy produce-free and diabetic diets.

VEGETABLE ACCOMPANIMENTS

The vegetable accompaniment doesn't often get the chance to shine as other more glamorous courses take centre stage. However, vegetables do play a crucial and delicious part in a balanced diet, adding fibre, vitamins and minerals especially vitamin C, vitamin A (in the form of beta-carotene), iron and calcium. Try *Sweet Roasted Fennel* (page 283) which is valued for its digestive properties and *Leek, Potato and Goat's Cheese Cakes* (page 284) which are high in beta-carotene and excellent for fighting off disease.

SALADS

A salad can be as simple or as elaborate as you like, just make sure all the ingredients you use are as fresh as possible, so you are guaranteed the optimum benefits. Sprouted beans are remarkable foods, cheap, nutritious and high in vitamin C. Herbs are best used raw to make the most of their high content of vitamins and iron, and bitter salad leaves such as chicory, watercress and baby spinach contain the largest amount of vitamins. Try *Leafy Salad with Pink Peppercorns* (page 307) for a light accompaniment or *Apple, Fennel, Ham and Pecan Salad* (page 294) for a more filling main course.

DESSERTS

Desserts can be the downfall for many people, but if you have a sweet tooth, you can't go wrong with simply serving fresh, ripe fruit. Packed with vitamins, minerals and fibre, fruit is also rich in antioxidants which are believed to reduce the risks of cancer and heart disease. However, if you are looking for a pudding to make for an everyday or special occasion there are more than 30 recipes to choose from. Try *Apple and Blackberry Snow* (page 310) at only 125 calories per serving and virtually fat free, or *Strawberry and Custard Tarts* (page 316) for a more indulgent treat. These are still low in calories and are suitable for people on a nut-free, low-calorie or diabetic diet.

BAKING

You may be surprised to find a baking section in this book as it's often considered stodgy and unhealthy. However, all the recipes we have included are good for low-fat, high fibre, low-cholesterol and diabetic diets. If you are on a wheat-free diet try *Chilli Cornbread* (page 336) or *Coconut Squares* (page 349) and if you are on a gluten-free diet and love chocolate try *Chocolate Brownies* (page 348).

AILMENTS AND DIET

This section gives information on 60 common ailments such as travel sickness, tension headaches, hayfever and fatigue to more serious illnesses such as ME, multiple sclerosis, depression and cancer. All the ailments are covered comprehensively with suggested foods and beneficial vitamins to help care for yourself.

Caroline Marson
Cookery Editor
Good Housekeeping

A GUIDE TO NUTRITION

THE ROLE OF ESSENTIAL NUTRIENTS

UNDERSTANDING THE TERMS FOR NUTRIENT INTAKE

■ The United States publishes a Recommended Daily Allowance (RDA).

■ The European Community publishes a Recommended Daily Allowance (RDA) for use as a food labelling reference.

■ The UK Department of Health uses several different terms including Estimated Average Requirement (EAR), Reference Nutrient Intake (RNI) and Lower Reference Nutrient Intake (LRNI). RNI is the amount of a nutrient that is enough for almost everybody, including people with higher needs. LRNI is the amount that is enough for people with low requirements.

■ Where there is insufficient evidence to establish an EAR, RNI or LRNI, the term 'Safe Intake' is used.

WHAT EXACTLY IS AN ESSENTIAL NUTRIENT?

Essential nutrients are classified as those that cannot be produced by the cells in our bodies and therefore must be supplied by food. A nutrient is also considered essential if it is known consistently to cure a specific deficiency disease or if it has a specific function within the body. Using these criteria, the nutrients we need to maintain health are protein, vitamins, minerals and those that supply energy, eg carbohydrates and fats. We also need oxygen from the air, and water; these are not classified as nutrients but are essential for survival.

ACHIEVING OPTIMUM HEALTH

In addition to simply maintaining health, however, most of us would probably like to achieve a state of optimum health. This is usually classified as a state of consistent physical and mental well-being, along with high levels of energy and a resilient immune system. There is now growing scientific evidence which suggests that by increasing our intake of certain nutrients we may not only increase our chances of enjoying optimum health but actually alleviate or even prevent certain diseases.

For example, a group of vitamins and minerals known as antioxidants (page 14) are widely believed to play a major role in protecting against coronary heart disease, some types of cancer and possibly many other degenerative diseases. Another group of substances called phytochemicals (page 37), found in vegetables, fruit and some beverages, though currently classified as non-nutrients, have similar protective effects. Certain enzymes (see opposite) also provide protection against disease.

HOW MUCH DO I NEED?

Unless you're an expert, it's often hard to know for sure whether you're getting the right amount of a nutrient, particularly as everyone has different requirements. Your needs for some nutrients will be higher if you smoke, drink alcohol, use certain prescription drugs, are on the pill, or if you are vegetarian (page 61), pregnant or breastfeeding (page 58).

Government nutritional experts in over forty countries publish figures for the amounts needed per day. Confusingly, the figures vary from country to country, as do the terms used to describe them, and the manner in which they are intended to be used. Some are actual recommendations, while others are simply a reference tool.

Some nutritionists feel that the UK levels are set too low, and that there is also a need to define the desirable level for optimum health. In the United States it has been suggested that the figures for this would lie somewhere between the RDA and upper safe levels.

For comparison, we have shown, where possible, both the UK and EC figures in the nutrient descriptions that follow. These refer to nutrient intake per day and are generally for the 19-50 age group. The nutritional requirements for babies and children, pregnant women, vegetarians and older people are discussed separately.

CAN I TAKE TOO MUCH?

It is tempting to take the view that if a little is good, more must be better. In some situations this is true – for example, there is strong evidence that high doses of vitamin E decrease the risk of heart disease. However, large doses of some nutrients, particularly minerals and fat-soluble vitamins such as vitamins A and D, can be detrimental to health. Though it is highly unlikely that the amount of nutrients we get from food could reach dangerous levels, people who take vitamin and mineral supplements may be putting themselves at risk. The upper safe levels for daily supplementation of vitamins and minerals are therefore included, where known, in the nutrient descriptions.

ENERGY FOODS

Without energy, we cannot survive. We need it to breathe, to grow, to pump blood around the veins and, of course, to move, to work and to exercise. The fuel that provides that energy comes mainly from carbohydrates and fats, but also from protein and alcohol.

The UK Department of Health has calculated an Estimated Average Requirement for energy (measured in kilocalories), but it is no more than an average – some people need more, others less. The actual amount depends on your age, sex, build, activity levels (see *High Energy Requirements*, page 55) and several other factors, including the climate you live in and whether or not you are pregnant or breastfeeding.

EAR FOR ENERGY	AGE	CALS/DAY
Women	19-50	1940
	51-59	1900
Men	19-59	2550

There is some evidence that a poor mix of energy-providing nutrients in the diet is a risk factor in diseases such as coronary heart disease and certain types of cancer.

The current recommendations are that we should increase the energy we get from carbohydrate and reduce the amount from fat. Carbohydrate intake should provide at least 50%, fat no more than 33–35%, protein a maximum of 15%, and alcohol a token 0.5%.

Pasta is a particularly good source of energy-providing carbohydrate.

ENZYMES

■ Enzymes are protein-like substances produced by the cells in the body. Though not a nutrient themselves, enzymes play a vital role in bodily processes. They act as a biological catalyst, and speed up a vast number of chemical reactions which would otherwise take place too slowly to sustain life within the cell.

■ Some enzymes help with digestion by breaking down large food molecules into smaller units so they can be absorbed by the body. For example, amylase, an enzyme found in saliva, reduces starch in carbohydrates (page 15) to simple sugars such as glucose or fructose.

■ Other enzymes, such as peroxidase and catalase, work in a protective way by disarming free radicals (page 14).

FREE RADICALS AND ANTIOXIDANTS

Since oxygen is part of the air that we breathe, we tend to think of it as a safe substance, but it is, in fact, a two-edged sword. We cannot survive without it, yet oxygen also harms the body, just as it can produce rust on a car. It does so by generating highly unstable, chemically reactive particles known as free radicals. These are atoms or molecules which contain an unpaired electron (a negatively charged particle of electricity). Free radicals are constantly on the lookout for another electron to make up the pair, so they wreak havoc by stealing electrons from other molecules. When they do so, the cells of the molecule under attack get damaged. Particularly vulnerable is DNA, the genetic material in the cell nucleus. If this is harmed, mutations take place which may then lead to cancer. Oxidative damage has also been linked to the onset of premature ageing, cataracts, heart disease, dementia and a whole slew of degenerative diseases.

UNDER ATTACK

We are currently exposed to a higher level of environmental sources of oxidative stress than ever before. Car exhaust fumes, ozone, cigarette smoke, pesticide residues and ultraviolet light all stimulate the production of excess free radicals, as do lifestyle factors such as smoking, alcohol, emotional stress and even strenuous exercise. Our cells are under attack from uncontrolled free radicals thousands of times a day, and the need for protection has never been greater.

THE DEFENDERS

Fortunately we have a bodyguard in the form of a powerful group of vitamins, minerals and other substances, collectively known as antioxidants. As the name suggests, they protect the cells from the harmful effects of oxidation. They shore up the body's natural enzymic defence system, and they act as scavengers, mopping up and neutralising free radicals on the rampage in the body.

The main antioxidants include beta-carotene, vitamin C and vitamin E; the minerals selenium, zinc, copper and manganese which work with protective enzymes (page 13); and an amino acid complex called glutathione. Equally important are the less well-known carotenoids such as alpha-carotene, lycopene and lutein (page 37). Vegetables, fruits and grains, now the superstars of the nutritional world, contain high levels of antioxidants, and it has been demonstrated over and over again that a diet rich in these foods offers powerful protection against disease.

CARBOHYDRATES

Carbohydrates, derived solely from plant foods, are a major source of energy in the diet. They are vitally important to health because they not only provide fuel, but they are low in fat and therefore decrease the risk of some diseases. They also provide nutritional extras such as vitamins and minerals.

Carbohydrates are often confused with calories (or kilocalories as they are more properly known) as both are concerned with energy. It's easier to understand the difference if you think of a calorie as a measurement of energy, and carbohydrate as the nutrient that provides it.

HOW MUCH DO I NEED?

The current advice suggests that at least 50% of our daily energy needs come from carbohydrates. But what does this mean in real terms? If we take as an example a 19-50 year-old woman with an energy requirement of 1940 calories, 50% would be 970 calories. Divide this by 3.75 (the number of calories in a gram of carbohydrate) and we have a figure of 258 grams of carbohydrate (1940÷2=970÷3.75=258). In terms of food, this is the equivalent of a bowl of muesli, a banana, a large serving of brown rice, a baked potato AND three slices of wholemeal bread – probably quite a lot more than we're used to.

SUGARS

There are two main groups of carbohydrates: simple sugars and complex starches. Simple sugars include glucose and fructose, found in fruit and vegetables; sucrose (table sugar), found in sugar cane, beets and some fruits and root vegetables; and lactose, found only in milk. With the exception of lactose, simple sugars are known as 'fast-releasing'. This means they raise blood sugar levels quickly, causing peaks and troughs of energy. This is why a sugary snack gives us an instant hit of energy, only to be followed by another dip.

Sugars can be further split into two groups – intrinsic sugars found within the cells of plants, and extrinsic, or free sugars, which are not part of the cellular structure. Intrinsic sugars are those in fruit and vegetables, while extrinsic sugars are found in table sugar, honey, confectionery and milk – extrinsic sugars are the cause of tooth decay. The DoH has suggested an upper limit of 10% of total energy from extrinsic sugars. That's about 50 grams of table sugar, or the equivalent of a can of cola and a bowl of sweetened breakfast cereal. It's easy to go over the limit.

STARCHES

Complex starches are made up of long spiralling chains of glucose units (polysaccharides) that are broken down into single glucose units when digested. They are found in foods such as cereals, beans, potatoes and bread. They provide slow-release energy which stabilises blood sugar levels, eliminating peaks and troughs. It's a good idea to eat as much of these foods as possible.

If not needed immediately for energy, glucose from all types of carbohydrate is stored in the muscles and liver as glycogen, which is then converted back to glucose when the body needs it. Any excess glucose ultimately turns to fat in the body.

■ Requirements

UK EAR: 258 g (women aged 19-50), 340 g (men aged 19-59). No more than 10% from extrinsic sugars.

■ Risks

Extrinsic sugars are a major cause of tooth decay. Very high quantities can also contribute to diabetes and high blood cholesterol.

■ Deficiency

None likely since complex carbohydrates tend to be staple foods.

■ Special needs

People who perform hard physical work, exercise intensively (page 55), are on low-fat diets (page 64), or suffering from mild depression.

■ Good sources

Grains, pulses, bread, pasta, root vegetables, squash, sweetcorn, dried fruits, bananas.

■ Requirements
UK EAR: 18 g.

■ Interactions
Fibre absorbs fluid in the gut so you'll need to drink more water as your intake increases. Phytate, found especially in wheat bran, binds with iron, calcium, zinc and copper, and may prevent absorption. Make sure you're getting enough minerals in your diet.

■ Risks
Because of their bulk, fibre-rich foods may prevent small children from eating enough other foods to maintain growth and energy needs. They may also cause a mineral deficiency in older people.

■ Deficiency
Low intakes are associated with increased risk of bowel disorders, heart disease and diabetes.

■ Good sources
Fibre-rich foods contain a mixture of soluble and insoluble fibre but some contain more of one type. Oats, beans, root vegetables, fibrous green vegetables, citrus fruits, stone fruits, rhubarb, grapes, bananas and apples contain more soluble fibre. Wheat bran, wheat germ, wholemeal products, barley, rye, nuts, seeds, lentils, chick peas, brown rice and corn contain more insoluble fibre.

FIBRE
Dietary fibre, now referred to as non-starch polysaccharides (NSP), is a form of complex carbohydrate made up of the indigestible substances in the structural material of plants. Once synonymous with bran, dietary fibre is, in fact, a collective term for a complex mixture of substances that have different physiological benefits. They are divided into two groups: soluble and insoluble. Nutritionists therefore recommend that we eat a variety of fibre-rich foods, so that the body has an adequate supply of both types.

SOLUBLE FIBRE
Soluble dietary fibre consists of pectins, gums and other mucilaginous substances. Better known for its jam-making properties, pectin is a type of sticky gel which binds with unwanted substances and helps remove them from the system. Gums and mucilages work in much the same way. There is strong evidence that soluble fibre not only lowers blood cholesterol levels (page 19), but also stabilises blood sugar levels by slowing down the rate at which glucose is absorbed.

INSOLUBLE FIBRE
Insoluble fibre – that's the kind that used to be referred to as 'roughage' – is made up mainly of celluloses, hemicelluloses and lignin. Cellulose is important because of its ability to absorb water and thus increase faecal bulk. This stimulates the intestinal muscles, making the transit of food easier and quicker, which in turn reduces the risk of infection and potential damage to the cells in the bowel. The bulkiness of insoluble fibre makes you feel full which means you can eat less – handy when you're trying to cut down on calories. Insoluble fibre is the most useful for dealing with constipation. It may also help control blood sugar levels. Though hemicellulose has its own characteristics, it's usually found alongside cellulose and acts in a similar way.

Lignin is a tough woody substance which is not strictly a non-starch polysaccharide. It is found mainly in fibrous vegetables such as old carrots and parsnips – it's the hard woody core that no amount of cooking will soften. Lignin is thought to lower blood cholesterol levels by binding with bile acids which, in turn, emulsify fats and reduce the likelihood of clogged-up arteries.

FATS

Even though we should all probably cut down on the amount of fat we eat, the human body could not survive without it. Fat is a necessary part of every cell in the body, it insulates us from heat loss, and it supports and cushions internal organs from damage. Fat provides essential fatty acids, and it aids the absorption of fat-soluble vitamins. It not only improves the flavour and palatability of food, but, because we digest it relatively slowly, it gives a satisfying feeling of fullness or 'satiety'.

Fat is also a concentrated source of energy. Weight for weight, it provides nearly three times as much as carbohydrates. Any that is surplus to requirements gets stored as body fat, which is why we need only small amounts.

WHAT'S MY LIMIT?

The current advice suggests that fat should make up no more than 33% of our total energy intake (page 13). For a 19–50 year-old woman with an energy requirement of 1940 calories, this is 640 calories (1940 x 33÷100=640). Since each gram of fat provides 9 calories, 640 calories represents 71 grams of fat (640÷9=71).

In terms of actual portions, 6 grams of fat is roughly the amount of butter you spread on a slice of bread; half an avocado is 20 grams. Unless you watch your intake like a hawk, it's remarkably easy to use up your allowance. It's a good idea to get to know the fat content of a typical serving of food (see *Weight Management*, page 64).

WHAT IS FAT?

Technically, fat should be referred to as 'fats' since there is more than one type. Whatever the type, however, fats consist mainly of compounds called triglycerides. These, too, come in various forms, but they all share a common chemical structure of three fatty acids and a unit of glycerol.

Fatty acids can be further subdivided into saturated and unsaturated. The easiest way of telling the difference is to bear in mind that saturates are solid at room temperature, and unsaturates are liquid. All fat-containing foods contain both types of fatty acids, but if the proportion of saturates is greater, then the fat is said to be saturated and vice versa. Some foods contain roughly equal amounts. Red meat, surprisingly, contains about the same amount of unsaturated and saturated fatty acids, though it is usually the saturates that get the mention.

■ Requirements

Percentage of total energy intake:
Total fats: maximum 33% (women 71 g, men 93.6 g).
Saturates: maximum 10% (women 21.5 g, men 28.5 g).
Monounsaturates: 12% (women 26 g, men 34 g).
Polyunsaturates: minimum 6%, maximum 10% (women 13–21.5 g, men 17–28.3 g).
Trans: maximum 2% (women 4.5 g, men 5.6 g).

■ Risks

A high-fat diet increases the risk of heart disease, obesity and a host of other 'modern' ailments.

■ Deficiency

Unlikely.

■ Special needs

Children under two need more fat in their diet.

■ Sources

Saturates: beef, lamb, pork, poultry, dairy products, eggs, offal.
Monounsaturates: Beef, lamb, pork, poultry, white fish, oily fish, seafood, eggs, avocados, olives, olive oil, nuts and nut oils.
Polyunsaturates: White fish, oily fish, soya milk, margarine, nuts, nut oils, vegetable oils, seed oils.

■ Stability

Some oils and fats oxidise at very high temperatures.

17

SATURATED FATTY ACIDS

In simple chemical terms, saturated fatty acid molecules carry a full set of hydrogen atoms, which is why they are known as 'saturated'. They can be made by the body and are often called non-essential fatty acids. They are found in solid fats such as butter, lard and suet, and in the fat in meat and poultry. Though saturates come mainly from foods of animal origin, two exceptions are coconut oil and palm oil. Unusually for plant foods, both contain a high percentage of saturates and are therefore solid at room temperature.

Saturated fatty acids are strongly associated with raised levels of 'bad' LDL cholesterol (see box opposite), and they can cause the blood to thicken and clot more easily. As such, they are considered the chief offenders in coronary heart disease.

UNSATURATED FATTY ACIDS

These are a group made up of monounsaturated, polyunsaturated and trans fatty acids.

Monounsaturates are deficient in only one pair of hydrogen atoms. They are usually liquid at room temperature though they may solidify when chilled. Like saturated fatty acids, they can be made by the body and are therefore often classified as non-essential. They are found in both plant and animal foods, but the best sources are olive oil, groundnut oil, nuts, olives and avocados. The typical 'Mediterranean' diet is rich in these foods and is associated with fewer cases of coronary heart disease, obesity and some cancers, as well as increased longevity. There is strong evidence that monounsaturates lower 'bad' LDL cholesterol, and maintain or even raise 'good' HDL cholesterol.

Polyunsaturated fatty acids are deficient in two or more hydrogen atoms, and are liquid at room temperature or below. They include two groups of essential fatty acids (EFAs) that must be supplied by food. These are called omega-6 and omega-3, and are derived from linoleic and alpha-linolenic acids respectively.

Omega-6 EFAs are involved in the production of a certain type of prostaglandin – a hormone-like substance with a therapeutic effect on many conditions, including skin complaints, allergies, premenstrual syndrome and rheumatic complaints. They are found in safflower, grapeseed and sunflower oils, evening primrose oil, soft polyunsaturated margarine, seeds and nuts.

Omega-3 EFAs are found in vegetable oils, seeds and nuts too, but additionally include eicosapentaenoic acid (EPA) and docosahexaenoic acid (DHA), which come almost solely from fish oils. Omega-3 EFAs are essential for brain development in unborn and newborn babies (see *Nutrition in Pregnancy*, page 59), and are thought to protect against heart disease, stroke and certain cancers. There is also evidence that they may alleviate, or even prevent, conditions such as high blood pressure, arthritis, certain immune diseases, skin complaints and even depression.

For good health, both EFAs must be present in the diet in the correct proportions. Ideally, omega-6 intake should be no more than four or five times that of omega-3 – about 2 grams and 0.5 grams respectively. In Britain, omega-6 intake is almost twice what it should be, and the imbalance is now recognised as a serious contributor to ill health.

TRANS FATTY ACIDS

Though small amounts of trans fatty acids are naturally present in meat and dairy products, they are mainly mono- or polyunsaturates in vegetable or fish oils that have been artificially hardened by an industrial process called hydrogenation. They are widely used in soft margarines, spreads, vegetable oils, and many processed foods. There is strong evidence that trans fats are as bad, or even worse than saturates in terms of heart disease. They not only increase levels of 'bad' LDL cholesterol, but may also lower the 'good' kind.

CHOLESTEROL

Cholesterol is a waxy substance belonging to a group of substances known as lipoproteins, and found in the membrane of every cell in the body. It is manufactured in the liver and used to carry essential fatty acids round the bloodstream. Although the body makes nearly all the cholesterol it needs, we also get some from animal foods such as meat, offal, egg yolk and dairy produce – all high in saturates as well as cholesterol.

WHAT'S THE PROBLEM?

Cholesterol travels round the bloodstream in tiny droplets of lipoprotein. This comes in three densities: very low density lipoprotein (VLDL), low density (LDL) and high density (HDL). If we eat a lot of saturated fats, the liver goes into overdrive and produces huge quantities of VLDLs and LDLs, both rich in cholesterol. Excess cholesterol then accumulates on the walls of the arteries, restricting the passage of blood and oxygen, and hugely increasing the risk of heart disease. HDLs, on the other hand, are thought to help prevent blocked arteries. This is why HDL cholesterol is sometimes referred to as 'good' and LDL as 'bad'.

It was once thought that cholesterol-rich foods contributed to excess cholesterol in the blood, but it now seems that blood levels are affected more by the amount of saturated fat in the diet than by the amount of cholesterol. Prawns – low-fat, high-cholesterol – are therefore a healthier choice than a high-fat, high-cholesterol food such as egg yolk.

■ Requirements

UK RNI: 45 g (women),
55.5 g (men).

■ Upper safe limits

90 g (women), 111 g (men).

■ Interactions

Amino acids in one food
can compensate for those
missing in another.

■ Risks

Very high doses may
aggravate poor kidney
function.

■ Deficiency

Unlikely, but infants in
undeveloped countries
suffer from a range of
disorders collectively
known as protein energy
malnutrition.

■ Special needs

Babies, young children,
pregnant/breastfeeding
women, vegetarians,
people recovering from
injury or surgical operations,
people under stress.

■ Good sources

Dairy products, eggs, meat,
fish, poultry, pulses
(particularly soya beans), nuts,
grains and grain products.

■ Stability

Methionine, an amino acid
found in milk, eggs and
beef, may be reduced
during cooking. Collagen,
a meat protein, dissolves in
the liquids that flow from
meat as it cooks.

PROTEIN

Derived from the Greek and meaning 'of prime importance', proteins are an essential constituent of virtually every cell in the body. They are complex molecules made up of chains of amino acids. The arrangement of amino acids within the molecule determines the function and characteristics of a particular type of protein.

The body manufactures literally thousands of different proteins with very varied functions. Some are structural and are found in muscle, connective tissue, skin, hair and bones. These are essential for the growth of body tissues in babies and children, and for the repair and replacement of tissues in adults. Others make up enzymes (page 13) and hormones which together play a regulatory role in cell metabolism and specific cell functions. Insulin, for example, is a protein that helps control glucose levels in the blood.

Some proteins are neurotransmitters. These include tryptophan, one of the essential amino acids, which sends signals to the brain to produce serotonin, a chemical that helps regulate appetite and sleep. Some work with the immune system and fight infection. Yet others work as transporters – haemoglobin, for example – moving essential fatty acids and minerals round the bloodstream. Protein is also used as a source of energy when carbohydrate and fat stores in the body are low.

PROTEIN IN FOOD

Interestingly, the protein we get from our food is not used directly. Instead, it has to be broken down during digestion into various amino acids which are then reassembled into specific body proteins.

The nutritional value of dietary protein is called its Protein Efficiency Ratio (PER) and is a measure of how adequately it supplies the essential amino acids. In general, foods from animal sources have the highest PERs. Proteins from vegetable sources tend to have lower PERs (soya is an exception) and must be combined with other protein foods to compensate for deficiencies (see *How to Achieve a Balanced Diet*, page 39). Fortunately, many commonly eaten combinations provide a natural balance – beans on toast, for example.

Most of us probably eat more protein than we need. The current DoH advice is to allow 0.75 gram of protein per day for every kilogram of body weight, which works out at about 10% of total energy needs.

AMINO ACIDS

There are about twenty amino acids that occur in proteins, eight of which are 'essential' since the body cannot make them for itself. These are:

isoleucine	phenylalanine	leucine	threonine
lysine	tryptophan	methionine	valine

Histidine and arginine are two 'semi-essential' amino acids which the adult body can produce but babies and young children may not be able to make enough of them (see *Feeding Babies, Children and Teenagers*, page 73).

VITAMINS

Vitamins are complex organic substances needed by the body for various metabolic processes (see box, page 29), and are vital for good health. Since many chemical reactions take place only in their presence, they act as essential catalysts. Beta-carotene, vitamin C and vitamin E are also antioxidants (page 14) and work as scavengers, protecting the body from the damaging effects of free radicals.

With the exception of vitamin D, which is produced by the action of sunlight on the skin, most vitamins cannot be made by the body and have to be provided by food.

VITAMIN A

Also known as retinol, vitamin A is found in foods from animal sources, but can also be made from some carotenoids (page 37) found in plant foods, which convert to vitamin A in the body. Vitamin A is fat-soluble and stored in the liver.

As well as being vital for children's growth, vitamin A helps protect the skin and mucous membranes, such as those lining the mouth, nose, breathing passages and the gut. It is essential for normal colour vision and for the cells within the eye which enable us to see in dim light. It promotes healthy skin and hair.

■ Requirements
UK RNI: 600 µg (women), 700 µg (men). EU RDA: 800 µg.
Upper safe levels 7000 µg (women), 3300 µg (during pregnancy), 9000 µg (men).

■ Interactions
A zinc deficiency can affect the function of vitamin A and vice versa.

■ Risks
Very high intake over long periods can lead to liver damage. Large amounts can also cause headaches, vomiting, double vision and hair loss. Because of a suggested link with birth defects, DoH advice is not to eat liver nor take supplements of more than 800 µg during pregnancy.

■ Deficiency
Rare in developed countries. Poor night vision is one of the first signs. Dryness of the eye is another symptom.

■ Special needs
Pregnant and breastfeeding women (page 58), vegans (page 61).

■ Good sources
Liver, kidney, oily fish, fish oils, egg yolk, milk, butter, margarine.

■ Stability
Vitamin A is stable throughout most cooking processes although there is some loss when frying butter or margarine at high temperatures.

Vitamins A, D, E and K are fat-soluble and absorbed with fat in our food. With the exception of vitamin K, the body can store fat-soluble vitamins for relatively long periods. You should take care if you use supplements as high levels of these vitamins can be toxic.

The B complex group, beta-carotene and vitamin C are water-soluble. Risk of toxic build-up is unlikely since any excess is flushed out by the kidneys. These vitamins are highly unstable and easily destroyed by prolonged storage, exposure to light and by cooking. You therefore need to maintain a steady supply.

BETA-CAROTENE

This is the pigment that gives yellow-, orange- and red-fleshed fruit and vegetables their colour. It is also found in dark green vegetables. The most abundant carotenoid in the diet, beta-carotene is converted to vitamin A in the body (6 µg beta-carotene = 1 µg vitamin A). Together with vitamins C and E, it is an important antioxidant and it may reduce the risk of some cancers. It is also believed to protect the skin from UV light. Beta-carotene seems to be better absorbed from lightly cooked vegetables rather than raw.

■ Requirements
Part of total vitamin A intake. No officially recommended separate dietary intake established, but 6 mg is recognised as an optimum figure.

■ Upper safe limits
25 mg.

■ Interactions
There is some evidence of an increased risk of lung cancer in smokers who take beta-carotene supplements.

■ Risks
None, apart from harmless yellowing of the skin if intake regularly exceeds 30 µg.

■ Deficiency
As for vitamin A. Additionally, people suffering from diabetes, hypothyroidism and severe liver disease have difficulty in converting beta-carotene to vitamin A. They therefore should not rely on beta-carotene as the sole source of vitamin A.

■ Special needs
People frequently exposed to strong sunlight. Vegetarians and people with a low vitamin A intake.

■ Good sources
Dried apricots, carrots, broccoli, kale, lettuce, mangoes, papaya, pink grapefruit, red peppers, pumpkin, sweet potato, spinach.

■ Stability
Some loss during storage and from exposure to the air.

B VITAMINS

These are a group of almost a dozen different substances, at one time identified by the letter B and a numeral, but now usually referred to by their chemical names. They each have their own role within the body but they work as a team. If you take supplements, it's best to take a B complex type to avoid causing any imbalances.

B vitamins need to be supplied on a daily basis as the body does not store them. They are depleted by exposure to light and air, and by cooking.

THIAMIN (B1)
Needed for the release of energy from carbohydrates, fats and alcohol, and for healthy nerve and muscle function.

▩ Requirements
UK RNI: 0.8 mg per 1940 cals (women), 1 mg per 2550 cals (men). EU RDA: 1.4 mg.

▩ Upper safe limits
100 mg.

▩ Interactions
More effective if absorbed with other B vitamins.

▩ Risks
Non-toxic. No harmful side effects known.

▩ Deficiency
Rarely seen in the West, but can cause depression, memory loss, lack of concentration and irritability. Severe deficiency causes beri-beri which affects nerves and muscle function.

▩ Special needs
Anyone with increased energy requirements or under mental stress. People who smoke and drink heavily.

▩ Good sources
Bread, flour, yeast extract, most breakfast cereals, meat (especially pork), potatoes, pulses, milk.

▩ Stability
Thiamin is one of the least stable vitamins, losing up to 50% during cooking at high temperatures. It is also destroyed by bicarbonate of soda, the preservative sulphur dioxide and UV light.

RIBOFLAVIN (B2)
Riboflavin is involved in energy release from proteins, fats and carbohydrate. It is also needed for healthy skin and mucous membranes, especially in the mouth and nose.

▩ Requirements
UK RNI: 1.1 mg (women), 1.3 mg (men). EU RDA: 1.6 mg.

▩ Upper safe limits
200 mg.

▩ Interactions
More effective if absorbed with other B vitamins. Unstable with some broad spectrum antibiotics.

▩ Risks
Non-toxic. No harmful side effects known.

▩ Deficiency
Sore, burning lips and tongue, clogged pores, skin rashes.

▩ Special needs
People on long courses of antibiotics. People with high energy requirements.

▩ Good sources
Meat (particularly beef and liver), kidney, milk, eggs, fish, yeast, cheese, pulses.

▩ Stability
Destroyed by bicarbonate of soda, and especially sensitive to light.

NIACIN (B3)

Two related substances – nicotinic acid and nicotinamide – are both called niacin. Niacin is needed for energy release from food. Although it is supplied in the diet, niacin can also be made in the body from the amino acid tryptophan. Large doses of nicotinic acid are thought to lower blood cholesterol levels, but should be taken only under medical supervision.

■ Requirements
UK RNI: 13 mg (women), 17 mg (men). EU RDA: 18 mg.

■ Upper safe limits
Nicotinic acid 150 mg, nicotinamide 450 mg.

■ Interactions
More effective if absorbed with other B vitamins. Nicotinic acid may cause flushing of the skin at intakes over 20 mg.

■ Risks
Excessively high doses of nicotinic acid may cause liver damage. Supplements should not be taken by people suffering from diabetes, gout or stomach ulcers.

■ Deficiency
Rare in the West but still widespread in some undeveloped countries. Leads to pellagra which causes skin rashes, diarrhoea and dementia. Minor deficiency causes tiredness, depression and memory loss.

■ Special needs
During the last months of pregnancy and when breastfeeding.

■ Good sources
Meat, liver, kidney, tuna, yeast extract, milk, cheese, eggs, nuts, wholemeal bread, brown rice, dried fruit.

■ Stability
Unaffected by exposure to light, air or bicarbonate of soda. Some loss in cooking water.

PANTOTHENIC ACID (B5)

Needed for the release of energy from carbohydrate, protein and fats. Contributes to cell growth, production of anti-stress hormones (steroids), antibodies and essential fatty acids. Of great importance in the functioning of the adrenal glands. Studies suggest that supplementation may help alleviate rheumatoid arthritis.

■ Requirements
UK RNI: None specified. EU RDA: 6 mg.

■ Upper safe limits
500 mg.

■ Interactions
More effective if absorbed with other B vitamins. Biotin and folic acid also help absorption.

■ Risks
No toxicity known, but excessive doses may lead to diarrhoea.

■ Deficiency
Unlikely, as found in food that is widely available.

■ Special needs
People under prolonged or heavy stress. Beneficial following injury and surgical operations.

■ Good sources
Liver, yeast, egg white, wheat bran, pulses, nuts.

■ Stability
Reasonably stable during cooking and storage. Some losses when thawing and cooking frozen meat.

PYRIDOXINE (B6)

Pyridoxine is involved in the metabolism of amino acids and fats, and the regulation of steroid hormones. It is needed for maintaining a healthy nervous system, and is also part of an enzyme which is involved in the release of energy in the muscles and liver. It is believed to relieve premenstrual tension, nausea and vomiting, especially during pregnancy.

■ Requirements
UK RNI: 1.2 mg (women), 1.4 mg (men). EU RDA: 2 mg.

■ Upper safe limits
200 mg.

■ Interactions
More effective if absorbed with other B vitamins. Zinc and magnesium also help absorption.

■ Risks
Very high doses may cause numbness and tingling of sensory nerves. The condition is reversible.

■ Deficiency
Rare. Minor deficiency can cause oily, flaky skin, irritability and muscle weakness.

■ Special needs
Pregnant and breastfeeding women, women taking the contraceptive pill, heavy drinkers and smokers, elderly people.

■ Good sources
Meat, liver, kidneys, yeast, egg white, milk, grains, pulses, nuts, green vegetables.

■ Stability
Fairly resistant to heat, but some loss in cooking water, and depleted by bicarbonate of soda. Sensitive to UV light.

CYANOCOBALAMIN (B12)

Vital for the production of red blood cells and normal growth. Involved in the metabolism of essential fatty acids and in maintaining the myelin sheath around nerves.

■ Requirements
UK RNI: 1.5 µg (women and men). EU RDA: 1 µg.

■ Upper safe limits
500 µg.

■ Interactions
Absorption is dependent on a substance in the gastric juices known as the 'intrinsic factor'. A deficiency may be masked by taking folic acid supplements.

■ Risks
Unlikely.

■ Deficiency
Causes a condition known as pernicious anaemia, which results in a drop in the red blood cell count. Vegans (page 61) are at particular risk as the vitamin is mainly found in animal foods. Deficiency is otherwise unlikely as adequate supplies are stored in the liver.

■ Special needs
Vegans.

■ Good sources
Liver, meat, eggs, milk, cheese, yeast.

■ Stability
Lost in cooking water. Depleted by acids (vinegar, lemon juice) and bicarbonate of soda. Sensitive to UV light.

THE B6 DEBATE

A major use for pyridoxine (vitamin B6) has been as a safe and effective high-dose supplement to relieve the symptoms of premenstrual problems. However, in 1997 the Government proposed a ban on over-the-counter sales of supplements containing more than 10 mg of B6. The ban was based on a single study which suggested that high levels could cause nerve damage. Many people claimed the research was flawed, and a number of scientists, consumers and retailers voiced objections to the ban. As a result, the Government is carrying out further research and the ban has not, as yet, been put into place.

FOLIC ACID

Vital for the formation of new cells and therefore for growth of the foetus and normal development in children. Supplements are routinely given to pregnant women or even to those planning to conceive.

■ Requirements
UK RNI: 200 µg (women/men). EU RDA: 200 µg.

■ Upper safe limits
400 µg.

■ Interactions
Supplements may mask a B12 deficiency. Prescription drugs can leach folic acid.

■ Risks
High levels may lead to reduced zinc absorption.

■ Deficiency
Can lead to megaloblastic anaemia in young children and pregnant women, and growth defects in babies and young children.

■ Special needs
Pregnant and breastfeeding women, babies and young children, heavy drinkers, women on the pill, elderly people who may have poor diets.

■ Good sources
Wheat germ, wheat bran, nuts, liver, leafy green vegetables, wholemeal bread, eggs, fortified cereals.

■ Stability
Up to 50% lost in cooking. Depleted by bicarbonate of soda and exposure to air.

BIOTIN

Biotin is involved in energy release from carbohydrates and fats, the metabolism of amino acids and the production of fats and glucose. It is thought to help treat Candida albicans, an invasive fungal disease.

■ Requirements
UK safe limits: 10-200 µg. EU RDA: 150 µg.

■ Upper safe limits
500 µg.

■ Interactions
Best absorbed with other B vitamins.

■ Risks
None recorded.

■ Deficiency
Rare. Slightly more common in babies and results in skin complaints.

■ Special needs
Babies and young children suffering from seborrhoeic dermatitis.

■ Good sources
Brewer's yeast, kidney, liver, wheat bran, eggs, wheat germ, chicken.

■ Stability
Biotin is thought to be stable.

VITAMIN C

Unlike most animals, humans cannot make vitamin C for themselves and therefore need a regular supply. Many nutritionists believe we would benefit from consuming more than the RNI.

Vitamin C helps the white blood cells fight infection. It helps the skin maintain its elasticity by producing collagen (a type of protein in the connective tissue). It also prevents bruising and speeds up wound healing. Vitamin C is an important antioxidant (page 14).

■ Requirements
UK RNI: 40 mg (women and men). EU RDA: 60 mg.

■ Upper safe limits
2000 mg.

■ Interactions
Bioflavonoids have been shown to increase the uptake of vitamin C. Works with vitamin E and beta-carotene as an antioxidant. Assists the absorption of iron.

■ Risks
High intakes sometimes result in diarrhoea.

■ Deficiency
A deficiency can leave you more susceptible to infection, and lead to slow wound healing, bleeding gums and irritability. A severe deficiency results in scurvy.

■ Special needs
Elderly people, those who don't eat fruit and vegetables, people who eat a lot of processed food, heavy drinkers, smokers, pregnant/breastfeeding women.

■ Good sources
Strawberries, blackcurrants, citrus fruit, kiwi fruit, mangoes, papaya, chillies, sweet peppers, cabbages, tomatoes, new potatoes.

■ Stability
Vast amounts are lost during cooking, storage, long-term deep-freezing and exposure to light.

VITAMIN D

Technically a hormone, vitamin D is produced in the body by the action of sunlight on the skin. It is also supplied by food. If you live where winter makes itself felt, you can build up enough vitamin D in the liver to last you the rest of the year, provided your skin is regularly exposed to the sun from April to October. Vitamin D is vital for calcium absorption and helps maintain the correct ratio of calcium to phosphorus. It promotes strong healthy bones and teeth.

■ Requirements
UK RNI: none, provided skin is regularly exposed to the sun. Otherwise 10 µg. EU RDA: 5 µg.

■ Upper safe limits
10 µg.

■ Interactions
None known.

■ Risks
Since vitamin D is stored in the liver, high doses are dangerous, especially for babies and young children.

■ Deficiency
A deficiency can lead to rickets (malformed bones) in children and osteomalacia (thinning of bones) in adults.

■ Special needs
Children under five, pregnant and breastfeeding women, elderly housebound people, people who are deprived of sunlight because of cultural restrictions on dress. Birth-control pill users have reduced levels. Post-menopausal women may need supplements to lower risk of osteoporosis. Absorption decreases with age.

■ Good sources
Oily fish, fish oils, liver, butter, margarine, cheese, evaporated milk, eggs.

■ Stability
Vitamin D is stable during normal cooking.

VITAMIN E

Claims have been made that vitamin E improves sexual performance, increases fertility and retards ageing – but there's little satisfactory evidence to support any of this. Vitamin E's major role is as a natural antioxidant (page 14), strongly believed to reduce the risk of heart disease. It is also involved in red blood cell formation and may help treat arthritis and some skin conditions. It is thought to help with wound healing, poor circulation and varicose veins.

■ Requirements
UK RNI: 5 mg. EU RDA: 10 mg.

■ Upper safe limits
800 mg.

■ Interactions
Aided by selenium and vitamin C, and vice versa.

■ Risks
Very little risk of overdosing, but large doses may cause diarrhoea.

■ Deficiency
Unlikely, but research shows some evidence of muscle wasting and red blood cell damage when blood levels of vitamin E are very low. Prolonged deficiency is thought to be a contributing factor in heart disease and cancer.

■ Special needs
People who eat a lot of food fried in polyunsaturated fats and oils. These oils are easily oxidised, and the need for vitamin E is therefore increased. Smokers may benefit from adequate intake.

■ Good sources
Wheat germ, safflower and sunflower oils, nut oils, olive oil, nuts, pulses, eggs, margarine, avocados.

■ Stability
Destroyed by exposure to air.

VITAMIN K

Vitamin K's most important function is in the production of a substance called prothrombin which causes the blood to clot and thus prevents haemorrhaging. Vitamin K is partially produced in the body from the friendly bacteria naturally present in the gut, but we also need some from food. Research suggests that it may reduce bone calcium loss, and thus play a role in the prevention of osteoporosis (brittle bones).

■ Requirements
UK Safe Intake: 1 μg per kg of body weight.

■ Upper safe limits
Naturally occurring vitamin K is considered safe at up to 100 times the Safe Intake. Synthetic supplements are not advised.

■ Interactions
As a fat-soluble vitamin, it is best absorbed with fat-containing foods.

■ Risks
Women on the pill may have increased levels of prothrombin which increases the likelihood of blood clotting, and therefore the risk of heart disease.

■ Deficiency
Rare, as the vitamin is found in a variety of foods. A deficiency may occur if fat is poorly absorbed, or if there is a blockage in the intestines, eg gall stones. A deficiency results in bleeding disorders.

■ Special needs
Menopausal and post-menopausal women, the elderly, people on long-term antibiotics.

■ Good sources
Green leafy vegetables, carrots, soya beans, turnips, liver, meat, oily fish, grains, honey, kelp.

■ Stability
Not destroyed by heat or exposure to air, but quickly destroyed by exposure to UV light.

CO-ENZYME Q10

Though not classified as an essential nutrient, co-enzyme Q10 (also called ubiquinone) works at a very fundamental level within the cell acting as a vital link in the complex system that converts the energy from nutrients to a form in which it can be used by the body. It is naturally present in all our cells, though production appears to fall off with age. It is especially concentrated in the heart, liver and muscles – organs that have high energy requirements. Quinone-like substances are also found in food, and these are converted to Q10 in the liver.

Q10 is also an antioxidant (page 14), working in tandem with other antioxidants to protect the body from free radicals. It is thought to enhance the immune system by stimulating the formation of antibodies, and to boost energy levels. It has been used to good effect in treating heart disease, high blood pressure and gum disease.

■ Requirements

UK RNI: None established. Daily requirement estimated at 30–90 mg. EU RDA: None established.

■ Upper safe limits

Doses of up to 200 mg have not caused side effects.

■ Interactions

Fat helps absorption. Works with B complex vitamins to produce energy.

■ Risks

None known.

■ Deficiency

Low energy levels, poor immune functioning, bleeding gums.

■ Special needs

Elderly people, sportsmen/women doing intensive training.

■ Good sources

Meat, poultry, sardines, mackerel, wholemeal products, nuts, dark green leafy vegetables.

■ Stability

Easily destroyed by cooking.

METABOLISM

Nutritionists often refer to metabolism and metabolic rate but what exactly do these terms mean? Metabolism is a general term used to describe chemical reactions that take place inside all living organisms. The term refers to the never-ending cycle of ingesting food, converting it to energy and eliminating waste products. It is to do with building up and breaking down; the growth, development and ageing process of the body; and the formation, processing and shedding of cells.

The metabolic rate is the rate at which the body uses energy. The basal metabolic rate is the rate at which energy is used simply to maintain life – for breathing, for the growth and repair of cells, for the heart to beat.

MINERALS

Minerals are as essential as vitamins. We need them for several reasons: they are part of the body's structure, they help regulate bodily fluids, and, as components of enzymes, they are involved in all the body's metabolic processes. Some minerals are antioxidants – zinc, selenium, copper and manganese, for example. They work with antioxidant vitamins in preventing damage to the cells from free radicals (page 14).

Minerals are found mainly in the bones and teeth, but there are small amounts in the liver, muscles, red blood cells and the fluid inside and outside the cells. The major minerals, for example calcium, phosphorus, magnesium, potassium and sodium, are needed in the largest amounts. Others, known as trace elements, are needed in much smaller quantities, but are no less important. Trace elements include iron, zinc, selenium, iodine and copper.

MINERALS IN FOOD

Different foods supply different minerals, so eating a varied diet is essential for good health. Even so, it is easy to become deficient. Certain minerals enter the food chain through plants, and the amount in our food depends on the amount in the soil. For example, selenium intake in the UK has dropped quite dramatically in the last few years because of a switch from selenium-rich bread-making wheat from North America, to low-selenium European wheat. The bioavailability of minerals can vary, too. For example, phytate (found in whole grains) and oxalates (found in spinach and rhubarb) inhibit the absorption of calcium, iron and zinc. An excess of one mineral may hinder the absorption of another. Different people have different absorption rates; and the amount we need may change, depending on health, age and other factors.

CALCIUM

Calcium is the most abundant mineral in the body with 99% of it in the bones and teeth; the rest is in the blood and tissues. Adequate intake throughout life is essential to ensure peak bone mass, and to help prevent osteoporosis in later life. Calcium absorption decreases with age. Weight-bearing exercise helps maintain bone mass.

Calcium's main function is to develop and maintain healthy bones and teeth. It is also needed for the absorption of vitamin B12, and it is essential for nerve function, enzyme activity and blood clotting. The current UK RNI of 700 mg is thought to be too low for optimal intake, and the amount is being reviewed.

■ Requirements
UK RNI: 700 mg (women and men). EU RDA: 800 mg.

■ Upper safe limits
1500 mg.

■ Interactions
Vitamin D essential for calcium absorption. Phosphorus also helps with effective absorption and use. A high calcium intake increases the need for magnesium.

■ Risks
Unlikely, although excessive intakes may hinder the absorption of other essential minerals including iron, manganese and zinc.

■ Deficiency
A severe deficiency in children may cause rickets. Insufficient intake throughout life is related to osteoporosis in menopausal and post-menopausal women. Minor deficiency can result in muscle cramps, insomnia and irritability.

■ Special needs
Pregnant, breastfeeding and post-menopausal women, adolescents, people with an inadequate vitamin D intake, vegans, vegetarians, those with a high salt intake.

■ Good sources
Dairy products, small oily fish with edible bones, nuts, tofu, fruit, green leafy vegetables, sea vegetables, white bread, fortified flour.

CHROMIUM

This trace element is involved in maximising the activity of insulin, the hormone which controls blood sugar levels. It therefore helps to reduce sudden hunger and cravings. Some studies suggest that by raising levels of HDL cholesterol and lowering LDL cholesterol, chromium may be of benefit to people with heart disease.

■ Requirements
UK Safe Intake: more than 25 µg. EU RDA: None.

■ Upper safe limits
200 µg.

■ Interactions
See Risks.

■ Risks
Should be taken only under medical supervision by insulin-dependent diabetics.

■ Deficiency
May be associated with high blood cholesterol levels and glucose intolerance.

■ Special needs
People who rely on processed food.

■ Good sources
Egg yolk, molasses, brewer's yeast, calf's liver, cheese, wholemeal products.

COPPER

Copper is an essential trace mineral involved in fundamental bodily processes. It participates in many enzyme systems but is best known for its role in an antioxidant enzyme which scavenges free radicals (page 14). It is involved in red blood cell production, formation of bones, energy production and healthy functioning of the brain and nervous system. Levels in the blood increase with diseases such as arthritis.

■ Requirements
UK RNI: 1.2 mg (women and men). EU RDA: None.

■ Upper safe limits
5 mg.

■ Interactions
High intake of zinc may interfere with copper absorption.

■ Risks
Toxic at high intakes.

■ Deficiency
Possibly increased risk of heart and circulatory problems, especially if associated with selenium deficiency. A deficiency in children may result in increased respiratory infections.

■ Special needs
None.

■ Good sources
Oysters, mussels, whelks, liver, brewer's yeast, whole grains, nuts, cocoa.

IODINE

Iodine is a constituent of the thyroid hormones that are vital for normal growth and development, both physical and mental. It is also involved in maintaining the metabolic rate. Cooking, particularly boiling, significantly reduces the iodine content of food.

■ Requirements
UK RNI: 140 µg (women and men). EU RDA: 150 µg.

■ Upper safe limits
500 µg.

■ Interactions
See Risks.

■ Risks
High intakes should be avoided when pregnant, or by people taking medication for thyroid problems.

■ Deficiency
Rare in the UK. Characterised by goitre – a swelling of the thyroid gland in the neck – and cretinism. Increases the incidence of miscarriage, still births and congenital abnormalities in the foetus.

■ Special needs
Pregnant and pre-pregnant women.

■ Good sources
Oily fish, fish fingers, sea vegetables, meat, milk, iodised table salt.

IRON

The body contains 3–4 grams of iron, over half of which is in the form of haemoglobin, the red pigment in blood. Iron is also stored in the bone marrow, liver and spleen. There are two types of iron – haem iron from meat and fish, and non-haem iron from vegetables and fortified foods. Haem iron is more easily absorbed than non-haem. Iron is needed for the production of red blood cells, transportation of oxygen round the body and the functioning of enzymes.

■ Requirements
UK RNI: 14.8 mg (women), 8.7 mg (men). EU RDA: 14 mg.

■ Upper safe limits
15 mg.

■ Interactions
Vitamin C is needed for the absorption and use of iron to be fully effective. Molybdenum is also important for iron uptake. Aspirin may increase requirements. Phytic acid (found in whole grains) and oxalates (found in rhubarb and spinach) bind with iron and inhibit absorption.

■ Risks
Ordinary supplementation can cause constipation, diarrhoea, stomach pains. Very high doses can be toxic and even lethal.

■ Deficiency
Iron deficiency causes anaemia, one of the commonest deficiency diseases in the world. It reduces the red blood cell count and thus the amount of oxygen carried to the tissues.

■ Special needs
Women suffering from heavy periods, pregnant women, people suffering from iron-deficiency anaemia, vegetarians, athletes, the elderly.

■ Good sources
Red meat, liver, oysters, eggs, dried apricots, chocolate.

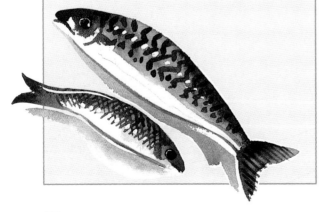

MAGNESIUM

Magnesium is concentrated mainly in the bones and muscles, but it is also an essential part of all cells. Required for energy release, cell division, enzyme production, and muscle and nerve function. Studies suggest that magnesium can lower blood pressure and may help alleviate asthma.

■ Requirements
UK RNI: 270 mg (women), 300 mg (men). EU RDA: 300 mg.

■ Upper safe limits
350 mg.

■ Interactions
Calcium is needed for absorption and use of magnesium to be fully effective. Pyridoxine (vitamin B6) and phosphorus are also helpful.

■ Risks
Unlikely.

■ Deficiency
Some nutritionists consider deficiencies to be more widespread than previously believed. Symptoms include muscle cramps, twitching, low blood sugar, irritability and insomnia. Studies suggest that low levels of magnesium in the blood may be associated with increased risk of heart disease.

■ Special needs
Women suffering from premenstrual syndrome, people who drink a lot.

■ Good sources
Meat, poultry, fish, dairy products, grains, nuts, pulses, green leafy vegetables, sea vegetables, dried fruit.

MANGANESE

Manganese is an essential trace mineral that interacts with various enzymes. It plays an important role in fundamental metabolic processes and also works as an antioxidant (page 14). It is involved in the development and maintenance of healthy bones, nerve development and function, glycogen formation (see *Carbohydrates*, page 15) and the synthesis of sex hormones.

■ Requirements
UK Safe Intake: in excess of 1.4 mg (women and men). EU RDA: none.

■ Upper safe limits
15 mg.

■ Interactions
None known.

■ Risks
None likely since absorption decreases dramatically if excess consumed. One of the least toxic minerals.

■ Deficiency
Unlikely.

■ Special needs
None.

■ Good sources
Wholemeal bread, wheat germ, nuts, avocados, peas, tea.

MOLYBDENUM

This is a little known but essential trace mineral found mainly in the liver, kidneys, adrenal glands, bones and skin. It is a component of various enzyme systems including one that works as an antioxidant (page 14). It is needed for normal sexual functioning in men. It is found in a variety of foods.

■ Requirements
UK Safe Intake: 50-400 µg (women and men). EU RDA: None.

■ Upper safe limits
200 µg.

■ Interactions
Helps with iron absorption. Works with riboflavin (vitamin B2).

■ Risks
Unlikely.

■ Deficiency
May affect reproductive capacity in men. May also increase susceptibility to tooth decay.

■ Special needs
Men, for normal sexual functioning.

■ Good sources
Liver, kidney, wheatgerm, lentils, sunflower seeds, eggs, beans.

PHOSPHORUS

Second to calcium, this is the most abundant mineral in the body. It is present in all the cells, mostly in the form of calcium salts in the skeleton. It plays a fundamental role in the complex system that converts the energy from food to a form in which it can be used by the body. It is found in most foods.

■ Requirements
UK RNI: 540 mg (women and men). EU RDA: 800 mg.

■ Upper safe limits
1500 mg.

■ Interactions
None known.

■ Risks
Rare unless kidneys are malfunctioning.

■ Deficiency
Unlikely.

■ Special needs
None.

■ Good sources
Dairy products, eggs, meat, fish, soya beans, soya products, pulses, wheat bran.

POTASSIUM

Potassium is among the minerals present in the largest quantity in the body. Almost all potassium is found in the fluid inside the cells. It is very easily excreted, especially if taking diuretic medicines, so a daily intake is essential. Higher intakes of potassium may counteract the effects of sodium (salt) and therefore reduce high blood pressure and the risk of stroke. Potassium is essential for the correct functioning of the heart, the muscles and the nerves. It also assists in protein metabolism. Potassium is found in almost all foods, but particularly fruit and vegetables.

■ Requirements
UK RNI: 3.5 g (women and men). EU RDA: None.

■ Upper safe limits
None established. See Risks.

■ Interactions
Prescription drugs can leach potassium from the body. Works in balance with sodium.

■ Risks
Unlikely, since excess is excreted.

■ Deficiency
Unlikely in normal situations but can arise from diarrhoea, excessive sweating or blood loss. A deficiency can lead to fatigue, muscle weakness, bloating, constipation, cardiac arrhythmia and insomnia.

■ Special needs
People who consume a lot of alcohol, coffee, sugar and salty foods. People who sweat excessively, eg manual workers and those who exercise strenuously. People on long-term antibiotics.

■ Good sources
Raisins, green vegetables, potatoes, wholemeal products, pork, fruit (especially bananas), juices, dairy products, grains and coffee.

SELENIUM

Selenium is an important trace element which enters the food chain through the soil. The amount present in the soil varies from country to country, and some areas are very low, especially in parts of China.

Selenium is part of an antioxidant enzyme and thus protects against damage from free radicals (page 14). It is also known to play a role in increased resistance to infections, protection from heart disease, strokes, arthritis and auto-immune diseases. It is thought to inhibit the harmful effects of toxic substances such as heavy metals and cigarette smoke. Selenium has also been used to treat rheumatoid arthritis as it may have an anti-inflammatory function.

■ Requirements
UK RNI: 60 µg (women), 75 µg (men). EU RDA: None.

■ Upper safe limits
200 µg.

■ Interactions
Vitamin E enhances the benefits of selenium and vice versa.

■ Risks
High intakes have been reported to cause diseased nails, hair loss, upset stomach and skin complaints. Very high doses can damage the liver and kidneys.

■ Deficiency
May increase the risk of heart disease and can cause Kaschin-Beck disease which affects the cartilage in the joints.

■ Special needs
Young adults and elderly people, vegetarians, pregnant and breastfeeding women, smokers, heavy drinkers.

■ Good sources
Nuts (especially Brazil nuts), seeds, pulses, bread, fish, meat (especially pork).

SODIUM

Sodium helps regulate body fluids and is involved in energy release, functioning of nerves and muscle contraction. It is found in small amounts in many foods, and since it is also added during processing and cooking, most of us have a higher intake than necessary. Excessive sweating can cause a temporary depletion.

■ Requirements
UK RNI: 1600 mg (women and men). EU RDA: None.

■ Upper safe limits
See Risks.

■ Interactions
Works in balance with potassium.

■ Risks
Intakes of more than 3.2 g may lead to raised blood pressure in those who are susceptible.

■ Deficiency
None likely.

■ Special needs
People exposed to high temperatures, and/or undergoing intensive physical activity.

■ Good sources
Bacon, ham, olives, shellfish, oysters, smoked fish, soy sauce.

ZINC

The body contains about 2 grams of zinc, mostly found in muscle and bone.

Zinc regulates genetic material and the activities of an enormous number of enzymes. It reinforces the immune system and protects against infection. It is involved in the metabolism of protein and carbohydrate, the production of male sperm and female ova, the formation of bone tissue and healing of wounds.

Zinc is not stored by the body so a daily intake is needed. Zinc from animal sources is usually much better absorbed than that from plant foods.

■ Requirements
UK RNI: 7 mg (women), 9.5 mg (men). EU RDA: 15 mg.

■ Upper safe limits
15 mg.

■ Interactions
High doses interfere with copper metabolism. Alcohol uses extra zinc when metabolised. Necessary for the absorption and effective use of vitamin A and the release of insulin.

■ Risks
High doses may cause nausea and vomiting.

■ Deficiency
The commonest symptoms of deficiency are skin problems, general fatigue, skin disorders, white marks on nails, hair loss, prolonged wound healing and reduced appetite.

■ Special needs
After injury and surgical operations, pregnant and breastfeeding women, growing children, the elderly, vegetarians and vegans.

■ Good sources
Meat, liver, poultry, seafood (especially oysters), eggs, milk, wheat germ, nuts, pulses, bread.

PHYTOCHEMICALS

Phytochemicals (from the Greek *phyto*, meaning plant) is the current buzzword in the field of nutritional research. There are around five hundred of these pharmacological substances, naturally present in fruit, vegetables and some beverages. Since our bodies do not depend on them in the same way as vitamins, for example, they are not classified as essential nutrients. Nevertheless, phytochemicals are biologically active compounds that potentially play a vital role in protecting us from chronic and life-threatening diseases.

Numerous scientific studies indicate that phytochemicals can significantly boost the power of antioxidants, and some are even antioxidants in their own right. Other groups of phytochemicals are known to activate cancer-fighting enzymes, and others still are capable of preventing tumour growth.

There is a long way to go before scientists can conclusively determine their effectiveness, how much we need for protection, and the extent of their bioavailability. However, a strong and consistent pattern is emerging which suggests that diets high in vegetables and fruit can decrease the risk of many cancers and degenerative diseases. The good news is that many of the common vegetables and fruit that most of us eat every day – onions and apples for example – are rich in this new generation of vital nutrients.

BIOFLAVONOIDS

This is a vast and important group of phytochemicals widely acclaimed for their cancer-fighting properties. They act as powerful antioxidants (page 14), fight infection, and reduce inflammation. Bioflavonoids also strengthen the capillaries – the small veins close to the surface of the skin – which means they are useful for dealing with uncomfortable complaints such as bleeding gums, varicose veins and haemorrhoids.

Found in a wide selection of plant foods, bioflavonoids include hesperidin (in citrus fruits), resveratrol (in red wine and grape juice) and rutin (in buckwheat). Quercetin, found in cabbages, green tea and apple peel, is believed to be a powerful anti-inflammatory, anti-viral and anti-tumour agent. It also has antihistamine properties and therefore may help prevent or alleviate hay fever.

CAROTENOIDS

This is a large group of phytochemicals currently the focus of much attention as scientists realise their pharmacological importance. Carotenoids are colourful pigments found in yellow-, orange- and red-fleshed fruit and vegetables. They are also present in dark green vegetables but their colour is masked by the green pigment chlorophyll.

Over five hundred carotenoids have been identified, of which a few are found in the human body. These include the better-known beta-carotene (page 22), as well as alpha-carotene, cryptoxanthin, lutein, zeaxanthin and lycopene.

Carotenoids have a range of biological functions. They are effective antioxidants (page 14) and as such may help protect against a whole host of degenerative diseases. Alpha- and beta-carotenes and cryptoxanthin are converted to vitamin A in the body. Though they perform the same functions as vitamin A, they also have separate functions as carotenoids.

CHLOROPHYLL

Chlorophyll is the pigment responsible for the green colour of plants, although it exists in all plants even if they are not green. There is some evidence that chlorophyll binds with carcinogens (tumour-inducers) and prevents them from damaging DNA in the cell nucleus.

Chlorophyll is anti-bacterial, anti-fungal and anti-inflammatory, and is also thought to stimulate the production of red blood cells in bone marrow. The richest sources are very green plants – for example wheat grass, seaweeds, and algae such as spirulina and chlorella.

Some carotenoids appear to have functions related to specific parts of the body or are associated with decreased risk of specific cancers. For example, lutein and zaxanthin, found in huge amounts in kale, beet greens and spinach, are linked to the part of the retina that is responsible for sharp and detailed vision. They thus have implications for degenerative eye conditions.

A major American study suggests that lycopene, found mainly in tomatoes and tomato products, red-fleshed grapefruit and watermelon, significantly reduced the risk of prostate cancer in men who ate plenty of tomatoes. Cryptoxanthin, found in mangoes, papayas and oranges, is associated with decreased risk of cervical cancer. Beta-carotene is thought to protect against UV radiation.

GLUCOSINOLATES, ISOTHIOCYANATES (ITCs) AND INDOLES

Glucosinolates are broken down into compounds known as ITCs and indoles, which appear to be responsible for their bioactive properties. They are found almost exclusively in cabbage and other Brassicas – turnips, horseradish, kale, broccoli and Brussels sprouts, for example. Numerous case-control studies suggest that glucosinolates are likely to protect against cancers of the rectum, colon and thyroid. It has also been suggested that indoles speed up oestrogen metabolism, and thus may offer some protection against hormone-related cancers, such as breast and womb cancer.

PHYTOESTROGENS

These have a similar structure and function to the human hormone oestradiol. Overproduction of the hormone may stimulate breast cancer, but recent research on animals has indicated that a group of phytoestrogens called lignans and isoflavones (found in soya beans and other pulses) block the absorption of oestrogen and therefore may offer some protection from hormone-related cancers. Genistein, an isoflavone in soya beans, is currently receiving great attention from the scientific community as it has been shown not only to inhibit tumour formation but also to lower blood cholesterol levels.

POLYPHENOLS

High concentrations of polyphenols have been found in green and black tea, red wine and some tree barks. Pycnogenol, found in pine bark, may help delay skin ageing by strengthening connective tissue. Ellagic acid, found in strawberries, blackberries, cherries and grapes may inhibit tumour growth.

SULPHUR COMPOUNDS

Plants from the allium family – for example onions, garlic, leeks and chives – are a major source of sulphur compounds. These appear to offer protection from tumour formation. Some studies suggest that diets high in alliums may decrease the risk of stomach cancer. Garlic is of particular interest, since it is rich in allicin, a substance known for its anti-bacterial, anti-viral and anti-fungal properties. Allicin also lowers LDL blood cholesterol (page 19) and raises HDL cholesterol, thus reducing the risk of heart disease and stroke.

HOW TO ACHIEVE A BALANCED DIET

WHAT EXACTLY IS A BALANCED DIET?

Government nutritionists, food manufacturers and supermarkets are among those who steadfastly bombard us with messages that centre around the importance of a 'balanced diet'. But what should be balanced with what? And why does the advice seem to change so often?

The term 'balanced diet' dates back to the days of post-war food shortages when people ran the risk of going short of the nutrients essential to good health. This meant that meals had to be 'balanced' by using a judicious mixture of whatever foods were available which would between them supply essential nutrients in more or less correct proportions. A balanced diet, therefore, is one that supplies the body with the necessary energy, dietary fibre, protein, vitamins and minerals in adequate but not excessive amounts.

The problem we face today, however, is not one of shortage but of excess – of food, of information, of choice, and of advice. So without a basic knowledge of the relationship between food and health, it can be hard to decide what to eat, and what not to eat. This section gives you the facts you need to put together a balanced diet that is suitable for you and anyone you regularly cook for.

A balanced diet has definite benefits – you'll have more energy, improved resistance to disease and a greater sense of physical and mental well-being. It's not hard to put in place. The key things to remember are variety and – let's not forget this – enjoyment. Variety makes for more interesting eating, and ensures that you get a good spread of nutrients. Enjoyment means you are more likely to pay attention to what you are eating.

LIFESTYLE CHANGES

Ideally we should all eat at least one balanced meal a day. However, the way we live may make this difficult. For many of us life is a hectic rush, and we sometimes have to rely on snacks and convenience foods to keep going. More and more people live alone – often from choice – and may feel disinclined to bother with traditional meals and meal times. Family life has changed too. People don't always eat together; and with the majority of women now in paid

STRIKING A BALANCE

■ Enjoy what you eat.

■ Eat a variety of foods.

■ Try new ways of cooking.

■ Eat the right amount to maintain a healthy weight.

■ Eat lots of starch and fibre.

■ Cut down on fat.

■ Keep sugary foods and drinks to a minimum.

■ Look after vitamins and minerals when you cook.

■ Keep alcohol within sensible limits.

BIOAVAILABILITY

Though we may think we are getting the right balance of nutrients, there is the question of 'bioavailability' – a term scientists use to describe the proportion of a nutrient that is actively absorbed and used by the body. Even though some foods may be rich in vitamins and minerals, there are situations in which a nutrient may either help or inhibit the absorption of other nutrients. Unless you are a trained nutritionist, it is almost impossible to fully understand the intricate mechanisms of bioavailability and the implications in terms of what you actually eat. However, the fact that such interactions exist makes it vital to eat as many different foods as possible. By doing so, you widen the net of available nutrients and stand a better chance of compensating for any that might be poorly absorbed.

employment, who's going to shop and get the meal ready anyway? Another factor is that the food we eat today has changed. The archetypal balanced meal used to be the traditional 'meat and two veg'. But now we live in a multi-cultural culinary world in which we can flit from cuisine to cuisine at whim, often relying on takeaways and ready meals.

THE BEAUTY OF BALANCE

Attempting to maintain a balanced diet usually boils down to juggling what we know we should eat with what can be practically achieved and what we actually enjoy. The great thing about balance, however, is that it always achieves equilibrium over time. In terms of diet, this means that you don't necessarily have to eat nutritionally sound meals every day, but you should aim to do so over a week or ten days.

The tables on the following pages are a useful reference for comparing the amounts of nutrients in various foods. To help you check out your intake, we have given the values for an average serving instead of the more usual 100 grams of food. However, don't feel you have to start weighing food and calculating nutrients every time you plan a meal. If you eat a wide variety of foods from the following five food groups you should be getting enough of each nutrient:

- Cereals and potatoes
- Fruit and vegetables
- Dairy foods
- Protein foods
- Fats and sugary foods

We should not eat an equal amount from each group. To get an idea of the correct proportions, think of the food groups as a pyramid, with the ones we should be eating most at the bottom, and those for eating occasionally at the top. Fats and sugary foods form the tip of the pyramid; cereals and potatoes form the base.

BALANCING THE FIVE FOOD GROUPS

This table shows you in more detail what each group includes, the main nutrients provided, and the recommended number of servings a day:

Group	What is included	Main nutrients	Servings per day
1 Cereals and potatoes Pulses can make up part of this group.	Bread, pasta, couscous, rice, oats, polenta, whole grains (eg buckwheat, millet, quinoa) breakfast cereals, potatoes, yams, sweet potatoes.	Complex carbohydrates, NSP (dietary fibre), B vitamins, calcium, iron.	Six
2 Fruit and vegetables Pulses can make up part of this group.	Fresh, frozen, canned fruit and vegetables, dried fruit, vegetable and fruit juices.	Vitamin C, carotenoids and other phytochemicals, B vitamins, vitamin K, calcium, magnesium, potassium, NSP.	Five
3 Dairy foods This group excludes butter and cream.	Milk, cheese, yogurt, fromage frais.	Protein, fats, vitamins A and D, B vitamins, calcium, magnesium.	Two
4 Protein foods Meat, poultry, fish, eggs, pulses and nuts.	Salami, bacon, sausages and other meat products. Fresh, frozen and canned fish. Fresh, canned or dried beans, chick peas and lentils.	Protein, fats, complex carbohydrates and NSP (pulses and nuts only), B vitamins, vitamin D (eggs) vitamin E, iron, zinc. magnesium.	Two
5 Fats and sugary foods	Butter, lard, ghee, margarine, other spreading fats, oils, oil-based salad dressings, mayonnaise, cream, chips, fried savoury snacks, pastry, cakes, biscuits, chocolate, sweets, ice-cream, soft drinks, pickles, jams, sugar.	Fats, extrinsic sugars, vitamins A, E and D.	Keep to a minimum

FOOD AND MOOD

If you suffer from mild depression, especially in winter, a diet rich in complex carbohydrates can help lift your mood. The brain contains chemicals, known as neurotransmitters, which pass messages from one nerve to another. The two neurotransmitters that affect mood – serotonin and noradrenaline – come mainly from carbohydrate foods. This may explain why a jacket potato or a dish of pasta can be deeply comforting at times.

INCREASING YOUR INTAKE

■ Base your main meal on a grain. For variety, choose a different one each day.

■ Middle Eastern, Asian and Mexican cuisines are all based on carbohydrates. Try a new dish each week.

■ Eat two slices of wholemeal or high-fibre bread with each meal.

■ Use thicker slices of bread for sandwiches.

■ Use wholemeal flour in baking.

■ Eat wholegrain breakfast cereals or those made with oats.

■ Make salads with pasta, rice, couscous or pulses. Mix them with plenty of chopped raw vegetables, herbs and spices.

■ Add cooked rice or bulghar wheat to soups.

■ Eat jacket potato skin (wash well before cooking).

■ Eat malt bread, scones or currant buns for a snack, instead of sugary foods or crisps.

GROUP 1: CEREALS AND POTATOES

Foods from this group should form the main part of most meals and snacks. They provide energy-rich complex carbohydrates, B vitamins, and non-starch polysaccharides (fibre). Potatoes, sweet potatoes and yams are especially valuable because they provide vitamin C too. Yellow- or orange-fleshed varieties are also rich in beta-carotene, an important antioxidant (page 14) which may reduce the risk of some cancers.

Wholegrain foods such as brown rice and wholemeal bread contain more NSP and vitamins than refined versions. However, if you simply cannot abide wholemeal pasta or brown rice, for example, it's better to use the ordinary kind rather than forcing yourself to eat something you don't enjoy. There are plenty of other fibre-rich foods you can use to make up the balance. Make sure you include some containing soluble NSP, as this can help keep cholesterol levels under control (page 19).

Many people mistakenly believe that carbohydrate foods are fattening. On their own, they are not intrinsically so, but it depends how you cook them, what you cook them in and what you add to them. For example, a portion of plainly boiled potatoes contains about 100 calories, but if you roast them the calories more than double. It's the same with pasta – a tomato sauce doesn't add many calories, but a creamy sauce or lashings of olive oil and Parmesan cheese send them sky high.

DAILY INTAKE

The current advice is that at least 50% of our daily energy needs should come from carbohydrates. This is 258 grams for a healthy woman of normal weight, and 340 grams for a man. Look at the table (below) to check the carbohydrate content of various foods. Then calculate what you should be eating to meet the target. The serving sizes are for a woman with an average appetite; men might need a bit more.

MAIN NUTRIENTS IN SELECTED CEREALS, POTATOES, PULSES

Average serving	Cals	Carbohydrate g	Total NSP g	Soluble NSP g
1 slice wholemeal bread	75	14.5	2.0	0.5
Wholemeal pitta bread	159	34.8	3.4	1.3
Naan bread	571	85.0	3.2	1.5
Bowl of muesli	364	71.1	6.1	1.8
Bowl of porridge	186	21.9	1.3	0.5
2 heaped tbsp wheat bran	31	4.0	12.7	0.5
Pasta, plain, cooked	156	33.3	1.8	0.9
Brown rice, cooked	211	48.1	1.2	trace
Jacket potato with skin	272	63.4	5.4	3.0
Yam, boiled	172	42.9	1.8	0.8
Kidney beans, cooked	77	13.1	5.0	2.4
Lentils, cooked	79	12.6	2.9	0.7

GROUP 2: **FRUIT AND VEGETABLES**

Fruit, vegetables and salads are the real superfoods of nutrition. They do more than simply provide vitamins and minerals; they are packed with biologically active substances called phytochemicals (page 37), which scientists believe may help protect against cancers and heart disease.

Top of the fruit league are mangoes. One delicious fruit provides nearly three times your daily vitamin C requirement, as well as a massive amount of beta-carotene (a major phytochemical) and a good dose of the all-important soluble fibre. Papayas, guavas and melons also score highly. Leafy greens such as kale, spring greens and spinach are also counted as superfoods, along with butternut squash, red peppers and broccoli. They all provide an abundance of beta-carotene and generous amounts of vitamin C and folic acid.

FIVE A DAY

There is almost universal agreement among government nutritionists that we should be eating a minimum of five servings of fruit and vegetables a day, not counting potatoes. That's about 450 g (1 lb) in total. Along with carbohydrate foods, they should form the largest part of our diet.

There are major health benefits to be had from following the advice. There's strong evidence that a diet rich in fruit and vegetables not only protects against specific cancers and damage to the cells from free radicals, but also reduces the risk of heart disease. The fibre in fruit and vegetables makes the bowel work more efficiently, and their vitamin C content helps the body to absorb iron.

DECIDING ON SERVINGS

The table overleaf gives you an idea of the main nutrients in selected fruit and vegetables, based on average servings. In the case of salad leaves, the serving is based on a decent-sized handful that takes up at least half your plate – not a few leaves in a sandwich or a simple salad garnish. A serving of cooked vegetables is about four heaped tablespoonfuls (or two large serving spoons).

Fruit and vegetables have different nutritional qualities, so you should aim to vary your choice as much as possible. For example, strawberries are rich in vitamin C but low in beta-carotene; parsnips are low in vitamin C and beta-carotene, but contain relatively high levels of soluble NSP.

Frozen and canned fruit and vegetables count as part of your five servings, though canned products are generally not as nutritious as fresh or frozen. With the exception of canned tomatoes, they should be kept for emergencies only. Dried fruit can be included – a serving is about eight dried apricots (50 g) or a handful of raisins (35 g). Fruit and vegetable juices can also make up the total, though not fruit squashes. A wineglass (125 ml) of juice counts as a serving. Since fruit juices contain no fibre, it's best to count them towards only one serving a day.

INCREASING YOUR INTAKE

Although the latest statistics show that intake of fruit and vegetables is on the increase, most of us still don't eat enough. However, once you get into the 'five a day' habit, it's relatively easy to build up your intake.

INCREASING YOUR INTAKE

- Have a bowl of fruit salad or berry fruits for breakfast.

- Top muesli or yogurt with sliced fresh fruit.

- Use the juice of two oranges to moisten muesli or wheatflake bars.

- Mash a banana and spread on to toast.

- Have a handful of dried fruit as a mid-morning snack.

- Take sticks of crisp raw vegetables for lunch – eat with cottage cheese.

- Treat yourself to a juicy nectarine or papaya as an afternoon snack.

- Keep frozen peas, sweetcorn or broad beans in the freezer, and add to soups and casseroles, or serve with fresh leafy veg.

- Serve pasta with a side dish of green beans, spinach or mushrooms.

- Aim to serve a root vegetable (excluding potatoes), a green vegetable and a yellow- or orange-fleshed vegetable with your evening meal.

- Aim to eat broccoli, kale or spring greens three or four times a week.

MAIN NUTRIENTS IN SELECTED FRESH FRUIT (edible parts of medium-sized fruits)

Average serving	Vitamin C mg	Beta-carotene µg	Potassium mg	Total NSP g	Soluble NSP g
Apple	9	10	130	2.0	0.9
Banana	11	21	400	1.1	0.7
Blackberries, 15	11	59	120	2.3	1.2
Cherries, small bowl	11	23	210	0.9	0.5
Dates, 5	18	23	513	2.3	0.6
Figs, 2	2	165	220	1.7	1.0
Grapefruit, pink, ½	29	224	200	1.0	0.7
Grapes, small bunch	3	17	210	0.7	0.4
Guava	230	380	230	3.7	1.0
Kiwi fruit, 2	74	43	363	2.4	1.1
Mango, 1 large	111	4365	540	11.2	4.8
Melon, cantaloupe, ½	78	2970	210	3.0	0.9
Nectarine	41	50	187	1.3	0.7
Orange	86	38	240	2.7	1.8
Passionfruit, 3	10	162	90	1.5	0.2
Pineapple, large slice	10	14	128	1.0	0.1
Plums, 2	4	325	264	1.8	1.2
Strawberries, 8	77	8	160	1.1	0.5

MAIN NUTRIENTS IN SELECTED FRESH VEGETABLES (boiled or baked weight unless stated otherwise)

Average serving	Vitamin C mg	Beta-carotene µg	Folate µg	Potassium mg	Total NSP g	Soluble NSP g
Asparagus, 5	13	656	194	275	1.8	0.9
Bean sprouts, raw	4	10	31	37	0.8	0.3
Beetroot	3	7	55	255	1.0	0.5
Broad beans	16	114	26	152	4.3	1.0
Broccoli	44	475	64	170	2.3	1.0
Cabbage, Savoy	19	625	39	140	2.0	1.0
Carrots	2	5144	13	96	2.0	1.1
Courgettes	11	440	31	210	1.2	0.6
Kale	71	3350	86	160	2.8	1.7
Lettuce, raw	2	107	17	66	0.3	—
Onions	6	22	41	360	3.1	1.8
Parsnips	8	24	38	280	3.8	2.2
Peas	11	172	19	161	3.1	0.9
Peppers, red, raw	98	2215	15	112	1.1	0.5
Spinach	10	4966	117	230	0.6	1.0
Spring greens	77	2255	66	160	2.6	1.3
Squash, butternut	23	3525	29	420	2.1	0.9
Sweetcorn kernels	5	17	24	240	1.5	0.1
Tomatoes, raw, 2	14	527	14	213	0.9	0.3
Watercress, raw	19	756	not known	69	0.5	0.2

GROUP 3: DAIRY FOODS

Dairy foods have traditionally been highly valued, associated with energy, health and wholesomeness. A glass of creamy milk, crusty bread thickly spread with butter, a wedge of crumbly fresh cheese – what could be more delectable? However, though packed with nutrients, they are also high in saturated fat – the kind that clogs up your arteries. The advice is therefore to eat them in moderate amounts – no more than two servings a day, with low-fat versions if possible.

Dairy foods are the biggest single source of dietary calcium, essential for healthy bones and teeth. They also provide protein, vitamins A, B2, B12 and D. Lower-fat versions are equally useful sources of these nutrients. We should try to have at least a glass of milk every day, along with a piece of cheese. If you don't like milk, have yogurt instead.

KEEPING AN EYE ON THE FAT

Dairy foods should be chosen carefully so that you make the most of their beneficial nutrients without unduly pushing up your fat intake. The maximum daily fat allowance for a woman of normal weight and energy requirements is 71 grams. Use the tables to calculate your intake, bearing in mind the additional fat you get from meat, fish, fatty spreads and snacks.

MAIN NUTRIENTS IN SELECTED DAIRY FOODS

Average serving	Cals	Protein g	Fat g	Vitamin A µg	Calcium mg
Cheese					
Brie, 1 slice	128	7.7	10.8	114	216
Cheddar, 1 slice	165	10.2	13.8	130	288
Cottage, 3 tbsp	44	6.2	1.8	20	33
Edam, 1 slice	133	10.4	10.2	70	308
reduced-fat, 1 slice	92	13.0	4.4	30	308
Feta, 1 slice	100	6.2	8.1	88	144
Fromage frais, 3 tbsp	57	3.4	3.6	50	45
Mozzarella, 1 slice	116	10.0	8.4	96	236
Parmesan, 2 tbsp	45	3.9	3.3	35	120
Quark, 2 tbsp	22	4.4	trace	trace	36
Ricotta, 2 tbsp	43	2.8	3.3	56	72
Stilton, blue, 1 slice	164	9.1	14.2	142	128
Milk					
Skimmed, glass, 200 m	66	6.6	0.2	2	240
Semi-skimmed, glass, 200 ml	92	6.6	3.2	42	240
Whole, glass, 200 ml	132	6.4	7.8	104	230
Buttermilk, 100 ml	37	3.4	0.5	7	120
Yogurt					
Whole milk, small carton	99	7.1	3.6	35	250
Low-fat, small carton	70	6.4	1.0	10	238
Greek, small carton	144	8.0	11.4	143	188

FAT FACTS

■ Hard cheeses such as Cheddar and Parmesan are highest in fat. They are strongly flavoured so you don't need too much. Grating makes them go further.

■ Reduced-fat Edam is a useful all-purpose hard cheese.

■ Ricotta and cottage cheeses are low in fat. Add flavour with herbs and spices, and serve a large spoonful with a leafy salad.

■ Try fromage frais or smetana (a low-fat cultured milk product) instead of cream or soured cream.

■ Use skimmed milk or buttermilk in sauces, custards and baking.

■ To make yogurt more palatable, add fresh fruit, honey or a few drops of vanilla essence.

GROUP 4: **PROTEIN FOODS**

Although we get protein from dairy foods and some carbohydrates, the major source comes from the foods in this group. There are two types of proteins: those from animal sources and those from plants.

AMINO ACIDS

During digestion, protein is broken down into amino acids, eight of which are essential (page 20). Animal protein supplies all eight, but some amino acids are missing from plant proteins (with the exception of soya beans). However, if you combine plant proteins with dairy products, or eat a mixture of different types (pulses, cereals and nuts), the amino acids missing in one type will be provided by those in another. For example, cereals lack an amino acid called lysine, and pulses (except for soya beans) do not contain methionine. However, if you eat chilli beans with a wheat tortilla, or baked beans on toast, all the amino acids will be present. (See also *Vegetarian Needs*, page 61.)

The table opposite lists the protein content of various foods. An average healthy woman needs 45 grams of protein a day; a man needs about 55 grams. It is relatively easy to clock up two daily servings, especially if you eat meat.

FAT WATCH

When choosing protein foods, keep an eye on your fat intake. Animal foods tend to be high in fat, much of it saturated. Exceptions are venison, rabbit, chicken breast without skin, and exotic meats such as ostrich and kangaroo – now making an appearance in some supermarkets. These meats may not be a regular part of your diet, but are worth including when you can.

Unless you are counting calories, don't worry too much about the fat in oily fish, such as mackerel and salmon. It's the omega-3 kind that we should be eating more of in our diet.

Relative to weight, eggs are high in fat – mainly monounsaturated but some saturated. Pulses contain very little fat; nuts contain lots, though it is mainly polyunsaturated. Nuts are also an excellent source of vitamin E, which is an important antioxidant.

VITAMIN AND MINERAL CONTENT

The protein foods in this group are a source of iron and zinc. Iron is well absorbed from animal foods, but needs help from vitamin C to be adequately absorbed from plant foods. Generally speaking, the darker the meat the higher the iron content. Protein foods are also a major source of energy-releasing B vitamins, including the vital vitamin B12. With the exception of sea vegetables, B12 is found only in foods of animal origin such as liver, eggs and milk.

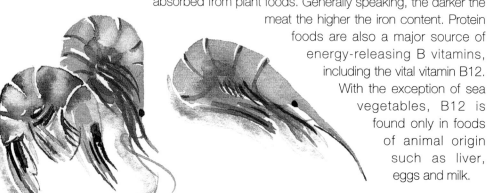

NUTRIENTS IN SELECTED PROTEIN FOODS (not cooked in fat unless stated)

Average serving	Cals	Protein g	Fat g	Iron mg	Zinc mg
Meat and poultry					
Bacon, 3 lean rashers	131	13.7	8.5	0.7	1.7
Beef, minced	209	21.8	13.5	2.2	5.0
Lamb chops, loin, 2	488	42.4	35.4	3.0	5.0
Pork, leg joint, lean	185	34.7	5.1	1.2	3.3
Rabbit	143	26.5	4.0	1.4	2.1
Venison	206	44.5	3.1	6.4	4.9
Chicken breast, meat only	184	37.2	3.9	0.6	1.0
meat and skin	216	36.1	8.0	0.8	1.0
Duck, meat only	244	31.6	13.0	3.4	3.3
Fish					
Cod fillet	100	22.3	1.1	0.1	0.6
Mackerel	382	33.3	27.7	1.3	1.1
Mussels, 10	73	11.7	1.9	4.8	1.6
Prawns, 6 large	50	11.3	0.5	0.6	1.1
Salmon steak	344	38.7	20.9	0.8	1.1
Tuna, canned in brine, drained	99	23.5	0.6	1.0	0.7
canned in oil, drained	189	27.1	9.0	1.6	1.1
Alternatives					
Egg, large	88	7.5	6.5	1.1	0.8
Soya beans	106	10.5	5.5	2.3	0.7
Tofu	44	4.9	2.5	0.7	0.4
Kidney beans	77	6.3	0.4	1.9	0.8
Chick peas	91	5.9	1.6	1.6	0.9
Almonds, raw, 25	153	5.3	14.0	7.6	0.8
Brazil nuts, raw, 10	273	5.6	27.3	1.0	1.7

CHOOSING PROTEIN FOODS

■ Eat the meat but not the fat. Trim off visible fat and choose lean cuts. Eat game meats such as venison and rabbit more often. They are low in fat.

■ Eat fish two or three times a week. Be adventurous – try monkfish, red snapper or parrot fish. Include oily fish such as sardines, trout and salmon.

■ Keep canned sardines or mackerel in your storecupboard. Spread on crackers as a snack.

■ Add pulses to meat casseroles and reduce the meat content.

■ Make protein-rich pâtés with mashed pulses, garlic and lemon juice.

■ Use tofu in stir-fries to give it more flavour.

(see also *Cooking for Health*, page 97)

◼ Use moist fillings in sandwiches then you'll need only a smear of spread or butter.

◼ Use whipped cream to top desserts and soups. Because it contains air, you won't need so much.

◼ Choose low-fat alternatives. Try smetana instead of soured cream, or Quark instead of cream cheese.

◼ Use reduced-sugar alternatives, but check labels (page 93). Many products contain more sugar than you would expect.

◼ Choose malt loaf, muffins and scones for snacks. They are lower in fat than other cakes.

◼ Cut down, or cut out, sugar in tea and coffee.

GROUP 5: FATS AND SUGARY FOODS

This group includes all fats, oils, dressings, spreads and cream, as well as fatty savoury snacks, sauces, preserves, ice-cream, soft drinks, foods that contain sugar, and sugar itself. These foods should make up the smallest part of your diet. With the possible exceptions of spreads and cooking oils, you don't need to eat them every day.

FATTY FOODS

We all need some fat in our diet to supply essential fatty acids (page 18). Babies and toddlers especially need fat for growth and as a concentrated source of energy. However, the foods in this group tend to be high in saturated fatty acids which can cause raised blood cholesterol levels and increase the risk of heart disease. Over-consumption of saturated fatty acids also leads to obesity and diabetes, and is associated with some cancers.

Foods like hard margarine, biscuits and cakes also contain trans fats (page 19) which are just as harmful as saturates. Be wary of products with the word 'hydrogenated' on the label – it means they contain trans fats.

Soft fats and oils contain mono- and polyunsaturated fatty acids. Though they are better for you in some respects, they contain just as many calories, and should be kept to a minimum if you are watching your weight.

SUGARY FOODS

Sugar crops up in many guises, and where you least expect it – in baked beans, tomato ketchup and some breakfast cereals, for example. The most harmful sugars are the free-floating extrinsic type (page 15), found in foods such as jams, honey, syrup, soft drinks and table sugar. They are loaded with calories, contain very few nutrients, and are a major cause of tooth decay. The one exception is milk sugar (lactose). Although this is an extrinsic sugar, its chemical structure is such that it does not damage the teeth.

The sugars in fruit and vegetables are contained within the structure of the cell, and because of this do not contribute to tooth decay. However, if these sugars are released from the cells, as they are in fruit juice, they can cause tooth decay in the same way as extrinsic sugars.

TABLE SUGAR

Because sugar is found in so many foods, we don't really need table sugar at all – except to make strongly acidic fruits such as rhubarb or blackcurrants more palatable. However, if you do use table sugar, don't be misled into thinking muscovado or raw sugars are a healthier choice. They may sound more wholesome, but they are no better for you than white.

The table opposite shows you the calorie, fat, sugar and sodium (salt) content of a range of commonly used foods. Many of the foods are processed and consequently contain high levels of sugar and sodium. The recommended maximum intakes for a healthy woman are 71 grams of fat, 50 grams of extrinsic sugars and 1600 milligrams of sodium for a healthy diet.

BREAKDOWN OF COMMONLY USED FOODS

Average serving	Cals	Fat g	Sugars g	Sodium mg
Butter, salted, on 1 slice bread	74	8.2	trace	75
Ghee, vegetable, 2 tbsp	269	30.0	trace	trace
Low-fat spread, on 1 slice bread	27	2.8	trace	46
Margarine, polyunsaturated,				
on 1 slice bread	52	5.8	trace	48
Oil, 1 tbsp	99	11.0	none	trace
Cream, double, 2 tbsp	157	16.8	0.9	13
whipping, 2 tbsp	130	13.8	1.1	14
single, 2 tbsp	69	6.7	1.4	17
soured, 2 tbsp	72	7.0	1.3	14
Biscuits, chocolate digestive	89	4.3	5.1	81
Breakfast cereal:				
Rice crispies	129	0.3	3.7	441
Sugar Puffs	162	0.4	28.3	5
Chocolate, plain, small bar	255	14.0	31.3	3
Crisps, small bag	159	10.2	0.2	252
Danish pastry, medium	411	19.4	31.4	209
Flapjack, medium	290	16.0	21.3	168
Fruit cake, 1 slice	319	11.6	38.8	225
Honey, on 1 slice bread	29	none	7.6	1
Ice-cream, vanilla	146	7.4	16.6	52
Jam, on 1 slice bread	26	none	7.0	3
Mayonnaise, 2 tbsp	207	22.7	0.4	135
Pickle, sweet	49	trace	11.9	564
Salad dressing, French, 2 tbsp	196	21.7	0.1	282
Soy sauce, 1 tbsp	6	trace	1.1	1068
Sugar, 1 tsp	20	none	5.0	trace
Carbonated drink, small can	98	trace	25.8	20

SALT

Most of us eat more salt than we need. This can contribute to high blood pressure, which in turn can lead to heart disease, stroke and kidney problems.

A little salt is useful in cooking as it brings the flavours together, but don't add more than a pinch or two, and try not to use it at the table. Learn to use spices, herbs, lemon juice and vinegar to add flavour in cooking, instead of salt.

Many processed foods are high in salt, and not always the obvious ones. Shop-bought cakes and pastries, for instance, contain a surprising amount; sweet pickle is loaded with it; and 1 tbsp soy sauce contains over 1 g. Even foods like digestive biscuits contain a minute amount, but it all adds up to an unhealthy level.

PUTTING IT INTO PRACTICE

Ideally, the day should begin with a low-fat, energy-boosting breakfast, the main meal should be taken at lunch time, and the final meal of the day should be relatively light. If your job involves lunch-time entertaining, this schedule may suit you best of all. However, many of us are likely to wait until evening for the main meal. If this is the case, try and eat early enough to allow the body time to digest – two or three hours at least. If you go to bed on a full stomach, you are likely to wake up feeling sluggish and muzzy-headed.

How you plan your meal schedule is a matter of personal choice. Body clocks and metabolic rates vary from person to person, so we get hungry at different times. When and how often you eat also depends on lifestyle and activity levels. Some people prefer four or five light meals a day, others feel better with one or two largish meals a day, supplemented by snacks.

BREAKFAST

Breakfast normally follows a long period of fasting during sleep, and your blood sugar levels will be at rock bottom. It's important to refuel if you are to avoid that mid-morning energy dip. You don't have to eat a substantial breakfast but it should be a sustaining one. Make enough time for breakfast, rather than eating on the run. By doing so, you will feel more in control, and this in turn reduces stress levels. Breakfast is also a great opportunity to start clocking up the recommended five servings of fruit and veg.

A BALANCED BREAKFAST SHOULD CONTAIN:

■ About 25% of your daily calorie intake

■ A mix of starchy carbohydrates, sugars and fibre

■ A small amount of fat

■ A reasonable amount of protein

■ Some calcium

BREAKFAST IDEAS

Fruit juice, muesli and wholemeal toast are an excellent nutrient-rich choice. Juice counts as one serving of fruit and provides vitamin C and minerals. If you find orange juice too acidic early in the morning, try something else. Pear, pineapple or tropical fruit juices are deliciously refreshing and easier on the stomach. Muesli and toast are packed with energy-giving carbohydrates, B vitamins and fibre. Milk on your cereal provides calcium and protein. Oats in muesli are particularly nutritious since they provide soluble fibre, which can help lower bad LDL blood cholesterol. Porridge would be another good choice in this respect.

■ A second serving of fruit can be squeezed in by slicing a couple of kiwi fruit or a few strawberries over your cereal, or mixing in chopped dried apricots or a handful of raisins, or spreading your toast with mashed banana.

■ Although it's a good idea to start the day with carbohydrate-rich foods, it's not the end of the world if you don't. But you will need to make up for the deficit in other meals during the day.

■ For a calcium-rich breakfast, a bowl of yogurt with a sprinkling of sunflower seeds or chopped nuts would provide just over a third of your daily requirement and a useful amount of protein. Nuts and seeds provide essential fatty acids.

■ For a light but vitamin-packed breakfast, try a bowl of fruit salad made with fresh or dried fruit, or a mixture, topped with a dollop of yogurt and a few nuts. The fruit will raise your blood sugar but you will need to boost your energy with a mid-morning starchy snack.

■ For a protein-oriented breakfast, try the continental habit of a slice of cheese or ham with a tomato and a hunk of decent bread. Or a smoked salmon-filled bagel spread with a small amount of very-low-fat fromage frais. Eggs are another option. They are a good source of protein but are high in fat, so make sure you don't exceed the WHO's upper limit of ten a week. Boil or poach them to avoid adding extra fat.

■ Eating healthily doesn't mean saying goodbye to the traditional British cooked breakfast. Poach the egg, or fry it in a non-stick pan sprayed with oil. Reduce the fat in bacon by grilling on a rack until crisp.

LUNCH

This should be the largest meal of the day so the body has time to digest it properly. For many of us, this simply isn't practical, especially during the working week. Nevertheless, even a light lunch should be nutritionally balanced and sustaining enough to keep up your energy levels until the evening.

No matter how packed your schedule, don't be tempted to grab a sandwich and eat on the run. Your body will absorb more nutrients if you take the time to sit down, relax and enjoy your lunch. Resting quietly for five or ten minutes afterwards will give the body an opportunity to digest. If you take a packed lunch to the office, or if you work from home, prepare food ahead of time so everything is on hand when you need it. When choosing your lunch, think about what you're going to have in the evening, so you don't double up or miss out on various nutrients.

GO FOR PROTEIN

A lunch based on carbohydrates can leave you feeling sluggish, so leave these for your evening meal and concentrate on protein foods instead. Useful protein foods include cooked chicken breast (without skin) or lean meat, canned tuna, fingers of smoked trout or mackerel, hard-boiled egg, a wedge of thick omelette, marinated tofu, or a portion of nut or bean pâté. Make these the basis of a substantial salad, or use as a filling for a baguette, pitta bread or a sandwich made with thick slices of wholemeal bread.

Bread will contribute sufficient carbohydrate, as will small portions of hummus, cooked kidney beans, rice, bulghar wheat, potatoes or oat cakes. Cheese, yogurt, white bread, lentils, chick-peas, beans and nuts are good sources of calcium. Make it a rule to finish with a piece of fresh fruit or some dried fruit, especially if lunch hasn't included a salad.

SALADS

If you're going to have a salad, make it a big one. Almost anything can go into it – not just lettuce, tomato and cucumber, but grated raw root vegetables, sliced peppers, cooked grains and pulses, yogurt or cottage cheese, nuts and seeds, nuggets of crisp lean bacon, olives, cheeses. The choice is endless.

For nutritional balance, base your salad on a protein food, then add smaller portions of calcium and carbohydrate-rich foods, an orange- or yellow-fleshed vegetable, and plenty of greenery. Keep dressings simple – a splash of good olive oil or extra-virgin sunflower oil, and a few drops of lemon juice, soy sauce or balsamic vinegar are all that's needed. A salad consisting of a piece of cold cooked trout, a few waxy new potatoes, a portion of cottage cheese sprinkled with sunflower seeds, carrot sticks, a handful of cherry tomatoes, crisp lettuce leaves, watercress and an olive or two would provide you with a good balance of protein, calcium, carbohydrate, vitamins and essential fatty acids. See right for more ideas.

A BALANCED LUNCH SHOULD CONTAIN:

■ A large proportion of your daily protein intake

■ A smaller amount of carbohydrate

■ Some calcium

■ One or two servings of fruit or veg

■ A little fat

SUBSTANTIAL SALADS

■ Crumbled feta cheese, grated kohlrabi, shredded green cabbage, diced green pepper, grated carrot, spring onions, pumpkin seeds, chives, pitta bread.

■ Diced smoked pork, shredded red cabbage, radishes, new potatoes dressed with yogurt, pistachio nuts, fresh dill.

■ Strips of turkey breast, chopped papaya, shredded Chinese leaves, bean sprouts, watercress, cashew nuts, cooked rice mixed with soy sauce and a few drops of sesame oil.

■ Kidney beans, shredded white, red and green cabbage, celery, grated carrot, cottage cheese, bulghar wheat, hazelnuts, dill, chives.

SOUP

Soup is ideal lunch material, as it can sometimes be too filling to eat with a main meal. Easily digested but satisfying, a thick, hearty soup served with a hunk of wholemeal bread will provide a good balance of nutrients. However, do beware of processed soups – they often contain lots of salt and fat, and very few real ingredients. If you buy a ready-made soup, choose the chilled type rather than canned or packet soups.

Home-made soup is best of all. Pulses and grains, chunks of omelette, morsels of meat or chicken, or cubes of cheese all add bulk and protein. Add extra nutrients with a swirl of colourful vegetable purée, yogurt, fromage frais or a slick of olive oil. Sprinkle with seeds, herbs, diced raw vegetables, croûtons, or crushed spices sizzled in oil. It is these embellishments that bring a soup to life and add to your enjoyment.

A BALANCED EVENING MEAL SHOULD CONTAIN:

■ 40% cereals or potatoes

■ 40% vegetables and fruit

■ 20% meat, fish or alternatives

■ A little fat

THE EVENING MEAL

The evening meal is an opportunity to go to town on carbohydrates. They have a calming effect, which can manifest itself as sluggishness during the day but allows you to wind down in the evening. We need less protein and fat at this time of day. Both take longer to digest, and are likely to lead to a restless night if the digestive process is still continuing when you go to bed. Try to eat the evening meal as early as possible. You can always top up with a light mid-evening snack or a piece of fruit.

PLANNING THE MENU

■ When deciding what to eat, think of the carbohydrate element first, then plan the rest of the meal around it. Be adventurous and try a variety of carbohydrates – don't just stick with potatoes, rice and pasta. As with fruit and vegetables, different carbohydrates provide different types and amounts of other nutrients, so the more you try, the wider your intake is going to be (see *A Healthy Storecupboard*, page 90). Carbohydrates form the backbone of healthy cuisines the world over – Middle Eastern, Asian and Latin American, to name but a few. Broaden your culinary repertoire and try a new dish each week – this will also add interest and variety to meals.

■ An equally important part of the menu are vegetables and salads. There is an ever-growing choice of vegetables and salad ingredients in the shops (see *Shopping for Fresh Food*, page 82). So again, try something different, but do include leafy greens at least every other day. Increase variety by serving a mixture of several vegetables in small amounts, then you can gradually introduce new ones.

■ Protein foods should make up the smallest portion on your plate, especially the fatty type from animal sources. A small amount of meat will go further if you chop it into small pieces and use in a stir-fry or casserole. Bulk out meat-based casseroles with chick-peas, lentils or beans, and reduce the meat content accordingly. Try to eat fish more often – aim for two or three times a week, and include oily fish such as sardines and trout as often as possible.

JUST DESSERTS!

For everyday eating, a dessert based on fresh fruit adds to your 'five a day' and provides vital vitamins and extra fibre. Alternatively, a milk pudding, fromage frais or yogurt can be used to top up calcium intake. Indulgences such as gateaux and flans are all high in sugar and fat, and are best reserved for an occasional treat.

HEALTHY INSPIRATIONS

An evening meal doesn't have to be the traditional British meat and two veg, although this can be adapted to become part of a healthy balanced diet. Here are a few ideas to whet the appetite.

For an Asian vegetable stir-fry recipe, see page 250.

■ **Taste of Asia** For an evening meal with an Asian twist, choose a large serving of jasmine rice or noodles, a large serving of stir-fried shredded green cabbage, bok choi, spring onions and shiitake mushrooms, and a plainly grilled salmon tail fillet.

Dessert could be a luscious tropical fruit salad of mango, papaya, passion-fruit and pineapple. White rice contains less fibre than brown, but there is plenty in the vegetables and fruit, which are also brimming with vitamins, antioxidants and phytochemicals. The salmon provides protein and the all-important omega-3 essential fatty acids.

For an Italian-style seafood pasta recipe, see page 256.

■ **Speedy Italian** For a quick, well-balanced Italian supper, make a large serving of pasta (shapes rather than ribbons are better for this) and mix with plenty of steamed courgettes or broccoli florets. Top with crispy snippets of grilled bacon or pancetta, plenty of chopped flat-leafed parsley, a splash of olive oil and a sprinkling of Parmesan cheese. The toppings are undeniably high in fat but since they are strongly flavoured, you'll only need a little.

■ **Go Middle Eastern** Try a large portion of bulghar wheat or couscous with herbs, fresh tomato sauce, lean lamb and red pepper kebabs, and a large mixed salad, followed by grilled apricots and yogurt. Red peppers, tomato sauce and apricots make this meal exceptionally high in vitamin C and beta-carotene. Apricots also provide iron and fibre.

By serving small pieces of lamb on skewers with peppers, the fat content of the meal is reduced but there is still adequate protein. Bulghar wheat provides the necessary carbohydrate, a little more protein, and is a useful source of iron, magnesium and B vitamins. Yogurt tops up the calcium and provides more protein still.

For a Middle-Eastern kebab recipe, see page 187.

■ **Best of British** The traditional British 'meat and two veg' is still on the menu as long as you think in terms of potatoes, three veg and some meat. Spray unpeeled small potatoes with oil and roast in a non-stick pan along with chunks of butternut squash or sweet potatoes. This will increase the beta-carotene and vitamin C content. For variety and extra fibre, add lightly parboiled chunks of swede or celeriac, or some baby turnips. Base the green veg on a leafy one, such as kale or Savoy cabbage – lots of phytochemicals here. Add a few slices of leek, celery stalk, courgette, or some broad beans (a good source of calcium). If you steam the vegetables, they can all be cooked together.

Poultry is a good choice for a roast. The fatty skin adds flavour and keeps the meat succulent, but there's no need to eat it. If you use a non-stick roasting pan, it won't be necessary to add much extra fat (see *Cooking for Health*, page 97). Make the gravy with vegetable water, a little wine and some cornflour, which doesn't need fat to thicken it.

For a British slow-braised beef recipe, see page 215.

SNACKS

The busier we get, the less time there is for cooking, so snacks have become an increasingly important part of our diet. They contribute to our overall nutrient intake and therefore must be taken into account as part of a balanced diet.

If your meal pattern includes breakfast, a light lunch and an evening meal, snacks can be kept small. Eat them mid-morning and mid-afternoon to prevent energy dips. If you have your evening meal early on, you may need a light mid-evening snack too.

■ The ultimate snack is a piece of fruit. It's ready to eat, conveniently packaged and counts as a 'five a day' serving. In fact, fruit is sometimes better digested if it is eaten on its own. Bananas are particularly good, since they contain plenty of carbohydrate and are also high in potassium.

■ Depending on season and availability, a luscious nectarine or peach is thirst-quenching and sustaining, and provides plenty of vitamins and fibre. In winter, an orange-fleshed fruit such as a mango, papaya or sharon fruit would provide valuable vitamin C and beta-carotene.

■ Dried fruit, such as apricots, apple rings, banana chips and raisins are concentrated sources of energy, vitamins and minerals.

■ Raw vegetables can also be eaten in abundance. Carrot sticks, baby sweetcorn, mangetout, cherry tomatoes, sliced peppers, fennel, radishes, cauliflower florets and celery are all deliciously crunchy and packed with vitamins and fibre. Dip them in hummus, puréed roasted aubergine, guacamole or low-fat cream cheese.

■ Instead of a bar of chocolate, have a handful of trail mix, nuts or sunflower seeds. They are much lower in fat and sugar than chocolate, and higher in vitamins, minerals and fibre.

■ Try bran muffins, tea bread, home-made fruit cake or flap jacks instead of chocolate biscuits.

■ Try oat cakes or rice cakes instead of crisps. Both are sustaining, particularly if topped with peanut butter, mashed banana or vegetable pâté.

DIFFERENT NUTRITIONAL NEEDS

Although the Government publishes reference figures for the intake of essential nutrients (pages 12–36), the figures are no more than indications of an appropriate intake. We all need different amounts, depending not only on age, sex, pregnancy and activity levels, but also on less quantifiable criteria such as lifestyle, stress, general state of health, the environment and so on. In this section we show you how to fine-tune your diet to cope with your particular needs.

HIGH ENERGY REQUIREMENTS

If your work is physically strenuous or you regularly practise vigorous exercise or sports, you should 'scale up' the normal balanced diet in order to provide extra nutrients. Your carbohydrate requirement will be higher and you may need more fat. You must also make sure you are well supplied with certain vitamins and minerals, including a plentiful supply of antioxidants (page 14).

NUTRIENTS FOR ENERGY

Of the energy-giving nutrients, only carbohydrate and fat provide the type of energy needed for strenuous physical movement. Carbohydrate, in the form of glycogen, is the most important fuel of the two. Glycogen is composed of glucose units produced when carbohydrates are digested. It is stored in the liver and muscles until needed. When we exercise or move vigorously, the body draws on this store, converting glycogen back to glucose. Together with fat, this provides the working muscles with the energy they need.

Unfortunately, only a relatively small amount of glycogen can be stored, and fatigue sets in when supplies get low. If strenuous activity is a regular part of your life, you need a consistently high intake of starchy carbohydrate-rich foods, such as pasta, rice and potatoes, to keep your glycogen topped up. Some athletes deliberately eat massive amounts of starchy foods two or three days before an event to ensure that their glycogen levels are at a maximum.

AEROBIC OR ANAEROBIC?

The proportion of glycogen and fat used depends on how hard and for how long you're exercising. Aerobic activity is generally less intense than anaerobic, and is sustained over a period of time – for example, very active physical work, long-distance cycling, or an 'aerobic' exercise class. Glycogen is used up first, but as the store is depleted, the body switches over to fat. Anaerobic activity, on the other hand, is of high intensity and short duration – sprints, rapid press-ups or weight lifting, for example. Because energy needs are so high and immediate glycogen is the only fuel in this situation.

KEY VITAMINS AND MINERALS

Certain vitamins play a key role in the way energy is processed by the body. The B vitamins, found in meat, eggs and pulses for example, work as a team to release energy from food. If you increase your carbohydrate intake, you may need to up your vitamin B intake too. Co-enzyme Q10 (page 29) is also involved in converting energy from food to a form in which it can be used.

Vitamin C is essential for combatting exercise-induced wear and tear on body tissues. It helps with the repair and maintenance of connective tissue, tendons and ligaments, and speeds up wound healing. Vitamin C is also involved in the absorption and use of iron, which, in turn, is essential for transporting essential oxygen to exercising muscles.

A good supply of minerals is vital for high energy users as profuse sweating can cause significant losses. Iron is probably the most important mineral because of its involvement in oxygen transportation. Calcium is needed for strong healthy bones and joints. A supply of sodium and potassium is essential, too, since both regulate the balance of fluids within and outside the cells. Magnesium is involved in energy release and healthy muscle function. Chromium plays a central role in regulating blood sugar levels.

ANTIOXIDANT DEFENCE

Intense exercise can lead to an increased metabolic rate, which in turn leads to increased production of free radicals – highly reactive molecules that can cause serious damage to healthy cells and tissues (page 14). Antioxidant nutrients such as vitamin C, E, beta-carotene, zinc, copper and other minerals, provide protection. If excess free radicals are produced, antioxidants will also need boosting. To get a full complement, eat a wide variety of foods.

FLUID INTAKE

Strenuous physical work and exercise result in heavy breathing and sweating, which deplete the body's fluids. It is vital to drink water before, during and after intense or prolonged activity to avoid dehydration, cramps, or even collapse.

TIPS FOR HIGH ENERGY USERS

■ Eat dense starchy foods, eg potatoes, yams, pasta, rice, tortillas, pulses. Foods with a high liquid content, eg soup or porridge, provide less energy even though they contain carbohydrates.

■ Eat three or four thick slices of bread with every meal.

■ Eat starchy snacks between meals eg cereal bars, toast.

■ Increase B vitamins and vitamin E by eating more liver, meat, eggs, wholemeal cereals, bread, nuts and pulses.

■ To increase antioxidant intake, make sure you have five servings a day of fruit and vegetables, plus nuts and pulses.

■ Increase carbohydrate-based meals to three a day.

■ Eat plenty of mineral-rich leafy vegetables, fish, eggs.

Very dilute fruit juices are also suitable, but steer clear of full-strength juices or fizzy drinks. Fizz can fill you up before you've drunk enough, and full-strength juices are absorbed too slowly to be of benefit.

COPING WITH STRESS

Most of us can cope with, or even thrive on, a certain amount of stress without any ill effects. However, excessive or prolonged stress can be intolerable. Even though you may not be able to eliminate the stress in your life, there are ways of increasing your ability to cope with it.

CALMING FOOD

The body needs more nutrients during periods of stress. It is essential to try and eat properly, even though this is the last thing you feel like doing. Make sure you have plenty of complex carbohydrate-rich foods, such as potatoes, wholemeal bread, rice and pasta. They provide steady, slow-release energy and can have a calming effect. B vitamins are important too. They release the energy from food and help maintain a healthy nervous system. Vitamin C helps boost the immune system and is vital if you're feeling run down. Zinc also helps resist infection. It is depleted by alcohol, so if you have been drinking more than you should, make sure you eat plenty of zinc-rich foods such as eggs and seafood.

A way of overcoming stress-induced loss of appetite is to eat small simple meals and healthy snacks. Make sure you eat something every three or four hours. Don't be tempted to keep going on adrenalin – you'll soon be running on empty which can only make matters worse.

For a comforting vegetable-based soup, see page 146.

De-stress with a vitamin-packed fruit and yogurt 'smoothie', see page 323.

STRESS-BUSTING FOODS

■ A bowl of warm soup is one of the most comforting of foods. It's simple to prepare and easy for your system to digest. Baked potatoes are also good in this respect.

■ Give yourself treats – a simple supper of grilled trout fillet and some tiny new potatoes will make you feel better. A bag of crisps won't.

■ Indulge in some luscious tropical fruits and eat these as snacks. Mangoes, papayas and passionfruit are vitamin-packed, sweet and delicious.

■ Whizz up a shake of strawberries, bananas and yogurt. It's easy to digest and provides plenty of vitamin C, B vitamins, calcium, potassium. Sprinkle with chopped nuts for extra sustenance.

■ Drink calming herb teas such as lime flower, lemon balm or chamomile. Try to avoid drinking excessive amounts of tea and coffee – they may temporarily stimulate the body, but they also serve to increase your anxiety levels, as will alcohol.

NUTRITION BEFORE PREGNANCY

Eating healthily before you conceive increases your chance of a problem-free pregnancy and gives your developing baby the best possible start in life. Now is the ideal time to build up a basic understanding of nutrition. It will be invaluable during pregnancy and will also help you pass on sound eating habits to your growing child.

VITAL FOLIC ACID

One of the most important things to be aware of is folic acid intake. Folic acid plays a vital role in the development of your baby's organs and tissues. It also reduces the risk of neural tube defects such as spina bifida. The DoH recommends that women who intend to become pregnant should take a daily supplement of 400 µg, continuing until the twelfth week of pregnancy. The supplement is in addition to increasing by 100 µg the amount of folic acid in the diet. Fortunately, breakfast cereals and some breads and milk drinks are now fortified with folic acid, and are identified by a special label.

The healthiest sources of folic acid for a preconceptual or pregnant woman are plant foods such as vegetables, cereals, pulses and nuts. Although liver is also an excellent source, it contains high levels of vitamin A (retinol) which may damage the developing baby. Some vitamin supplements also contain vitamin A, so seek professional advice before taking any supplements. Fresh fruit and vegetables containing beta-carotene, which is converted to vitamin A in the body, are not a problem.

WEIGHT AWARENESS

A healthy body weight before pregnancy is important too. If you are underweight, it can be more difficult to conceive. It also means that your baby is likely to have a low birth weight which, in turn, increases susceptibility to ill health. If you are overweight, you risk complications such as diabetes or high blood pressure. Find out the correct weight for your height (see *Weight Management*, page 64), and try to lose or gain if necessary. Avoid crash dieting – a steady loss or increase will have longer lasting results. Aim to reach the correct weight three or four months before you plan to conceive.

GOOD SOURCES OF FOLIC ACID

- Grapenuts
- Asparagus, lightly cooked
- Muesli
- Purple sprouting broccoli, lightly cooked
- Swiss chard, lightly cooked
- Brussels sprouts, lightly cooked
- Spinach, lightly cooked
- Pinto beans, boiled
- Sweetcorn, lightly cooked
- Fortified soft grain bread
- Fortified cornflakes

WEIGHT GAIN

An additional 11-16 kg (25-35 lb) is a reasonable amount to gain during pregnancy.

However, if your pre-pregnancy weight was lower or higher than normal, your weight gain targets will differ accordingly.

BMI at start of pregnancy	Recommended kg	total weight gain lb
Low: under 20	12.5-18.0	27-39
Normal: 20-26	11.5-16.0	25-35
High: 26-29	7.0-11.5	15-25
Obese: over 29	6.0	13

The section on Weight Management, page 64, shows you how to calculate your Body Mass Index (BMI).

NUTRITION IN PREGNANCY

Pregnancy is one of the most nutritionally demanding periods in a woman's life. It is vitally important to have sufficient nutrients and energy to meet the needs of your developing baby, and to support the growth of your breasts, placenta and uterus during this time.

The same principles for a balanced diet – variety and enjoyment – still apply, but you will need to increase your intake of certain vitamins and minerals, particularly if you plan to breastfeed. To find out which foods are the best sources, check the individual nutrient descriptions on pages 15–38, or the food tables in the section on *How to Achieve a Balanced Diet*.

CALORIE INCREASE

You will need to consume an extra 200 calories per day during the last three months of pregnancy. This represents roughly two glasses of milk or two slices of medium-hard cheese – both of which will provide extra calcium as well. Alternatively, a bowl of porridge, muesli or a baked potato will provide the additional amount.

ESSENTIAL FATTY ACIDS

There is no additional requirement in pregnancy for carbohydrates and fats (except as part of an overall increase in calories). However, there is some evidence that good levels of essential fatty acids (EFAs) are linked with longer-term pregnancies and therefore higher birth weights and healthier babies. EFAs are also associated with reduced risk of high blood pressure in the mother.

In the final three months, when brain and eye development, and therefore intelligence, are at their peak, requirements for docosahexaenoic acid (DHA) from the omega-3 group of EFAs start to rocket. DHA is found almost exclusively in oily fish such as sardines, trout and mackerel. Try and eat some every other day.

If you are a vegetarian, you can get another type of omega-3 fatty acid, known as alpha-linolenic acid (ALA), from linseed (flaxseed) and rapeseed oils. The conversion process is somewhat inefficient, however, as many times more ALA must be consumed to produce levels of DHA comparable to those that can be obtained from oily fish.

PROTEIN NEEDS

A small increase in protein is required, but if you are eating a well-balanced diet, a conscious effort to increase intake is unlikely to be necessary. If you are vegetarian, a variety of cereals, nuts and pulses together with tofu, soya milk, eggs, cheese and cow's milk will provide all the protein you need.

MINERAL REQUIREMENTS

Although there is no official recommendation to increase mineral intake during pregnancy, do make sure you are getting adequate supplies, especially if you plan to breastfeed. Once breastfeeding is under way, your requirement for major minerals increases quite sharply.

DRINKING AND SMOKING

If you drink alcohol, try to keep your intake well below the levels advised for non-pregnant women. One unit of alcohol a day – a small glass of wine, or ½ pint of beer or cider – is considered acceptable. If you smoke, cut it out, or cut down drastically.

If your calcium intake is low during pregnancy, you risk losing some of your bone calcium to your baby. Vegans should take particular care to eat plenty of non-dairy calcium-rich foods, such as tofu, soya milk, tahini, sunflower seeds, spinach, broccoli and fortified bread and breakfast cereals.

Zinc deficiency during pregnancy has been linked with increased rate of abortion, low birth weight babies, growth retardation and preterm delivery. Deficiency is unlikely if you regularly eat meat and fish. Nuts, pulses and wheat germ are the best source for vegetarians.

Iron is particularly important, since you may become anaemic if you start your pregnancy with depleted stores. Vegetarians and vegans should have a daily intake of iron-rich foods such as fortified bread, cereals, soya products, pulses, nuts, dark green vegetables and dried apricots.

VITAMIN LEVELS

Though you should avoid foods (eg liver) containing excessively high levels of vitamin A, you do need to slightly increase your intake of this vitamin. A glass of milk, a portion of oily fish or well-cooked eggs would provide the extra amount.

Provided you are eating a variety of foods which include plenty of fruits, vegetables and wholegrain cereals, you are probably getting sufficient B vitamins and vitamin C. The most important B vitamin is folic acid which is discussed under *Nutrition Before Pregnancy*, page 58.

If you follow a vegan diet you will need foods fortified with vitamin B12 since it is not found in plant foods – seaweed is an exception. Such foods include soya products, yeast extract, breakfast cereals and some margarines. You should take a supplement if the amount of vitamin B12 in your diet is intermittent.

FOOD SAFETY IN PREGNANCY

Special precautions should be taken when pregnant to avoid infections such as listeriosis, toxoplasmosis and salmonella. To guard against the latter, do not eat anything containing raw or lightly cooked eggs.

Listeriosis is a dangerous bacterial infection which can cause miscarriage, stillbirth, deformities or severe illness in a newborn baby.
■ Avoid soft and blue-veined cheeses such as Brie, Camembert, Stilton or Danish Blue; soft unpasteurised sheep and goat's milk cheese.
■ Avoid meat, vegetable and fish pâtés unless canned or shrink-wrapped and pasteurised.
■ Reheat ready-cooked meals, particularly those containing poultry, until piping hot.

Toxoplasmosis is caused by a parasite. In rare cases the illness can be passed to the unborn baby from the mother, resulting in a range of problems, some of which can be serious.
■ Avoid undercooked or raw meat, including Parma ham.
■ Avoid unpasteurised goat's milk, goat's cheese or yogurt.
■ Wear rubber gloves if in contact with cat litter trays or soil contaminated by cat faeces. Scrub hands thoroughly as an extra precaution.
■ Thoroughly wash fruit and salads (even shop-bought pre-washed salads) to remove any traces of soil that might be contaminated.

VEGETARIAN NEEDS

The same broad principles for an omnivorous balanced diet apply equally to a vegetarian diet. Eat a wide variety of foods, including lots of cereals, potatoes, vegetables and fruit, moderate amounts of protein foods and limited amounts of high-fat, high-sugar foods.

You will need to find alternative sources of the important nutrients found in fish and meat – iron, zinc, selenium, B vitamins and protein. If you become a vegan and give up dairy foods as well, you must find other ways of getting calcium and vitamin D into your diet. You will also need a vitamin B12 supplement or foods fortified with that vitamin.

The greater the restrictions, the more care needs to be taken, particularly with babies, children and teenagers (page 73), the elderly (page 69) and if you are pregnant or breastfeeding (page 59). As with any restrictive diet, some nutritional knowledge and careful planning is required in order to maintain good health and to avoid deficiencies.

ENERGY-RICH FOODS

The starchy carbohydrate-rich foods that make up the bulk of a vegetarian diet are the main source of energy. Oils and nuts also provide some. Fruit and many vegetables have a high water content and contribute very little energy.

In order to supply adequate energy, vegan diets are of necessity quite bulky. This can cause problems for children who may not be able to eat enough carbohydrate foods to meet their energy needs. They will need adequate supplies of 'energy-dense' fats such as nut butters, tahini and vegetable margarine.

FAT INTAKE

Make sure you get plenty of essential fatty acids by eating avocados, seeds, nuts and the oils derived from them. Non-fish eaters will be missing out on the omega-3 essential fatty acids DHA and EPA (page 18). They can be replaced to some extent by alpha-linolenic acid (ALA) found in linseeds (flax) and linseed oil, but you will have to eat quite a lot to attain equivalent DHA and EPA levels. Sprinkle linseeds over breakfast cereal, muesli, salads, soups, or add them to cake mixtures and nut loaves – but note they have a laxative effect. Linseed oil has a strange taste and is best blended with other oils, such as olive oil or unrefined sunflower oil, and used in dressings. It should not be used for frying.

PROTEIN BALANCE

Vegetarians often worry needlessly about getting enough protein, but in fact a deficiency is unlikely, provided that staples such as bread, cereals and pulses are eaten every day. Don't make the mistake of eating lots of dairy foods. They may be high in protein but many of them are high in saturated fat too.

Although plant proteins do not contain all the essential amino acids (see page 20), it is easy for vegetarians to get the right amount if they eat a mixture of cereals, nuts, seeds, pulses and other vegetables. The amino acids missing in one type of food will be supplied by those in another. And if you eat plant proteins with dairy foods, which have the full complement of amino acids, the problem does not arise (see table on the next page).

VEGETARIAN VARIATIONS

■ **Semi- or demi-vegetarian**
Will eat fish, poultry (usually) and other animal products. Will not eat red meat.

■ **Ovo-lacto-vegetarian**
Will eat eggs, milk and dairy products. Will not eat meat, poultry or fish.

■ **Lacto-vegetarian**
Will eat milk and dairy products. Will not eat eggs, meat, poultry or fish.

■ **Vegan**
Will eat only plant foods. Will not eat any foods from animal sources, including honey.

■ **Fruitarian**
Will eat only fruits, raw vegetables, nuts, seeds and sprouted beans and seeds.

VITAL VITAMINS

Keep an eye on the amount of vitamins D and B12 in your diet. VITAMIN D is not available from plant foods, but it is found in eggs, margarine, milk and dairy products. It is also manufactured by the action of sunlight on the skin. If you are a vegan you will have to rely on fortified foods such as soya milk, bread, breakfast cereals and vegetable margarine for your dietary supply.

VITAMIN B12 is also unavailable from plant foods, although small amounts are found in seaweed and miso (fermented soya bean paste). Good natural sources are milk, cheese, eggs. If you drink less than 300 ml of milk, or eat less than 50 g of cheese or 1 egg daily, you should include fortified products, seaweed or miso in your diet. Fortified foods include breakfast cereals, bread and soya milk and these are a useful source of B12 for vegans.

BALANCING VEGETARIAN FOOD GROUPS

Group	What is included	Main nutrients	Servings per day
1 Cereals and potatoes	Bread, pasta, couscous, rice, oats, polenta, whole grains (eg buckwheat, millet, quinoa) breakfast cereals, potatoes, yams, sweet potatoes.	Complex carbohydrates, NSP (dietary fibre), B vitamins, calcium, iron, protein.	Three to four
2 Fruit and vegetables	Fresh, frozen, canned fruit and vegetables, seaweeds, dried fruit, vegetable and fruit juices.	Vitamin C, carotenoids and other phytochemicals, B vitamins, vitamin K, calcium, magnesium, potassium, NSP, iron, iodine, selenium.	Four to five
3 Pulses, nuts and seeds	Kidney beans, chick peas, lentils, peas, baked beans. All nuts. Sunflower, pumpkin and sesame seeds.	Complex carbohydrates, NSP, fat, protein, iron, calcium, zinc, selenium, vitamin E.	Two to three
4 Dairy foods, eggs, soya products	Milk, cheese, yogurt, fromage frais, tofu, tempeh, soya protein, soya milk.	Protein, fats, vitamins A and D, B vitamins, vitamin B12, magnesium, calcium.	Two
5 Vegetable oils and fats	Vegetable oils, nut oils, seed oils, butter, margarine.	EFAs, vitamins A, D and E.	A small amount

FIBRE FACTS
A vegetarian diet based on whole grain cereals and plenty of fruit and vegetables will naturally be high in NSP (fibre) of all kinds. However, excessive amounts can hinder the absorption of other nutrients, particularly calcium, iron and zinc. It is essential to make sure these minerals are well supplied. Foods containing vitamin C will help with iron absorption.

PROTEIN COMBINING

The following table shows you the combinations which supply complete protein. To check out a combination of cereals and nuts/seeds, for example, read horizontally along the cereals line to the point where it meets the nuts and seeds column.

	Cereals	Pulses	Nuts/seeds	Dairy products
Cereals	No	Yes	Yes	Yes
Pulses	Yes	No	Sometimes	Yes
Nuts/seeds	Yes	Sometimes	No	Yes
Dairy products	Yes	Yes	Yes	Yes

EXAMPLES OF PROTEIN COMBINING

■ Nut loaf made with nuts, breadcrumbs or lentils.

■ Rice or a wheat tortilla served with a bean casserole.

■ Lentils and rice mixed in a pilau.

ABSORBING MINERALS

Although a vegetarian diet can supply all the necessary minerals, some minerals from plant sources are less well absorbed. For instance, the iron in vegetables is in a form called non-haem, which is less easily absorbed than haem iron in meat. Non-haem iron also binds with a substance called phytate, found in bran and cereals, which limits absorption still further. However, foods containing vitamin C eaten at the same meal will help increase absorption.

To ensure an adequate supply of iron, you should have daily servings of leafy green vegetables, tofu, peas, beans, lentils, chick peas, barley, couscous, bulghar wheat, dried fruit or eggs, together with vitamin C-rich fruit and veg. Using cast-iron cooking pots provides some iron as well. Iron is also found in cocoa powder and ground spices such as cardamom, cumin, cayenne pepper and turmeric. The amount may be very small, but if you use spices regularly, it all adds up.

Milk and dairy products are excellent sources of calcium. If you don't eat these, you'll have to rely on eating lots of tofu, nuts, pulses, peas, leafy vegetables, tahini, bread and dried apricots. As with iron, the phytate in bran and cereals binds with calcium and limits absorption. Make sure you get enough vitamin D, without which calcium cannot be absorbed.

Vegetarians tend to have lower body levels of zinc than meat-eaters. Make sure you eat plenty of eggs and cheese to ensure an adequate supply. If you are a vegan, top up with peas, beans, lentils and chick peas. Selenium and iodine are also important minerals for vegetarians. Brazil nuts are an excellent source of selenium – just one nut can give you a day's supply. Cashews, pecans, walnuts and eggs provide smaller, useful amounts. Nuts and eggs are also a source of iodine, as are milk and dairy products.

63

FACTS ABOUT WEIGHT

■ If food eaten (measured in calories) is equal to energy used (in calories), weight remains constant.

■ If food eaten provides more calories than energy used, weight increases.

■ If food eaten provides fewer calories than energy used, weight decreases.

BASAL METABOLIC RATE

The basal metabolic rate is the rate at which the body uses up energy when you're lying still, relaxed and warm. Rates vary from person to person, which is why some people are naturally thin. The rate changes throughout life, too. It is highest at birth and gradually slows down with age. This may explain why some people tend to put on weight in middle age, even though they are eating and exercising the same amount as previously.

WEIGHT MANAGEMENT

Balancing the amount of energy you consume with the amount you use in physical activity is essential for maintaining a healthy body weight. If the food you eat provides more calories than you burn, then your body will store the excess as fat, which could ultimately lead to obesity and associated health risks. Conversely, if your food intake is not providing enough calories to fuel your activity levels, then you could be underweight, which may make you more susceptible to certain health hazards.

BODY MASS INDEX

A way of finding out whether you need to lose or gain weight is to use the scale known as the Body Mass Index (BMI), which indicates a broad range of acceptable weights for people of different heights. To calculate your BMI, divide your weight (in kilograms) by the square of your height (in metres). For example, if you weigh 60 kg and your height is 1.7m: $60 \div (1.7 \times 1.7) = $ BMI 20.7. A BMI of below 20 is underweight; 20–24 is desirable; 25–30 is overweight; 30 and above is considered obese.

You may be surprised to find your BMI falls within acceptable limits, even though you feel you should lose weight. Remember that we live in a society that places great value on thinness, with constant pressure to conform. If your BMI is on the border of underweight, don't be tempted to go on a diet just so that you can fit into a smaller pair of jeans. If, however, you are on the border of being overweight, then the loss of a kilo or so may be justified.

WAIST-HIP RATIO

Another simple indicator is the waist-hip ratio, which shows the amount of fat on the abdomen. Build-up of fat around the waist is thought to carry greater risks, such as high cholesterol and insulin levels, than build-up around the hips and thighs.

To calculate your ratio, measure your waist (including any protruding flab) and divide this by your hip measurement (measured around the widest part). A figure of higher than 0.8 (for women) and 0.95 (for men) indicates there is too much fat around the waist, and you may be well advised to lose weight.

LOSING WEIGHT

Although a short-term crash diet may help get you started on the road to weight loss, it is not a long-term or healthy solution. Weight tends to pile back on and frequently becomes more difficult to lose, and essential nutrients may not be adequately supplied. For healthy and sustained weight loss, you need a balanced and varied diet that cuts calories to a safe level without sacrificing essential nutrients, and one that encourages healthy eating habits that will continue after the dieting period is over. A healthy calorie-reduced diet should therefore include moderate amounts of lower-calorie foods such as lean fish, meat and low-fat dairy products, as well as plenty of fruit, vegetables, pulses and wholegrain cereals. Try and space out meals as evenly as possible.

Since fat contains more calories (nine per gram) than any other nutrient, keeping it to a minimum is the obvious way of reducing calories. The current guidelines are that we should limit our daily fat intake to no more than 33% of total calories, with a lower limit of 15%. So if you reduce your overall calorie intake, fat should be reduced proportionately (see table below). It is also important to cut right back on non-essential sugary foods such as cakes, biscuits and confectionery. If you stick to these guidelines and eat only when you are really hungry, weight loss takes place almost automatically.

EXERCISE HELPS

During the first week of dieting you can expect to lose about 1.3 kg (3 lb). This is mainly due to loss of fluids from the body. After that, aim for a slower reduction of about 450–900 g (1–2 lb) a week. However, if you combine a reduction in calories with an increase in exercise, you will increase your metabolic rate and lose weight more easily, as well as improving your general level of health. Try to increase your overall activity levels – running up the stairs instead of using the lift, for example – as well as making time for regular aerobic exercise at least three times a week. Vigorous exercise not only improves body shape, but can also improve mood, which can be helpful if you get downhearted by dieting.

HOW MANY CALORIES SHOULD I AIM FOR?

The DoH recommends an overall intake of 1940 calories per day for a woman who is not overweight, and 2550 for a man. (For different age requirements, see chart page 112.) For gradual but steady weight loss you might start off with a goal of 1500 calories, perhaps reducing to 1250 calories towards the end of the diet. Men could start off with 2000 calories and move on to 1500.

Fortunately, there is no longer any need for obsessive calorie counting every time a morsel of food crosses your lips. Once you have decided on your reduced calorie intake, use the table below to calculate the amount of fat that makes up 33% of this. Then look at the food tables which follow (and those on pages 44-45) to check the amount of fat in different foods. If you decide to aim for a daily intake of say 1200 calories, 33% would be 44 grams of fat. For even greater weight loss, a fat intake of 25% brings the fat down to 33 grams.

CALCULATING FAT INTAKE

Daily energy requirement	33% of energy from fat	Daily fat allowance at 33%	25% of energy from fat	Daily fat allowance at 25%
cals	cals	g	cals	g
3000	990	110	750	83
2550**	841	93	637	70
1940*	640	71	485	53
1500	495	55	375	41
1200	396	44	300	33
1000	330	36	250	27

** Estimated Average Requirement for a 19-59 year-old man with low levels of activity.
* Estimated Average Requirement for a 19-50 year-old woman with low levels of activity.

FAT-BUSTING TIPS

■ Always use fats and oils sparingly. If a recipe calls for 1 tbsp of oil, measure it rather than guessing.

■ Use fat-free cooking techniques (see *Cooking for Health*).

■ Choose extra-lean cuts of meat, trim off all visible fat and remove skin from poultry.

■ Steam, microwave or grill fish and poultry, rather than frying.

■ Avoid 'hidden fat' in red meat by having smaller portions. Cut into small dice and bulk out with vegetables and pulses.

■ Drain off any fatty liquid from meat after browning.

■ Allow soups and stews to cool, then chill and remove fat solidified on the surface.

■ Replace full-fat dairy products with low-fat alternatives.

■ Be wary of labelling, particularly on dairy products and spreads. Low-fat products may still contain more fat than you think.

■ Use moist, low-fat fillings in sandwiches so that you will not need to use a spread.

CUTTING BACK ON FAT

It's easy to use up your fat allowance unless you make a point of familiarising yourself with the fat content of various foods, especially those that you find hard to cut back on. If you eat a higher fat food in one meal, you can compensate by eating lower fat food later on. As with a non-calorie-reduced balanced diet, foods from groups 1 and 2 should make up the greatest proportion of your diet, with moderate amounts of low-fat foods from groups 3 and 4, and very little, if any, from group 5.

LOW-FAT SNACKS

Even if you are on a calorie-reduced diet, you still need tasty snacks.

■ **Fresh or dried dates**
They are sweet, energy-boosting and virtually fat-free.

■ **Fresh fruit**
Eat as much as you like.

■ **Hunza apricots**
Sweet and delicious. Plump up by soaking. Drain and keep in the fridge.

■ **Muscatel raisins**
Fat, silky and sweetly fragrant.

■ **Raw vegetables**
Cherry tomatoes, radishes, crisp sticks of carrots, fennel and celery are great on their own or dipped into yogurt.

■ **Fruit cake or tea bread**
These contain less fat and sugar than ordinary cakes and biscuits.

■ **Oat or rice cakes**
These contain very little fat. Top with chopped bananas or quark (very low-fat cheese).

■ **Yogurt**
'Light' Greek yogurt is deliciously creamy and contains only 5% fat. Mix with fruit purée for extra richness.

FAT CONTENT OF COMMON FOODS

Food group	Average serving	Fat content g
1 Cereals and potatoes	portion of chips	28.9
	bowl of muesli	5.6
	2 oatcakes	4.8
	2 slices wholemeal bread	1.8
	pasta, plain	1.1
	2 wheatflake bars	0.8
	jacket potato	0.1
2 Fruit and vegetables	½ avocado pear	25.4
	fried onions	13.3
	spinach	0.7
	broad beans	0.5
	sweetcorn	0.4
	1 banana	0.3
	broccoli	0.0
	carrots	0.0
	bowl of strawberries	0.0
3 Dairy products	1 slice Cheddar cheese	13.8
	small carton Greek yogurt	13.7
	small carton low-fat yogurt	12.0
	glass semi-skimmed milk	3.1
4 Protein foods	2 scrambled eggs	31.6
	handful Brazil nuts	27.3
	3 rashers bacon, grilled	15.2
	1 salmon cutlet, steamed	14.2
	roast chicken, meat and skin	11.9
	lean pork chop, grilled	8.5
	tofu	2.5
	2 plaice fillets, steamed	2.3
	chick peas	1.6
5 Fats and sugary foods	mayonnaise, 2 tbsp	22.7
	1 bar plain chocolate	14.6
	small bag of crisps	10.7
	butter on slice of bread	6.5
	low-fat spread on bread	3.2

GAINING WEIGHT

While most of us are preoccupied with losing weight, some people have diffi-culty putting it on. Being skinny is not normally a cause for concern, and, indeed, is a state most people envy. However, a BMI (page 64) of 20 or below could cause health problems. A diet-related illness such as anorexia nervosa can be life-threatening, but even less seriously underweight people may be more prone to respiratory infections and tiredness. Without a comforting layer of insulating fat under the skin, thin people can also have difficulty keeping warm when the temperature drops.

REASONS FOR BEING UNDERWEIGHT

Apart from underlying medical reasons, the most common reason for being underweight is exercising vigorously and/or eating fewer calories. Some people are naturally skinny – it's in their genes – and they may have difficulty in eating an amount of food that seems normal to other people. Some people are simply more active – they may need less sleep, or have a physically strenuous job, or like to pack as much as possible into the day.

HEALTHY BALANCE

In the same way as trying to lose weight, increasing your weight needs to be tackled gradually for successful long-term results. An increase of about 500 calories a day is a good starting point. You may need more than this if you practise vigorous exercise (see *High Energy Requirements*, page 55). Don't make the mistake of just eating more high-fat foods. Your diet should maintain a healthy balance so that you are still getting a spread of nutrients from the dif-ferent food groups. The proportion of fat to overall calorie intake should remain the same, at around 30%. Check the table on page 65 to see what this means in terms of actual grams of fat.

SMALL AND OFTEN

If you have difficulty increasing the amount you eat either because your appetite is poor or because you find the actual bulkiness of food off-putting, try smaller and more frequent meals rather than fewer large ones. To avoid increasing bulk, you could, in the short term, use energy-dense foods that are a little higher in fat – Brazil nuts, Greek yogurt, full-fat milk or plain chocolate, for example.

REGULAR EXERCISE

Even though exercise uses up energy, it's not a good idea to go without it even if you are trying to put on weight. Regular brisk walking or stretching exercises tone up the system, help circulation, stimulate the appetite and generally make you feel much healthier and better all round.

TIPS FOR GAINING WEIGHT

■ Maintain a balanced and healthy diet with plenty of carbohydrate-rich foods, vegetables and fruit.

■ Make sure that most of the fat in your diet is monounsaturated or polyunsaturated. Eating fried fish and chips or cream cakes every day is not the right idea!

■ Snack on unsalted nuts, dried fruit, oat cakes topped with peanut butter, wholemeal scones topped with mono- or polyunsaturated spreads.

■ Eat larger servings of basic healthy foods: fish, poultry, meat, pasta, rice, pulses and starchy vegetables.

■ Use more dressings and sauces: French dressing, mayonnaise, cheese sauce.

■ Increase calorie intake by adding simple desserts to meals.

■ Drink whole milk between meals rather than tea or coffee.

USEFUL FOODS IN A BUILD-UP DIET

Average serving	Cals	Carbohydrate g	Fat g
Group 1: Cereals and potatoes			
Naan bread	571	85.0	21.3
Bowl of muesli	364	71.1	5.9
Jacket potato with skin	272	63.4	0.4
Oat cakes, 4	230	32.8	9.6
Wholemeal bread, 2 thick slices	215	41.5	2.6
Yorkshire pudding	104	12.4	5.0
Group 2: Fruit and vegetables			
Avocado pear, ½	247	2.4	25.4
Dates, dried, 10	135	34.0	0.1
Banana	128	31.3	1.3
Apricots, dried, 5	94	21.7	0.3
Onions, baked	82	17.8	0.5
Sweetcorn kernels, boiled	77	13.7	1.6
Butternut squash, baked	48	11.1	0.2
Group 3: Dairy foods			
Cheddar cheese, 2 slices	330	0.1	27.6
Cream cheese	176	trace	18.9
Greek yogurt, small carton	144	2.5	3.6
Whole milk	132	9.6	7.8
Group 4: Protein foods			
Duck, meat and skin	529	0.0	47.6
Mackerel	382	0.0	27.7
Salmon steak	344	0.0	20.9
Smoked mackerel pâté	294	1.0	27.5
Brazil nuts, 10	273	0.0	27.3
Pork, leg, lean and fat	259	0.0	15.4
Chicken breast, meat and skin	216	0.0	8.0
Tofu, fried	157	1.2	10.6
Peanuts, dry roasted, 25	147	2.6	12.5
Baked beans in tomato sauce	128	20.6	1.0
Kidney beans, cooked	77	13.0	0.4
Group 5: Fats and sugary foods			
Fruit cake, 1 slice	319	52.1	11.6
Flap jack, medium	290	36.2	16.0
Chocolate, plain, small bar	255	31.7	14.0
Mayonnaise, 2 tbsp	207	0.5	22.7
Oil, 2 tbsp	198	0.0	22.0
Cream, double, 2 tbsp	157	0.0	16.8
Ice-cream	146	18.3	7.4

NUTRITION IN LATER YEARS

From the age of sixty and upwards, maintaining a balanced diet continues to be vital for good health and well-being. Old age is inevitable but senility may not be. Many of the obvious signs of ageing can be slowed down, and life may even be prolonged, by following a diet that is high in antioxidants, fibre and fish oils, and low in animal fats. This means eating plenty of fruit, vegetables, whole grain cereals, lean meat, fish, poultry, and low-fat milk and dairy products.

Although the nutritional needs of a healthy older person are not so very different from those of younger adults, a few adjustments are necessary to allow for increased or diminished requirements for certain nutrients, and to cope with physiological changes.

NUTRITIONAL PROBLEMS

Despite good intentions, the practicalities of following a balanced diet may be difficult to cope with as you get older. For example, it may be hard to get to the shops, or if you have moved to a smaller home or sheltered accommodation, you may not have sufficient storage space. If you have moved to a residential home, you will not be entirely in control of what you eat. Shortage of income may be another problem. Some people lose interest in food because of bereavement – the resulting depression and loneliness can both lead to a decrease in appetite.

Physical problems can occur too. Digestive disorders or difficulties in chewing narrow down the range of foods which can be enjoyed. Long-term prescription drugs can reduce the appetite and impede the absorption of important nutrients.

Because of this range of difficulties, many older people in the UK suffer from nutrient deficiencies and therefore do not enjoy optimum health. Whether planning your own diet, or helping an older person make choices about food, it makes sense to be aware of possible pitfalls.

According to research, the main area for concern appears to be deficiency of B vitamins, especially folic acid and vitamins B6 and B12. Deficiencies are also noted in vitamins C and D, beta-carotene, iron, magnesium and potassium. When your daily intake of these nutrients regularly falls below the necessary level, your health is bound to suffer. The immune system is weakened and the body becomes more prone to infections.

NUTRIENTS AND ENERGY BALANCE

As ageing progresses, the amount of energy needed from food becomes less. However, the requirement for vitamins and other nutrients increases. Since the foods that supply energy also supply other important nutrients, it is important that the bulk of your diet is made up of energy-rich complex carbohydrates, eg bread, wholegrain cereals, potatoes, rice and pasta. You will also need some fat, although it may be less than the amount required by a younger adult. For example, if you are at risk from heart disease, the amount of fat in the diet should be reduced to around 15–20% of total energy intake.

LOOK AFTER YOURSELF

Taking an interest in food is one of the best ways of improving nutrition and staying healthy.

■ Try and eat different foods each day.

■ Maintain an interest in cooking – experiment with new recipes.

■ If you are new to cooking, buy a beginner's cookbook. Planning menus and shopping can be a pleasurable part of the day.

■ Invite family or friends to share your meals.

ESSENTIAL FIBRE

A healthy and efficiently working bowel becomes even more vital as we get older. Though it may be tempting to opt for convenience foods, many are lacking in fibre and important nutrients. Make sure your diet includes some wholemeal bread and wholegrain versions of pasta and rice. These NSP-rich foods aid digestion and help prevent constipation and piles. They also reduce the likelihood of diverticulosis – a bowel disease associated with increased risk of bowel cancer. It is better to try and include these foods in your diet rather than adding bran to food, as this can reduce the absorption of important vitamins and minerals.

Another type of fibre, which helps reduce the amount of cholesterol in the blood, is found in oats, peas, beans and fruit and vegetables. Eating a wide range of foods ensures you get plenty of both types.

FAT WATCH

As age increases, so does the risk of developing coronary heart disease. If you are on the heavy side, watch your intake of fatty foods such as chips, fried foods and butter. Look for reduced-fat alternatives, and try to grill food rather than fry. If you are underweight, a higher fat diet is fine but try to use vegetable oils for cooking, rather than animal fats such as lard.

Scientists now believe that a diet containing oily fish provides particular types of essential fatty acids (page 18) that reduce the risk of heart disease, especially in the elderly. It's a good idea to eat oily fish (eg mackerel, trout or herrings) at least three times a week. If you don't have a local fishmonger, or can't get to the shops, stock up with canned fish, such as sardines or tuna. Sardines have an added bonus of edible bones which are a useful source of calcium.

PROTEIN FOR REPAIRS

Protein is essential for maintaining and repairing body tissues, especially after illness, surgery or injury. You need only have small portions, but do eat protein foods every day. The main sources are meat and fish, which also supply B vitamins, iron and other minerals. Canned fish is ideal and convenient, and liver, eggs and cheese are good sources. Beans such as butter beans, kidney beans and baked beans also provide protein as well as some fibre.

WHICH VITAMINS?

B vitamins are essential for releasing the energy from the food you eat. Some of them also help the nervous system to work correctly. Folic acid is particularly important in this respect. Together with iron and vitamin B12, folic acid is also involved in the formation of red blood cells. Low levels of these nutrients can lead to anaemia, and a B12 deficiency is associated with memory lapses and problems with co-ordination and balance. B12 is found mainly in foods of animal origin, so it is essential to include meat or dairy products in the diet.

You need some vitamin C every day. It helps you absorb iron from food and is especially important if you don't eat much meat. As we age, the skin gets more fragile, and cuts and bruises may take longer to heal. Vitamin C and zinc speed up the healing process and help fight infection.

Vitamin D is essential for calcium absorption and healthy bones. After the age of sixty five, both men and women need an extra 10 µg a day. Although vitamin D is found in some foods (eg eggs, margarine and oily fish) it is mainly formed by the action of sunlight on the skin. If you don't get out of doors regularly, try and eat more vitamin D-rich food, or consider taking a supplement, such as a daily spoonful of cod liver oil.

WHICH MINERALS?

Calcium and magnesium are vital for keeping bones strong and healthy. Osteoporosis, or thinning of the bones, is a major problem with elderly people – both men and women – resulting in fractures and loss of mobility. As ageing progresses, the ability to absorb calcium decreases, so it is important to have a regular daily intake. Dairy foods, canned fish with edible bones, fortified white bread, baked beans and green vegetables are all good sources.

Iron and zinc are important too. Although the need for iron reduces after the menopause, it is still vital for women to make sure they are getting enough. A deficiency can result in anaemia or reduce the amount of oxygen getting to the tissues, which results in tiredness and breathlessness. Meat and eggs are rich in both iron and zinc. Liver is a more concentrated source and easier to chew than meat. Chocolate and cocoa provide small but useful amounts of iron.

ANTIOXIDANTS

Scientists now believe that a group of nutrients known as antioxidants (page 14) can help protect the body from 'oxidative stress' caused by free radicals. Damage from free radicals has been cited as a leading cause of premature ageing and chronic disease. There is strong evidence that these nutrients can help reduce the risk of developing a wide range of age-related diseases, including Alzheimer's disease, cataracts, Parkinson's disease, heart disease and some cancers.

To maintain a good supply of antioxidants (eg vitamins C, E and beta-carotene), try to eat at least five servings of fruit and vegetables a day, excluding potatoes. Yellow-, orange- and red-fleshed fruit and vegetables are a particularly good source of beta-carotene. Vegetable oils such as sunflower and olive oils are a good source of vitamin E, so use these instead of hard fats for cooking.

NECESSARY EXERCISE

As you get older, bones start to lose minerals which leads to thinning, and sometimes to osteoporosis, in both men and women. Regular exercise, even just walking, helps keep your bones strong, and if you do it outside, you'll be boosting your store of vitamin D.

AFTER THE MENOPAUSE

Once the menopause is over, the risk of developing heart disease becomes as great for women as it is for men. It is important to keep an eye on overall fat intake, and make

FLUID FLOW

Even if you do not feel thirsty, or are worried about bladder control, aim to drink at least six to eight cups of fluid a day – tea, fruit juice, squash or plain water – otherwise you may risk becoming dehydrated. Extra fluids also help prevent constipation and are essential if you are eating fibre-rich foods.

FIVE A DAY

Five servings of fruit and vegetables may sound a lot, but is easy to achieve:

■ A glass of fresh fruit juice

■ A piece of fresh fruit

■ A bowl of stewed fruit

■ Two servings of vegetables

sure you eat as little animal fat as possible (see *Losing Weight*, page 64). The incidence of osteoporosis (loss of bone tissue) and the risk of fracture also increases rapidly over the age of sixty.

Latest research suggests that isoflavones (see *Phytoestrogens*, page 38) found in soya beans, may help raise 'good' HDL cholesterol in the blood. This, in turn, is thought to reduce the risk of heart disease. Isoflavones have also been found to increase bone density. So it may be worthwhile eating soya beans or soya products such as tofu, soya milk, or soya desserts, once in a while. It can certainly do no harm.

TIPS FOR A HEALTHY DIET

■ Try and eat oily fish at least three times a week. Canned sardines, salmon or mackerel are relatively bone-free and are a convenient way of getting more fish into the diet.

■ If food seems lacking in flavour, add lemon juice and your favourite herbs and spices, rather than extra salt, which can raise blood pressure.

■ Porridge makes a nutritious and warming start to the day. It is easy to swallow and high in soluble fibre, which is thought to help lower blood cholesterol levels.

■ Make sure you get enough folic acid by eating plenty of eggs, liver, wholemeal bread and leafy vegetables. Choose breakfast cereals that are fortified with it.

■ If you eat little meat, increase protein intake by adding beans, lentils or grated cheese to soups. Make sure you get vitamin B12 from dairy foods or yeast extract.

■ Eat more soya beans and soya products. Soya beans need lengthy soaking but can be added to soups and stews. Tofu (soy bean curd) is more convenient to use. Add it to scrambled eggs or stir-fries.

■ Make sure you get a daily supply of vitamin C. Strawberries, kiwi fruit, blackcurrants and oranges are excellent sources. Cabbage, red peppers and new potatoes also provide useful amounts.

■ Don't go short of minerals. Meat, liver, chicken, eggs and wholemeal bread supply iron and zinc. Milk, dairy products and leafy vegetables provide calcium. Fruit and vegetables – especially bananas – provide potassium.

FEEDING BABIES, CHILDREN AND TEENAGERS

It is now widely believed that nutrition in infancy has a significant and lasting effect on health in later years. Providing a healthy balanced diet and encouraging sound eating habits are therefore the greatest contributions a parent can make towards a child's development and future health.

DIFFERENT NUTRITIONAL NEEDS

The criteria which apply to an adult's balanced diet are not the same for children under the age of two – a fact that is not always realised.

■ Babies and infants have small stomachs and therefore need energy- and nutrient-dense foods. At this stage, fat is an essential part of the diet because a small amount provides concentrated energy, vitamins A and D, and the essential fatty acids crucial for the development of cells and tissues, especially those in the brain and nervous system.

■ Low-fat, high-fibre foods, such as pulses and muesli, may rob a child of some of the nutrients needed for proper growth and development.

■ Older children and adults require a wide variety of foods to get all the necessary nutrients, but babies must slowly build up a repertoire of foods at a rate dictated by their individual physical and mental development so it is important not to rush them.

THE FIRST FOUR MONTHS

A baby's digestive system and kidneys are too immature to handle solid food at this stage, so most babies need nothing more than breast milk. This provides all the energy and nutrients needed for development, in the correct proportions and in a highly available form. Breast milk contains particular proteins, antibodies and white blood cells which help protect the baby from infection. It reduces the risk of food allergies which sometimes occur as a result of early exposure to certain foods. Breast milk is also rich in the omega-3 essential fatty acids which are considered vital for healthy brain development.

Breastfeeding is the healthiest, most economical and practical way of feeding your baby, so even if you try it only for a few weeks it will be well worthwhile. If you then decide to switch to bottle feeding, the changeover should not be difficult since a feeding routine will already have been established.

If you bottle feed, you should use an approved infant formula rather than cow's, goat's or sheep's milk. Formula milk is modified to make its composition closer to that of human milk. Unmodified milks contain proteins and lactose which can cause digestive upsets, respiratory problems and allergies. Soya milk should not be given to babies without first seeking medical advice, as it contains natural oestrogens.

Up to the age of four to six months a baby has no need for solid foods. In fact, if they are introduced too soon, the amount of breast milk (or formula) taken will be reduced, and with it the essential nutrients that breast milk provides. After four to six months, however, milk no longer provides sufficient nutrients to meet the needs of a growing baby. Solid foods must therefore be gradually introduced, though you should continue giving breast milk or formula as the main drink throughout the first year.

INTRODUCING SOLID FOODS

4–6 MONTHS

A baby's first foods must be of a semi-fluid consistency since the swallowing reflex is not yet mature, and he or she still has to learn to chew. Start off by offering a teaspoon or so of cooked, sieved cereal moistened with breast milk or formula. It is preferable to use a single gluten-free cereal such as rice, cornmeal or sago. These are easy to digest and least likely to cause allergies. Wheat or cereals containing gluten are harder on the stomach and may cause an adverse reaction.

Introduce new foods one at a time at intervals of a few days. This will allow a baby to get used to different flavours, and also will indicate whether or not a particular food is causing upsets.

For the first month of weaning, stick with cereals, vegetables and fruit. After that, you can gradually add fish, poultry and well-cooked pulses. Breast or formula milk should still be the main drink, although water may be offered as well. Fruit juices are not necessary, or even advisable, at this stage.

In the early stages of weaning, commercial baby foods are sometimes more convenient. However, if home-cooked food is preferred, always sieve the food to get rid of indigestible residues. Puréeing the food in a food processor or blender does not do the job so effectively.

Foods for early weaning

■ Boiled, mild-tasting vegetables such as potatoes, carrots, squash or peas, sieved to a purée. Try mashed avocado as well.

■ Stewed apples, pears and apricots, sieved to a purée. Sweeten with mashed banana.

■ Steamed white fish, such as plaice or haddock, mixed with breast or formula milk and puréed.

■ Minced, steamed chicken or turkey, mixed with breast or formula milk and puréed. Mix with potato or carrot.

■ Well-cooked lentils or chick peas, sieved to a purée and moistened with breast or formula milk, or home-made salt-free stock.

Don't be tempted to add margarine or butter, salt, soy sauce or sugar to a baby's food. You may think you are improving the flavour, but babies have sensitive taste buds and bland food is what they like. Their kidneys are also too small to cope with salt.

GLUTEN

Gluten is a protein found in wheat, oats, barley and rye, and is therefore present in foods which contain them, eg rusks, bread, pasta, biscuits. Some people suffer from a permanent sensitivity to dietary gluten – a condition known as coeliac disease. It causes damage to the mucosa in the small bowel and prevents nutrients from being properly absorbed. In order to reduce the risk of the disease, it is better not to give your baby foods containing gluten until after six months of age.

6–9 MONTHS

By six months, breast or formula milk no longer provides enough iron, and the baby's internal iron store will be coming to an end. Solid foods are now the major source, so it is important to make sure that they contain iron in a form that is easily absorbed. Meat and fish are ideal; dark green leafy vegetables, tofu and fortified breakfast cereals are also a reasonable source. Since iron from plant foods is less well absorbed, improve absorption by giving your baby vitamin C-rich foods, such as fruit and fruit juices, at the same meal.

A baby can now tolerate foods with a coarser texture. Start giving finger foods to encourage chewing. Try softish foods first, such as a piece of banana or a sliver of mild cheese. After about a month, offer chunks of peeled apple or carrot. Remember never to leave your baby alone while feeding in case of choking.

Wheat- or oat-based cereals can be introduced from six months, as well as pasta and different types of bread. Dried toast, bread sticks and rusks are all good for teething. You can also start using cow's milk on cereal and in cooked dishes such as sauces and custards, but not as a main drink. Use whole milk (red or silver top), rather than skimmed and semi-skimmed milk – they are low in calories and vitamin A. Never use raw or unpasteurised milk. Other dairy products can be served as well. Try plain yogurt or fromage frais mixed with puréed fruit, cottage cheese and mashed banana, or a little finely grated mild cheese on mashed potato.

By about seven or eight months a baby will be ready for stronger tasting vegetables, such as broccoli and cauliflower. You can also start serving eggs. Start off with a teaspoon of well-cooked egg yolk. To avoid the risk of allergies, leave out the whites until about twelve months. If your baby is able to drink from a cup, you can start offering fruit juices occasionally. Remember, however, that they contain extrinsic sugars (page 15) which can decrease the appetite for other nutrient- and energy-rich foods, and cause tooth decay. Excessive amounts can also cause digestive upsets and diarrhoea. Always serve the juice well diluted and with a meal.

9–12 MONTHS

By now your baby will be eating a much wider variety of foods and enjoying three meals a day as well as healthy snacks between meals. Food can be chopped into tiny pieces rather than sieved, and fruit and vegetables may be served lightly cooked or raw. Fruit juices can be regularly offered with meals, and will help iron absorption in a meat-free diet. Cow's milk should still not be used as a main drink since it is low in iron and vitamin D. You can offer lightly buttered bread with jam as an occasional snack, but try to limit sweet foods and foods that contain additives.

Your baby now needs a minimum of one serving of protein food from meat sources, or two from vegetable sources each day. In a vegetarian diet, replace the protein provided by meat with a mixture of cereals, pulses, smooth nut pastes and dairy foods.

Although your baby's diet and meal schedule will now be closer to that of the rest of the family, remember that the dietary guidelines for adults – low-fat, high-fibre – do not apply to infants, nor do they need salt.

SUGAR AND TEETH

Children naturally like sweetness, but sugary foods and snacks have little nutritional value and are a major cause of tooth decay. Try and discourage a sweet tooth by getting your child used to savoury foods – if you don't serve sweet things, they won't miss them. Don't add sugar to desserts unless absolutely necessary, then add only the tiniest amount. Mashed banana is naturally sweet and can be mixed with other foods to provide sweetness.

NUTS AND SEEDS

Do not give whole nuts and seeds to children under the age of five, and even then do so only under supervision. Children can easily choke. Smoothly ground nuts and seeds such as peanut butter, almond butter or tahini (sesame paste) are fine. If there is a family history of allergies, avoid peanuts and products containing them until after the age of three years.

TODDLERS AND PRE-SCHOOL CHILDREN

By the second year of life, your child will be active and growing rapidly, so this is a time of high nutrient and energy needs. At this stage, the appetite fluctuates quite widely. During a period of rapid growth, your toddler's appetite will have you glowing with pride. When not much is happening on the growth front, there will be a corresponding lack of interest in food. Don't worry – it's normal. The second year is also a time when food is used to assert independence and test your control. Young children will start to exhibit strong preferences or dislikes for certain foods. They are also easily distracted and need to be encouraged to concentrate on eating. Again, all of this is normal.

A child's appetite is a good indicator of nutritional needs, so beware of falling into the trap of insisting that he or she eats more than they want. It is better to serve a very small portion and offer more when that is finished. If your child refuses a particular food, don't worry – offer it again another time.

The easiest way to ensure that a child's nutritional needs are being met is to offer a wide variety of foods from the four main food groups (see chart below). However, a young child will need fewer daily servings than an adult. There is no reason why your child should not try most of the foods eaten by the rest of the family, although it is too soon to serve highly spiced foods such as garlic and chilli. Remember not to add salt, sugar or other strong seasonings to your child's portion.

Toddlers and pre-school children still need plenty of fat in the diet as this is the most concentrated source of energy. Full-fat milk should be given up until the age of two. Semi-skimmed milk can be given between the ages of two and five, provided the diet also contains plenty of energy-dense foods. Skimmed milk should not be introduced until after the age of five, otherwise the child may lose out on essential nutrients.

You should continue to limit the amount of fibre, particularly if your child follows a vegetarian or vegan diet. If too many bulky high-fibre foods are served, your child may not be able to eat enough to satisfy energy needs. High-fibre foods also restrict the absorption of important minerals such as iron and calcium, which are vital to a child's development.

DAILY SERVINGS: ONE TO FIVE YEARS

Use the table as a guide only – there's no need to follow it rigidly. Serving sizes will vary depending on age and appetite.

Food group	Servings per day
1 Cereals (including bread) and potatoes	Three to four
2 Fruit and vegetables	Four (preferably including green leafy vegetables and citrus fruit each day)
3 Milk and dairy foods (or fortified soya)	Three
4 Protein foods (meat, poultry, fish, eggs, tofu, pulses and nuts)	One or two

SNACKS FOR TODDLERS

Healthy snacks make an important contribution to a young child's overall nutrient intake, and they also provide extra energy. Planning snacks is therefore as important as planning meals. Serve snacks well in advance of the next meal so they do not spoil the child's appetite. Variety is important as this will increase the amount of nutrients in the diet. Try the following healthy snack ideas.

- Raw carrot, celery or cucumber sticks.

- Cherry tomatoes.

- Fresh fruit cut into bite-sized pieces.

- Grated mild cheese.

- Greek yogurt swirled with mashed strawberries or puréed mango.

- Home-made whole milk shake with no added sugar. Add mashed strawberries or banana.

- Tiny sandwiches with energy-dense fillings. Try mashed banana and smooth peanut butter, avocado and cottage cheese, or mashed sardine. The fillings are rich in calcium too.

- Oat cakes or rice cakes topped with hummus or peanut butter.

- Muffins, tea bread or scones.

- Low-sugar cakes made with sweet fruit or vegetables, such as banana, dried apricots, pumpkin, carrot or beetroot.

SCHOOL-AGE CHILDREN

By the time children reach school age, they are beginning to take some responsibility for what they eat. It is therefore important that children understand that eating a balanced diet will keep them healthy and bouncing with energy. They will be strongly influenced by the example set by you and the rest of the family. Relaxed family meals during which everyone can enjoy conversation and good food will be more effective in instilling sound eating habits than leaving your children to eat in front of the television while you rush around doing something else. Giving them simple tasks to help with the cooking will also stimulate an interest in good food.

At this stage outside influences start to make themselves felt. As your children grow and become more sociable you will not necessarily be able to control what they eat. A recent survey revealed that over 40% of school-age

GOOD SOURCES OF CALCIUM
- Milk
- Fortified soya milk
- Yogurt
- Cheese
- Tofu
- Canned sardines (if bones are eaten)
- Almonds
- Sesame paste
- White bread
- Purple sprouting broccoli
- Spring greens
- Spinach

GOOD SOURCES OF ZINC
- Meat
- Liver and liver pâté
- Poultry
- Seafood
- Eggs
- Nuts
- Chick peas
- Lentils
- Bread

children buy sweets and snacks on their way to and from school. Crisps, biscuits and fizzy drinks were top of the list. It is inevitable that your child will want to eat these, and to do so every now and again causes no real harm. However, it is important to persist with sound eating habits at home.

As all parents know, sweet-eating is a natural part of childhood, but it also causes tooth decay and spoils the appetite. There is little point in banning sweets altogether since this causes difficulties if your children's friends are allowed sweets, and is more than likely to result in secret sweet-eating. The best solution is to let your children have sweets occasionally after a meal, but don't make an issue of it by using sweets as a reward or special treat. Explain the dangers of tooth decay and encourage regular teeth-cleaning.

NUTRITIONAL REQUIREMENTS

Between the ages of five and eleven, children are growing rapidly and becoming more active. Their need for energy-dense foods increases rapidly with age, as does the need for a good supply of protein, calcium and iron. As well as changes associated with age, the nutritional requirements for boys and girls start to differ. Teenage girls need more iron and calcium, while boys need more zinc (page 36), needed for the production of male sperm. The chart below shows nutrient requirements in more detail.

As long as a school-age child's diet includes cereals, bread, potatoes, milk, green vegetables, fruit, eggs, cheese, meat, fish, and poultry they will be getting a sufficiently wide range of nutrients. Vegetarian children will need energy-dense foods such as nut and seed pastes, tofu, cheese, avocados, beans and lentils. Don't serve high-fibre cereals and pulses too often as they inhibit iron absorption.

CHILDREN'S DAILY NUTRITIONAL NEEDS (girls/boys)

Age	Energy	Protein	Vitamin A	Folate	Vitamin B12	Vitamin C
	cals	g	µg	µg	µg	mg
1-3	1165/1230	14.5	400	70	0.5	30
4-6	1545/1715	19.7	500	100	0.8	30
7-10	1740/1970	28.3	500	150	1.0	30
11-14	1845/2220	41.2/42.1	600	200	1.2	35
15-18	2110/2755	45.4/55.2	600/700	200	1.5	40

Age	Calcium	Magnesium	Iron	Zinc	Potassium
	mg	mg	mg	mg	mg
1-3	350	85	6.9	5.0	800
4-6	450	120	6.1	6.5	1100
7-10	550	200	8.7	7.0	2000
11-14	1000/800	280	14.8/11.3	9.0	3100
15-18	1000/800	300	14.8/11.3	7.0/9.5	3500

BEGIN THE DAY WITH BREAKFAST

It is vitally important that school-age children start the day with breakfast. After a night's sleep, blood sugar levels are low, and a boost of slow-release energy is essential. Without a nutritious, energy-rich start to the day, children are less able to concentrate and performance at school may suffer.

Make sure your children have enough time to eat breakfast. A bowl of cereal (not the sugary sort) and refreshing cold milk takes no more than ten minutes to prepare and eat. Wholemeal toast spread with peanut butter and banana, and served with a glass of milk, is equally speedy. Both provide a good amount of carbohydrate, protein and calcium, and will keep energy levels stable until lunch.

SCHOOL MEALS

The Government abolished nutritional standards for school meals in 1980. With many school meal services now privatised, the nutritional quality of food served can be variable, though there are still guidelines for 'meal providers'. The policy in many places is to serve 'what the kids want', which makes it even more crucial to instill sound eating habits at home.

However, it is better for children to eat what is offered at school, no matter the quality, than to spend their lunch money on crisps and sweets. That way, they will at least be getting a few nutrients rather than empty calories.

PACKED LUNCHES

Packed lunches are potentially a healthy alternative to school meals, but even these can be fraught with problems. You may send your child off to school with a wholesome and nutritious packed lunch, only to have it returned barely eaten. It's important to take into account what he or she will actually eat, and what is acceptable within the peer group – children do not like to have their sandwiches ridiculed. If the child is very young, make sure the food is easy to unpack and simple to eat.

Small sandwiches or rolls with tasty fillings are always popular, as are finger foods such as small cubes of cheese or carrot sticks, or tiny cold cooked potatoes, or cherry tomatoes. Fresh fruit is easier to deal with than salad – grapes, cherries, satsumas and small apples are all good. Children also appreciate a piece of home-made cake, tea bread or fruit loaf. Small cartons of yogurt or fromage frais can be included, but don't forget to pack a spoon. A carton of fruit juice or a small flask of cold milk makes a refreshing drink.

Older children will enjoy large baps or pitta bread stuffed with shredded cold chicken. Mix it with thick yogurt or hummus and add tomatoes, grated carrot and perhaps some crisp lettuce. You could also add pasta, rice or bean salads, or coleslaw, to be eaten with a fork or stuffed into pitta bread. A cold rolled ham omelette or a wedge of potato tortilla provides protein and energy, and makes a change from a bread-based packed lunch. Nuts, raisins and other dried fruits are good energy boosters.

GOOD SOURCES OF IRON

■ Fortified breakfast cereals

■ Dried apricots

■ Dried figs

■ Almonds

■ Molasses

■ Wholemeal bread

■ Egg yolk

■ Lentils

■ Chick peas

■ Peas

■ Sea vegetables

■ Tofu

■ Lamb chops

■ Liver and liver pâté

■ Canned tuna

■ Spinach

■ Spring greens

ADOLESCENTS

Teenagers have higher nutritional needs than any other group and yet they sometimes seem to have the poorest diet. Adolescence is also a time when eating disorders like anorexia and bulimia are prevalent. It is now known that major health problems such as osteoporosis and coronary heart disease have their foundations in the diet and eating patterns of adolescence. It is therefore vital to steer teenagers away from the easy options of fast food and processed products. They are all likely to be high in saturated fat, salt and sugar.

Teenagers like to make their own decisions about when and what to eat. Appetites at this stage are gargantuan and a teenager standing before an open fridge is a familiar sight – make sure the fridge has something to tempt them. It is important to provide a variety of healthy foods that are not only easily and quickly prepared, but also supply adequate calcium, iron and zinc (see mineral sources and nutritional requirements, pages 77-79).

There is an increased need for energy, protein, and almost all vitamins and minerals to support the growth of bones and muscles, and sexual develop-ment. The teenage years are the most crucial time for building up bone density in order to reduce the risk of osteoporosis later in life, so adequate calcium intake is vital. Three glasses of milk, a couple of pots of yogurt or a hefty wedge of cheese are minimum daily requirements.

Iron deficiency can be a problem, too, especially with teenage girls who need more iron than boys to replace menstrual losses. It is estimated that about 17% of adolescent girls and 4% of boys suffer from iron deficiency anaemia. Teenagers who eat a badly planned vegetarian diet or are using an unsuitable method of slimming are particularly at risk.

THE TEENAGE VEGETARIAN

Teenagers are increasingly turning to vegetarianism for a variety of personal, ecological and economic reasons. It is vital that they are aware of their new nutritional needs and that they understand that a healthy vegetarian diet is not simply a matter of going without meat and stocking up on crisps and chocolate instead.

Make sure the protein content of meat is replaced by adequate dairy prod-ucts, using lower-fat versions if weight gain is a cause for concern. Bean chilli, veggie burgers and sausages are useful sources of protein and will also satisfy teenage appetites. If your teenage daughter follows a vegetarian diet, take spe-cial care that she gets plenty of iron- and folate-rich foods.

OFF TO COLLEGE

It's vitally important that teenagers going away to college for the first time know how to feed themselves, and have some idea of what constitutes a healthy balanced diet. They need to understand that food does much more than stave off hunger – that it also provides energy, keeps the mind alert, maintains a resilient immune system, and speeds up recovery from illness.

It's very easy for students to start skipping meals. If

they wake up late and then rush off to lectures, breakfast usually goes by the board. Lunch may be a quick sandwich or bar of chocolate, and dinner a plate of chips. To reduce the risk of poor eating habits, encourage your teenager to practice some simple but tasty recipes before he or she leaves the nest, perhaps inviting future flat-mates round so they get used to cooking together. Students are more likely to eat healthily if they take turns to cook for each other – it is far more fun than eating alone and it's easier on the purse.

Students need nourishing food that's cheap and easy to make. Make sure they know how to cook rice, dried beans, pasta and potatoes. Once the basics are mastered, a useful repertoire of recipes could include:

- a stir-fry
- a pasta dish
- an omelette
- roast chicken
- bean- or meat-based chilli

Knowing how to shop is also important. Some teenagers may not have been inside a supermarket since the days of riding the trolley. Before your offspring leave, take them with you on the next major shop and show them the ropes. Choice in supermarkets can be totally baffling if you're not used to it, so make sure your teenager knows how to identify the cheapest brands and what to look for when choosing fresh produce (page 82). It is also a good idea to give your teenager a stash of cans, bottles and basics – these are easily stored since they don't take up fridge space, and are invaluable when funds are short.

STUDENT STORECUPBOARD

- *Cans*: chopped tomatoes, chick peas, beans, lentils, tuna.
- *Bottles*: pasta sauces, curry sauces, Chinese sauces, fruit compote, soups, olives.
- *Basics*: easy-cook rice, dried pasta, beans, lentils, flour, stock cubes, mustard, olive oil, sunflower oil, wine vinegar, black peppercorns.

THE CONVENIENCE FACTOR

A huge number of foods come under the umbrella term of 'convenience foods'. Even items we take for granted, such as flour, could be labelled as such, since a ready-milled product is more convenient than grinding whole grains.

At the other end of the scale we have a whole host of ready-prepared products including entire meals, ready-made sauces, fresh soups and bulging pillow-packs of washed, trimmed and sliced vegetables.

There is no denying that food freshly prepared at home is likely to be better for you. In addition to the benefit of potentially higher nutrient levels, the actual process of preparing and cooking food can be therapeutic. However, there is also room in a healthy balanced diet for carefully chosen convenience products.

If you are in a rush, or if family members need to eat at different times, the occasional ready-prepared meal is fine. However, portions tend to be small and you will need to add fresh vegetables or salad, and perhaps some extra carbohydrate for nutritional balance. These extra items can also be ready-prepared if necessary: trimmed green beans, ready-shelled peas, prewashed spinach are all fine, as are frozen vegetables. Buy ready-prepared fresh produce on the day you need it, since any fruit or vegetable that has been cut or chopped will start to lose nutrients.

A situation to be avoided at all costs is relying on ready-prepared meals every day. Ready-meals are prohibitively expensive, especially for a family, they generate huge amounts of packaging which has to be disposed of, they invariably contain additives and preservatives, and they can never, ever be as nourishing as a competently cooked home-made meal. If you are too rushed to spend any time at all preparing your own food, then you probably need to re-evaluate your lifestyle.

SHOPPING FOR FRESH FOOD

Shopping for fresh food needs to be done every two or three days in order to enjoy it at its best. Fruit and vegetables in particular start to deteriorate and lose their nutrients even from the moment of harvest.

Highly perishable items should spend the absolute minimum time away from a chilled environment. It's no good buying fish in your lunch hour if you then have to keep it under your desk all afternoon. Bacteria could build up to unacceptable levels and there will be some loss of nutrients. If you have to drive several miles to a supermarket or specialist supplier, remember to take a cool bag or ice box to keep the goods fresh until you get home.

WHERE TO SHOP

There are advantages and disadvantages to each kind of retail outlet. Supermarkets obviously offer the widest variety, and there is the added benefit that fresh produce will have been packed and stored in optimum conditions. However, though convenient for a weekly shop, visiting a supermarket every two or three days not only becomes tedious but also means you may buy more than you need.

Smaller or specialist shops are good for topping up supplies, and they are more likely to stock seasonal or locally grown items. You can also potentially enjoy personal contact with the shopkeeper, who may be willing to procure items especially for you. However, choice in smaller outlets may be more restricted. You also need to check hygiene, storage facilities and the rate of turnover of goods.

If you buy meat from a butcher, choose a shop that has a steady turnover, then at least you will know that the meat is likely to be fresh. A look around the shop will also give you clues as to the standard of produce. The shop should smell fresh, have a clean floor, and a clean and tidy preparation area. There should be a separate area for any cooked produce.

Vegetables and fruit are often sold more cheaply in street markets. The produce is likely to be fresh as stall holders cannot as a rule stock more than they can sell in one day. However, quality can be variable. Fruit bought from street markets seems particularly prone to deterioration.

Shops catering to ethnic communities often sell good-quality fresh produce that is hard to find elsewhere. These shops tend to sell seasonal fruit and vegetables, albeit imported, which makes a change from a year-round diet offered by the supermarkets. They are also an invaluable source of realistically sized bunches of fresh herbs.

Many of the better healthfood shops stock good-quality cheeses and yogurt as well as organic fruit and vegetables (see also *Organic Food*, page 88). There is also an ever-growing number of mail-order companies willing and able to deliver quality fish, meat, fruit and veg. There are several directories on the market which give details.

'USE BY' AND 'BEST BEFORE' DATES

When buying pre-packed fresh food, always check the 'use by' and 'best before' dates. This also applies to frozen and canned food. Be ruthless about discarding any item that has gone beyond the recommended date.

CHOOSING FRESH FRUIT

As well as using a greengrocer or supermarket known for top-quality produce, the secret of choosing good fruit is to learn to recognise when it is at the peak of its growth cycle. At this stage, fruit will be at its best in terms of flavour and texture, and will also contain higher levels of nutrients such as vitamin C. Use your senses to assess quality – the way a fruit smells and feels are as important as its size and colour.

With some fruits – pineapples, melons, strawberries, peaches and nectarines, for example – smell is probably the best guide, so don't be shy of picking up fruit and having a sniff. If these types of fruit smell of nothing, don't buy them. On the other hand, if they give off a very sweet, almost fermented smell, they are probably overripe and should also be rejected.

Texture comes into play with mangoes, papayas and kiwi fruit. They have little or no smell, but when ripe they should give slightly when lightly pressed.

With any fruit, the heavier it feels relative to size, the greater the chance of a pleasing texture and plenty of juice. Large specimens are likely to be riper because they will have had a longer pre-harvest period, and thus time to develop flavour and sweetness.

All fruit should look plump and appetising. The skin should be free from wrinkles, cracks, browning or bruised bits. Citrus fruit should look bright and glossy. Loose-skinned citrus should be just that – loose but not squashy. Berries should look firm and have a good even colour. Don't buy any that are sprouting whiskers of mould or showing signs of staining at the base of the punnet.

UNDER-RIPE FRUIT

Some fruits are deliberately picked while still 'green' so that they will survive transportation and have a longer shelf life. Apricots, nectarines and plums are typical examples of fruit sold in this state. Some, such as bananas, mangoes and papayas, will continue to ripen post-harvest, but most types will never develop the depth of flavour and succulence of a fruit picked at its peak.

'RIPE AND READY TO EAT'

In response to consumer complaints concerning under-ripe fruit, some supermarkets sell produce marked 'ripe and ready to eat'. However, unless you buy from a supermarket geared to people who shop on a daily basis, there is a risk that the fruit may have languished on the shelves. Always carefully inspect 'ripe' fruit before buying, and eat on the day of purchase. If the fruit is past its best, take it back and ask for a refund.

WAXED FRUIT

Some types of apples and pears, and all citrus fruit are routinely waxed to improve appearance and prolong shelf life. Although the wax is said to be harmless, it is safer to buy unwaxed or organic produce if you want to use the peels in cooking. Scrubbing may remove some of the wax from citrus fruit, but doing so will also destroy the volatile oils.

CHOOSING FRESH VEGETABLES

Vegetables, including salad leaves and herbs, are the main providers of several essential vitamins and minerals in the diet. Some of the vitamins are highly unstable when exposed to air, heat and light, so it is vital that produce is stored in prime conditions once harvested. All vegetables, even humble root vegetables, should look lively and smell fresh.

Green leafy vegetables and salad leaves should be vibrantly coloured, full of bounce and sometimes literally squeaking with life. Any limpness or yellowing is unacceptable, as is sliminess or rot. This applies especially to Asian greens such as choy sum, bok choi and water spinach.

Stalks and shoots – celery and asparagus, for example – should snap crisply when the stems are removed from the base.

Root vegetables should feel firm and smell good. Reject any that are wrinkled, damaged, feel flabby or have started to sprout. Avoid potatoes with green patches; turnips with green patches are fine, however. Swede, celeriac and kohlrabi should be free from cracks and feel weighty for their size. Carrots should be a good strong orange with a smooth skin and no sign of sprouting. They should snap crisply when broken.

When buying onions, shallots and garlic, choose plump, solid bulbs with a tight skin. Reject any that are soft, mouldy or beginning to sprout. Look for sprightly spring onions and leeks. The white part should feel firm and there should be no sign of withering or sliminess.

Freshness is paramount when buying beans and peas. Beans with edible pods, eg French beans and runner beans, should be green and crisp with no wrinkling, limpness, brown patches or signs of mould. Mangetout and sugar snap peas should be crisp and bright green; peas for shelling should have plump, wrinkle-free pods. Shelling beans, such as broad beans, should have smooth evenly shaped pods without any pockmarks or brown spots.

Late-summer shelling beans, such as fresh borlotti, flageolet and cannellini beans, are beginning to appear on the market. These beans have long been enjoyed in southern Europe and the US, but are relatively new to Britain. They are worth buying for convenience alone – unlike their dried equivalent, fresh shelling beans do not need soaking and they cook in a matter of minutes. They are also packed with nutrients. Indications of quality are the opposite to those of broad beans and beans with edible pods: the pods should look leathery and lumpy – a sign that the beans within are plump and ready to be eaten.

Sweetcorn should have tightly packed kernels and the ears should preferably be completely enclosed in their green husks. Avoid any with pale or dried-out silks, or wrinkled kernels.

Vegetable fruits – that's tomatoes, peppers, chillies, squash, aubergines, avocados and cucumbers – should feel heavy for their size, and the flesh should feel firm. Any that are wrinkled, bruised or flabby are not worth buying. Tomatoes, peppers and chillies should have smooth, brightly coloured skins. Aubergines should be firm and glossy with no pockmarks, and feel heavy for their size.

Mushrooms should have a clean fresh smell, and the skin should feel smooth and dry with no blemishes or sliminess.

CHOOSING MEAT

Meat is one of the most difficult foods to assess for quality, and price is not necessarily a guide. Good flavour and texture are partly a result of breeding, what the animal was fed on, and where and how it was reared. However, the use of growth stimulants, the conditions in which the animal was slaughtered, how quickly a carcass has been chilled, and the length of 'ageing' or hanging time also affect flavour and texture. There is often no way of knowing these things, so eating the meat is the only test.

Appearance offers several clues to quality. Depending on the animal, the colour of meat should be in the pink to reddish-brown spectrum. The cut surface of the meat should look slightly moist but in no way should it look or feel wet. A freshly cut piece of red meat will be bright red, but after about twenty minutes of exposure to the air, the colour changes to reddish-brown. This may look less attractive but it does not affect flavour. Any greyness, however, is a bad sign.

The state of the animal before slaughter affects flavour and colour. A very dark beef steak could be from an animal not rested enough before slaughter. Though the meat may be tender it will lack flavour. Confusingly, a very dark steak could have come from an older animal, and so may be tougher and have a stronger flavour. With pork, stressful conditions before slaughter make the meat much paler. The meat also looks wet and may be tough after cooking.

FATTY ISSUES

Part of current healthy eating advice is to cut down on saturated fat, and one way of doing that is to eat less meat. Another way, however, is to eat leaner meat. Many animals are now specifically bred for leanness, and more meat is trimmed to remove excess visible fat before it is sold.

Lean meat has less 'marbling' or small streaks of white fat running through it. The amount of marbling appears to affect flavour – very lean meat with little marbling tends to be less juicy and tender. Beef and lamb tend to have more marbling than pork, and a lot of marbling in beef is an indication of quality.

Fat round the outside of meat has less effect on flavour but it does stop the meat from drying out during cooking, and thus influences eating quality. The fat that is left after trimming should be a firm creamy white with a waxy texture.

CHOICE OF CUT

When choosing meat, select a cut suitable for the dish you are planning to cook. The parts from the animal which do the most work – that is the front quarters, neck and shoulders – will have the most developed muscles, and these are the toughest cuts of meat. Though they are the cheapest, these cuts need long slow cooking at gentle temperatures to become tender, so the money you save at the butchers may end up being spent on the fuel bill.

The tenderest cuts are the loin and fillet from the back of the animal, which is the part that does the least work. These are suitable for quick cooking methods using intense direct heat, such as grilling or frying. Cuts from the flank and rump are midway between tender and tough, and are best cooked over moderate heat with the addition of some liquid, as in pot roasting or braising.

MODIFIED-ATMOSPHERE PACKAGING

Since customers tend to associate a nice bright colour with freshness and quality, supermarkets increasingly sell freshly cut red meat in transparent plastic packs and 'gas flush' it with nitrogen and carbon dioxide to stop the colour darkening. The process prolongs shelf life but does not appear to affect flavour.

CHOOSING FRESH POULTRY

As with meat, eating quality in poultry depends on breed, feed and the environment in which the bird was reared. The best-quality birds will be largely grain-fed and will have spent most of their days roaming freely out of doors.

Poultry deteriorates relatively rapidly, so when buying a fresh bird, check that it is well-chilled and within its sell-by date. If the bird is not embalmed in plastic, smell it and feel it. The smell should be clean and fresh with absolutely no 'off' taints. The flesh should be evenly coloured and feel smooth and almost powdery-dry to touch. Wet skin indicates that the bird may have been frozen. With prepacked birds, cling film smoothes out signs of age, so it's harder to evaluate freshness. However, the flesh should look plump and give slightly when pressed. Young birds should have a pliable breast bone.

CHOOSING FRESH FISH

Current nutritional advice suggests that we should eat more fish, particularly oily fish like mackerel, tuna and sardines, which are valued for their special omega-3 fatty acids.

Since fish is a food that deteriorates rapidly, it is vital to recognise when it is fresh. Smell is an obvious indication – fresh fish has a clean pleasant smell with absolutely no trace of fishy odours. Appearance offers several clues. When fresh, a whole fish has a bright skin with a good sheen. It feels stiff and firm and has tightly attached scales. The eyes are bright, clear and bulging rather than sunken or cloudy. The gills are bright pink or blood-red and moist, rather than dull brown and dry. An ungutted fresh fish is plump and resilient, especially around the belly.

Fillets and cutlets should not look dry or discoloured. There should be no blood clots or reddening along the backbone. Because exposed flesh is more vulnerable to bacteria, fish that has been cut deteriorates more rapidly than whole fish. It is therefore best to buy fish at a shop where it can be freshly cut, or buy pre-cut portions in modified-atmosphere packaging (see page 85).

SHELLFISH

With shellfish, freshness is so essential that they are often sold live – once dead, bacteria quickly multiplies to unacceptable levels and shellfish perish fast. Bivalve molluscs such as mussels are particularly prone to contamination. If you buy shellfish uncooked, make sure you go to an impeccable supplier. The same applies when buying ready-cooked shellfish, since once cooked it is difficult to assess freshness.

Fresh uncooked crustaceans (shrimps, crabs, lobsters etc) should look glisteningly moist, and have a clean, sweetish smell. Legs, heads and tails should be firmly attached to the body. Cooked crustaceans such as prawns are best bought while still in the shell as they seem to retain more

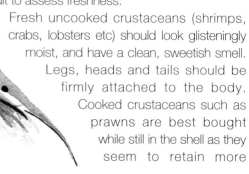

flavour. The shells should look pink and slightly moist – any with whitish marks may be dehydrated and tough.

Molluscs in the shell (mussels, scallops, clams, oysters) must be bought live. The shells should be tightly shut (although scallops and some clams are never completely shut). If they remain open when tapped they should be discarded.

CHOOSING FRESH CHEESE

When buying fresh cheese, resist the temptation to buy more than enough for two or three days. Once cut, cheese deteriorates quite easily. For the best flavour, it is best stored, or at least served, at room temperature – another reason for buying a small amount.

Freshness can be judged by colour, texture and smell. If possible, ask for a sliver to try before buying. There should be no whiff of ammonia coming from soft cheeses such as Brie and Camembert. The inside should look soft and buttery but not runny. There should be no discolouration or browning at the edges. Hard cheeses such as Cheddar should show no sign of sweating, cracks or mould. The inside should be firm and fresh with a hint of dampness when touched.

CHOOSING EGGS

The fresher the egg, the better the flavour and nutritional value. Always check the sell-by date. Hen eggs can be kept for up to three weeks, but it's best to eat them as soon as you can and use the older ones for baking and sauce making. Open the box and check for damage – a cracked egg should be used quickly. If the white has leaked out, don't buy them.

Even though brown or speckled eggs look more wholesome, shell colour has no effect on flavour. Flavour is affected by the diet of the hen, and the best eggs are those that have been fed on natural foodstuffs. 'Free-range' is not necessarily a sign of quality (see *Choosing Fresh Poultry*, left), but good free-range eggs can often be found in health food shops and specialist food shops. 'Four-grain' or organic eggs are the ones to look for in supermarkets.

EGG SIZES

In line with EC regulations, the number of egg sizes has been reduced from eight to four. The new sizes are Very Large, Large, Medium and Small. As a general rule, Very Large and Large are perfect for boiling, frying, poaching, scrambling and omelette-making, while Medium is the size recommended for use in recipes. Small is the most economical size for glazing, binding, stuffing and enriching or thickening sauces.

ORGANIC PRODUCE

Organic food includes not only fruit and vegetables, but also dry goods such as cereals and pulses, wine from grapes produced by organic methods, and meat and dairy produce from animals which have been reared on a diet free from hormones, additives and antibiotics. This includes:

- meat, poultry, game and fish
- meat products such as bacon and sausages
- dairy products
- eggs
- bread and flour
- grains and pulses
- pasta and pasta sauces
- breakfast cereals
- cakes and biscuits
- herbs and spices
- oils and vinegars
- sauces and seasonings
- sugar, honey and other sweeteners
- jams and spreads
- dried fruits
- ready-made meals and fresh soups
- baby food
- chocolate
- fruit and vegetable juices
- tea and coffee
- wines and beers

ORGANIC FOOD

Recently there has been a deluge of organic products coming into the shops. Fuelled by fears of BSE, GM foods, artificial fertilisers and pesticides, consumer demand has risen to such an extent that even supermarkets now devote sizeable sections entirely to organic produce. 'Organic-only' supermarkets are popping up in major cities, and more and more health food shops are now selling good-quality fresh organic produce along with packaged products. Organic food can also be bought by mail order and on the Internet.

WHAT DOES ORGANIC MEAN?

Although most people vaguely associate the word 'organic' with wholesomeness, how many of us really understand what it means?

The term basically refers to matter that has been formed from living things. Organic farming, therefore, relies on natural compounds from plant matter to fertilise crops. Pests and diseases are controlled without the use of artificial chemicals, natural predators are encouraged, and crops are timed to avoid certain pests. Crop diversity, as well as crop rotation, is used to build up soil fertility, and weeding is carried out mechanically rather than chemically.

Other characteristics of organic farming include the humane and responsible treatment of livestock. Animals used for meat or dairy products cannot be given antibiotics, hormonal growth promoters or feed that contains animal protein.

IS ORGANIC FOOD BETTER FOR YOU?

Despite Government claims that pesticide residues in fresh fruit and vegetables are negligible and harmless, and that GM foods are safe, nobody knows the long-term effects. Eating organic food is the only way of ensuring that your food is free of chemical cocktails and has not been genetically modified.

Regardless of the scientific evidence – or lack of it – people who eat organic food claim they feel better in themselves and they enjoy taking positive steps to safeguard their future health. The knowledge that organic farming helps to protect the environment also produces a sense of well-being.

Supporters claim that organic food contains higher levels of vitamins and minerals, and several studies have indeed shown higher levels of protein, calcium, iron, potassium and vitamin C in some organic vegetables. However, nutrient levels are likely to depend not only on the type of fruit or vegetable, but also other variables such as environmental conditions, stage of ripeness and time of harvest. In a study commissioned by MAFF (the Ministry of Agriculture, Fisheries and Foods), vitamin C levels were found to be higher in organically produced oranges, apples and tomatoes, but non-organic potatoes contained higher levels than the organic ones tested.

DOES ORGANIC FOOD TASTE BETTER?

Blind tastings by food writers, chefs and other interested parties have so far failed to produce consistent evidence that organic food tastes any better than conventionally produced food. However, organically produced raw fruit and vegetables tend to do well in tasting trials. The difference in organic carrots, for example, has been described as 'stunningly obvious'. Even so, it is important to bear in mind that the eating quality of fresh produce ultimately boils down to the skill of the individual grower, whether organic or otherwise.

With baked foods, there is an obvious improvement in flavour and texture when organic flour, eggs and butter are used.

WHY IS IT SO EXPENSIVE?

Because organic food is produced on a smaller scale, using traditional farming practices and manual labour, production is more labour intensive. Since small organic farms cannot benefit from the economies of scale enjoyed by the bigger conventional farming operations, the food costs more to produce.

Other costs are incurred by the use of cold storage after harvest rather than the post-harvest preservation treatments used by conventional farmers. This is not only more expensive but less reliable, so organic farmers lose more of their produce. Sorting, packaging and transporting organic food can also be more expensive because of the small volumes involved.

At the moment, UK supplies of organic produce cannot keep pace with demand, and much of what is in the shops is imported. However, the more organic food becomes available, the greater the likelihood that prices will fall.

THE LAW

By law, all food sold as organic must come from producers and importers whose methods have been inspected and approved by one of the six independent certification bodies officially recognised by UKROFS (the UK Register of Organic Food Standards):

■ *Bio-Dynamic Agricultural Association (Demeter)* Requires farmers to use mixtures of herbs and other natural substances to nourish the soil. To qualify, farms must have used these methods for three years.

■ *Irish Organic Farmers' and Growers' Association* Follows UKROF standards, and helps promote organic production and consumption in Ireland.

■ *Organic Farmers and Growers* Follows UKROF standards and helps market organic food.

■ *Organic Food Federation* Represents importers and manufacturers of organic food and drink.

■ *Scottish Organic Producers' Association* Follows UKROF standards, offers advice to members and helps promote organic produce in Scotland.

■ *Soil Association* In addition to UKROF standards, has further conservation standards which aim to protect the environment and wildlife habitats on organic farms.

ORGANIC STANDARDS:

■ prohibit the use of artificial pesticides and fertilisers.

■ prohibit genetically modified crops and ingredients.

■ promote wildlife conservation and natural enhancement of soil fertility.

A HEALTHY STORECUPBOARD

A storecupboard stocked with a variety of health-promoting ingredients means that you can always serve up a delicious nourishing meal with what's on hand. A well-stocked storecupboard does not have to be overflowing. It is better to keep a minimum of items that get used up and replaced, rather than a vast collection of cans and bottles that are past their 'use-by' date.

The list that follows is not a comprehensive one. For example, basics are not included unless there is a healthier or more flavourful version. What the list does include, though, are the items you need to follow a healthy diet. You may consider some things unusual but none are hard to find. They are all worth keeping and using regularly. By doing so, you will add variety to your diet and thus improve nutritional balance.

OILS

Oils derived from plant foods are a healthier option than hard fats and margarines. Of the three main types used, cold-pressed oils are the most superior. They are unrefined and have the best flavour and nutritional value. Semi-refined oils are made from second pressings and are subjected to heat treatment. They are nutritionally inferior to cold-pressed oils. Refined oils are highly processed, which removes most of the nutrients, but vitamins and antioxidants are reintroduced after processing.

It is worth investing in good-quality extra-virgin olive oil for drizzling over salads or vegetables. Extra-virgin oil is made from the first pressing and has a rich, fruity flavour. Light olive oil (often labelled 'pure') is better for shallow-frying. You might also want to try extra-virgin sunflower oil. It has a delicious satiny mouth-feel and is sometimes preferable to olive oil. Though relatively new to the market, it is widely available.

Groundnut oil is best for stir-frying since it has a high smoke point and therefore does not oxidise so readily as other vegetable oils. Grapeseed, safflower and refined sunflower oil are good all-purpose neutral oils, high in polyunsaturates and linoleic acid. Toasted dark sesame oil is extremely strong and should be used more as a flavouring agent than a cooking medium.

Richly flavoured and expensive, unrefined walnut and hazelnut oils add a wonderful depth of flavour to salad dressings, as does pumpkin seed oil. Buy these oils in small amounts as they do not keep well.

VINEGARS

Vinegars are useful not only for salad dressings but for sharpening the flavour of foods such as soups, casseroles, stir-fries, sauces and dips. There are differences in flavour, so you might want to keep three or four different vinegars to reflect the nature of the dish you are cooking.

Brown rice vinegar is mildly flavoured and good for Asian dishes. Chinese black vinegar has a meaty flavour but is quite light. Cider vinegar is a good all-purpose vinegar. It has a low acidity and a good mellow flavour. White wine vinegar is lighter than red wine vinegar and goes well with salad leaves.

Balsamic vinegar, made in Italy from sweet wine, is aromatic and full-bodied. A few drops go a long way. Sherry vinegar is also full-bodied but not nearly as sweet as balsamic vinegar.

HERBS AND SPICES

Fresh herbs are usually preferable to dried, but a few of the more robust types, such as rosemary, marjoram and thyme, keep their aroma when dried, and are good in pasta sauces and casseroles. For freshness and a better flavour, buy your spices whole whenever possible and grind them as you need them. Discard any that taste dry and musty. It is always wiser to buy herbs and spices in small amounts from a shop with a high turnover. Store them in airtight jars or containers away from light and moisture, and don't forget to add labels so that you can easily identify the contents.

SOYA PRODUCTS

A useful variety of protein-rich products are made from soya beans. Shoyu and tamari are naturally fermented soy sauces. Tamari is wheat-free and therefore suitable for people on a gluten-free diet. Both have a warmer, mellower flavour than synthetic soy sauces. They are widely available from healthfood shops and the better supermarkets.

Miso is a highly nutritious fermented soy bean paste which contains living bacteria and enzymes in the same way as 'live' yogurt. A spoonful added to soups or stews at the end of cooking enriches the flavour. Miso can also be used in spreads and dressings.

Tofu is soya bean curd, rich in protein, calcium, iron and B vitamins. It is an invaluable substitute for animal protein and is extremely versatile in cooking. It can be stir-fried, scrambled, grilled, beaten into dressings and sauces, or even used in desserts. It comes in various densities: silken, soft and firm, and is sold fresh, or in long-life packs which keep for several months.

DRIED PEAS, BEANS AND LENTILS

A wonderful range of pulses forms the basis of staple dishes the world over. We tend to limit our use of them in the UK, and therefore miss out on a variety of subtly different taste experiences. Earthy black turtle beans, pink borlotti beans, yellow split peas, and beautiful purple-brown Puy lentils are all delicious, highly nutritious and worth trying.

Because they contain almost no fat, dried pulses have a long shelf life and are therefore ideal storecupboard material. (Soya beans are an exception, since they are high in fat.) However, the older they are, the longer they take to cook. Always buy pulses from a shop with a rapid turnover. Discard any with flaking skins, small holes or that look dusty – all signs of possible insect infestation.

GRAINS

Like pulses, grains are one of the most widely used foods the world over, but in the UK we do not make as much use of them as we might. They are an invaluable source of carbohydrate, fibre, vitamins and minerals, so it's worth keeping a selection and trying a different one each week. Rice is a familiar enough grain, but you might like to keep different types for different dishes. Jasmine, or Thai fragrant rice is beautifully flavoured and ideal for stir-fries. Basmati is also delicious and nutty. Use the brown variety for added fibre and B vitamins. Red rice is another nutty sort. It makes delicious salads and pilaffs. Wild rice is succulent, earthy and expensive – best kept for special occasions only.

Bulghar wheat and couscous are both part-cooked, and are useful if you are short of time. Both are delicious in salads or with roasted vegetables. Buckwheat, quinoa and golden yellow polenta are good too. Whole grains keep indefinitely in a cool, dry place, but, like pulses, cooking time increases with age. Whole grain flours do not keep more than a few months, since the milling process exposes the oil which soon goes rancid. The vitamin E content also deteriorates with time.

NUTS AND SEEDS

A small selection of nuts and seeds is useful for adding to salads, rice dishes, curries, stir-fries, home-made cakes and biscuits, and as a snack. Almonds, Brazil nuts and walnuts are particularly delicious and contain valuable vitamins and minerals. Sunflower, pumpkin and sesame seeds are also useful.

Because they have a high oil content, nuts and seeds easily go rancid. It's best to buy nuts in the shell, but only when they are really fresh. Don't buy any that feel light or rattle when you shake them. Buy pre-shelled nuts in small quantities and store in an airtight container away from heat, light and moisture.

Nut or seed butters, such as peanut butter, almond butter and tahini (sesame paste) are an invaluable source of energy for young children. Buy low-salt versions if possible.

DRIED PASTA AND NOODLES

A selection of good-quality dried pasta is essential for whipping up tasty, energy-rich meals. Keep two or three different shapes, such as shells, spirals or butterflies, for chunky sauces, and use ribbon pasta for smoother sauces. Choose wholemeal varieties for extra fibre, B vitamins and zinc. Keep dried egg noodles and rice noodles on hand for stir-fries or oriental soups. Stored in a dry place, dried pasta and noodles keep indefinitely.

CANNED FOODS

Canned tomatoes, chick peas, kidney beans, sardines, tuna and salmon are all worth keeping on hand. When buying canned beans and chick peas, look for those with labels saying 'no sugar added'. If you are trying to reduce fat intake, choose fish canned in brine rather than oil. It doesn't always taste as good, but will be better for you. Always check the 'use-by' date and throw out any cans that are rusty, dented or swollen.

SEA VEGETABLES
Sea vegetables (or seaweeds) are high in fibre, low in fat and are one of the richest sources of minerals needed by the body. They are rich in protein and contain useful amounts of B vitamins, including B12 – rarely found in foods of vegetable origin. Most of the sea vegetables available in the UK are imported dried from Japan, and are sold in good health food shops. They will keep indefinitely in a dry place. The flavour and texture may seem strange if you are not used to them, so try a small amount in soups and stews to begin with. The mildest types are arame, hiziki and nori.

BREAKFAST CEREALS
Choose brands with a high-fibre content and preferably without any added sugar or salt. Wheat flake bars and shredded wheat biscuits are the least adulterated types available.

THE MYSTERIES OF FOOD LABELLING
Food labelling is a huge and complex subject, and the laws concerning it are constantly changing. Consumers' biggest complaints are to do with unclear and inconsistent wording and content of labels. Though new legislation has brought about some improvement, there is still a long way to go.

THE NAME
A seemingly straightforward product description can be misleading. If the name contains the name of another ingredient followed by the word 'flavour', the product does not have to contain that ingredient. So a drink marked 'orange flavour' does not have to contain real oranges.

STATEMENTS
Many packaged foods carry nutritional claims (eg low-fat, sugar-free), or claims which imply a health benefit (eg can reduce cholesterol as part of a low-fat diet). Where a claim is made, nutritional information is now required (see page 94). Understanding the real meaning behind the various messages will help you compare nutritional content of different foods.

INGREDIENTS
Ingredients are listed in order of weight and the percentage quantities of main ingredients are now included. For example, the label on a can of chicken soup has to state the percentage of chicken. Ingredients such as 'starch' or 'modified starch' have to indicate their specific vegetable origin if they are likely to contain gluten. New EC regulations require all foods containing ingredients from genetically modified soya and maize to be clearly labelled. Ingredients do not have to be listed if they are part of another ingredient which makes up 25% of the product. Flavourings must be mentioned but not necessarily by name.

Another problem is that manufacturers have a habit of using technical terms for ingredients they may not want to highlight. For example, sugar may be described as honey, sucrose, fructose, dextrose, glucose or syrups. This makes it harder to add up the total sugar content.

Additives are described by a word or an 'E number'. They have to appear after the word describing their function: eg 'stabiliser' (function) – 'carob gum'.

NUTRITIONAL INFORMATION

New regulations now require a statement of the energy, protein, carbohydrate and fat content, as well as sugars, saturates, fibre and sodium. Information about additional nutrients, such as selected vitamins and minerals, is optional, and is usually declared only if 100 g of the product contains at least 15% of the Recommended Daily Amount.

FOOD LABELLING MADE CLEAR

Claim	Meaning
Energy (calories)	
Reduced calorie	At least 25% fewer calories than the standard product.
Low calorie	Less than 40 cals per 100 g and per serving.
Fat	
Reduced fat	At least 25% less than the standard product.
Low fat	Less than 5 g fat per serving or per 100 g if typical serving is more than 100 g.
Virtually fat free	Less than 0.3 g fat per 100 g.
Saturated fat	
Reduced saturates	At least 25% less than the standard product.
Low in saturates	Less than 5 g per serving or per 100 g if typical serving is more than 100 g.
Free from saturates	Less than 0.1 g per 100 g.
Sugars	
Reduced sugar	At least 25% less than standard product (including added sugar and sugar naturally present).
Low sugar	Less than 5 g per serving or per 100 g if typical serving is more than 100 g (including added sugar and sugar naturally present).
Sugar free	Less than 0.2 g per 100 g.
No added sugar	No sugars from any source have been added (NB food may be high in natural sugars).
Fibre	
High fibre	At least 6 g per serving or per 100 g.
Source of fibre	At least 3 g per serving or per 100 g.
Sodium	
Reduced sodium	At least 25% less than the standard product.
Low sodium	Less than 40 mg per serving or per 100 g if typical serving is more than 100 g.
No sodium	Less than 5 mg per 100 g.
Vitamins and minerals	
High or rich in a vitamin or mineral	At least 50% of the Recommended Daily Amount in a daily serving.
Source of a vitamin or mineral	At least 17% of the Recommended Daily Amount in a daily serving.

THE HEALTHY KITCHEN

A healthy approach to cooking involves more than recipes and ingredients. The kitchen environment, how you organise your cooking and good hygiene practices all have a part to play too.

KITCHEN HYGIENE

Whether you like it or not, the kitchen is a favourite place for bacteria and pests. Only a few are likely to cause harm and these need to be present in significant quantities. Be aware that bacteria can multiply at an alarming rate, given warm, moist conditions where there is food. Most of the time, our immune systems can cope with this and any bacteria-related illness is shortlived. However, some people are more vulnerable and require scrupulous hygiene practices:

- babies and infants under two years old
- pregnant women
- elderly people
- anyone who is already ill or convalescing
- people with an impaired immune system or who are taking immuno-suppressant drugs

Following these guidelines will make your kitchen a safer place:
- Always wash your hands (not in the kitchen sink) before and after handling food, and between handling different types of food, eg raw and cooked meat, fish or vegetables.
- Avoid touching your mouth, nose and hair while preparing food.
- Keep cuts and grazes covered with a clean waterproof plaster.
- Always wash food, where appropriate, even if it looks clean. Soak fruit, vegetables and salads for a few minutes in a bowl of clean, cold water, then rinse under a running tap.
- Wash raw poultry under a running tap and pat dry with kitchen paper. Then thoroughly clean and disinfect the sink, plus any work surfaces and utensils that have come in contact with the bird.
- Keep a separate plastic chopping board for raw meat, poultry and fish, and another one for vegetables.
- Wash kitchen utensils between preparing raw and cooked foods.
- Never put ready-to-eat food on to a surface that has just had raw meat, poultry or fish on it.
- Wipe and disinfect work surfaces regularly and keep them dry.
- If you wash-up by hand, use hot soapy water and rinse under running water to remove detergent.
- Change tea-towels and disinfect the sink and washing-up bowl daily.
- Try to keep pets out of the kitchen, or at the very least keep them off work surfaces and tables.

COOLING FOOD

Warm food is an ideal breeding ground for bacteria. Once cooked, don't keep food warm for longer than necessary and don't leave it sitting about in the

---

THE KITCHEN ENVIRONMENT
Make the kitchen an enjoyable place to be. Clean and tidy work surfaces, shelves for books, favourite pictures or photos on the walls, lighting that allows you to see what you're doing but that isn't too harsh – these all help to create an environment in which you can cook with enjoyment.

kitchen or in a turned-off oven. One and a half hours is the maximum time that cooked meat can safely be left to cool at room temperature before storing it in the fridge. If you've cooked a large quantity of food for eating later or freezing, speed up cooling by dividing it into smaller portions. If necessary, stand containers in a larger bowl of cold water. Never cover food while it is cooling.

REHEATING FOOD

Where possible, avoid reheating leftovers or pre-prepared food. If you must do so, never reheat food more than once. Make sure it is piping hot all the way through. Stir microwaved foods to avoid cold spots, and leave for the recommended standing time so that the heat is conducted all the way through.

MOULDS

Moulds grow from microscopic spores in the atmosphere. If the spores come in contact with a suitable food, they germinate and produce a growth of mould on the surface. If only the outer surface is contaminated, foods may look safe to eat. However, there is concern that mycotoxins produced by the mould and which migrate into the food could be harmful.

There is particular danger with soft or liquid food such as jam or chutney, so throw away the whole jar if you see mould on the surface. With a more solid food, such as hard cheese, there is less danger of mycotoxins spreading. It should be safe to eat if you remove the mould with about 1.5 cm of the food underneath. If in doubt, throw it away.

FRIDGES AND FREEZERS

Storing perishable food at the correct temperature is vital. Cool temperatures will halt the growth of – but not destroy – harmful bacteria, with the exception of listeria (see page 60).

■ Make sure your fridge is operating at a temperature of between 1 and 5°C, and your freezer below −18°C. Use a fridge/freezer thermometer to check.

■ Your fridge stands more chance of maintaining the correct temperature if you don't open the door unnecessarily, don't put warm food in it and don't overload it.

■ Store raw meat, poultry and fish at the bottom of the fridge so that blood or moisture does not drip on to cooked foods. This prevents bacterial cross-contamination.

■ Keep all food in the fridge covered. Wipe up spills immediately using kitchen paper or a clean cloth.

■ Defrost fridges and freezers regularly, if they don't defrost automatically.

■ Thoroughly clean your fridge regularly using a specially formulated germicidal fridge cleaner or 1 tablespoon of bicarbonate of soda dissolved in 1 litre of warm water.

COOKING FOR HEALTH

A healthy diet isn't only about eating the right kind of food. The way that you store, prepare and cook your food, and even the pots, pans and equipment you use, all have a significant effect on nutritional value as well.

VOLATILE VITAMINS

The water-soluble B vitamins and vitamin C in fruit and vegetables are particularly volatile. Vast amounts of vitamin C are lost during storage and preparation, and yet more is destroyed by heat and lost through leaching into cooking liquid. Thiamin (vitamin B1) and folic acid are also extremely unstable with losses of up to 50% taking place during cooking or exposure to light. Vitamin E, found in nuts, pulses and vegetable oils, is destroyed by exposure to air. It is vital, therefore, not only to buy the freshest possible ingredients, but to store them correctly – in a cool place, away from light, in an airtight container if necessary, and for the briefest possible time.

Any chopping or slicing should preferably be done immediately before cooking. Once cut surfaces are exposed to the air, more vitamins are lost, and the action of enzymes can cause colour or textural deterioration.

Eat cooked fresh produce as soon as you can; keeping food warm or reheating results in more vitamin losses. If you have cooked a large quantity of food for the freezer, cool and chill it as quickly as possible before freezing. Divide the food into smaller containers to speed up cooling.

Some cooking methods are more health-promoting than others. The techniques described below are the most beneficial for a healthy diet. Remember, too, that using particular pots and pans can help preserve vital vitamins and minerals, and reduce the amount of fat in a dish.

STEAM CUISINE

Steaming is one of the best methods for cooking vegetables. It preserves texture and flavour and colours remain brighter. More importantly, since the food does not come in contact with the cooking liquid, more vitamins are retained, although inevitably some are lost through heat and a few leach into the cooking liquid. If you keep the liquid and use it in soups or sauces, or for wet-frying (see page 99), nutrient losses will be minimal.

Steaming is a fat-free method for cooking tender items such as fish fillets and chicken breasts. It is a useful way of reheating grains or pasta. The moist environment prevents the food from drying out, so no oil is needed.

Steamers range from simple plastic or stainless steel expanding baskets which sit above the liquid in the bottom of the saucepan, to sophisticated multi-tiered electric steamers. There are also oriental tiered types made of bamboo. Expanding baskets are good for cooking small amounts of food. Complete meals can be cooked simultaneously in the larger tiered steamers.

COOKING UNDER PRESSURE

Pressure cookers work by trapping steam by means of a specially designed tight-fitting lid which fits over a sturdy metal saucepan. As pressure builds up

TIPS FOR REDUCING FAT IN COOKING

■ For minimal use of fat during frying, grilling and roasting, use oil from a spray can. Or combine oil with stock, fruit juice or water in a plastic spray, and use to lightly mist food or cookware.

■ Allow soups and stews to cool, then chill. The fat that accumulates on the surface can easily be removed.

■ Use filo pastry instead of ordinary pastry. Spray it lightly with a flavourless oil instead of painting with melted butter.

■ Dress salads by using just enough oil to barely coat the leaves.

NON-STICK COOKWARE

Non-stick cookware is essential if you are trying to reduce the amount of fat in your diet, since you need only the minimum amount of oil, or none at all, to lubricate the food and prevent it from sticking. Choice and quality of pans have improved considerably in recent years. Many of the new ranges are dishwasher-safe, and some are so durable that they can even be used with metal spatulas. The following items are the most useful:

▪ two or three frying pans eg 15 cm, 23 cm and 30 cm in diameter, including a largish one with a lid

▪ a wok

▪ a ridged grill pan for use either on top of the stove or under the grill

▪ small and large roasting tins

▪ baking sheets

inside, the temperature rises above boiling point, forcing steam into the food. This cuts the cooking time by at least half, and because a relatively small amount of liquid is involved, fewer nutrients are lost through leaching, though some will be destroyed by heat.

Pressure cookers can be used for a variety of foods. They are particularly handy for vegetarians, or if you are trying to boost your fibre intake, since dried pulses can be cooked in a matter of minutes without pre-soaking. Tough cuts of meat become meltingly tender and don't need the usual lengthy cooking.

Pressure cookers are made in heavy-gauge aluminium or stainless steel. Some have non-stick interiors or internal dividing baskets which enable you to cook different foods at the same time. The most versatile are those operating at several rates of pressure.

BOILING

The water-soluble vitamins in vegetables are more easily lost during boiling. There are two schools of thought about the best way to preserve them: one is to use a large volume of ready-boiling water – the advantage being speed and therefore less time for vitamins to leach out. The second way is to use the minimum amount of water. This also limits leaching, but can sometimes result in uneven cooking if parts of the vegetables protrude above the surface of the water. It is a matter of preference and judgement as to which method to use. Bulky vegetables, such as a whole celeriac, or kale leaves with sturdy stalks, or wedges of cabbage, will probably be better cooked in a large volume of ready-boiling water. Smaller, uniformly shaped items such as beans and peas need only a small amount of water. Whichever method you choose, make the most of the vitamins by using the cooking water to make soup, stock or gravy.

MICROWAVE COOKING

Microwave cooking is excellent for vegetables and fish, and for defrosting and reheating food. Microwaves cook food very quickly with only a minimal amount of water or extra fat. This method therefore helps to minimise loss of water-soluble nutrients which might otherwise dissolve in the cooking water. However, a similar effect could be gained by steaming.

FRYING

Frying food in a large amount of fat will certainly pile on the calories and, depending on the oil or fat used, may raise saturated fat intake to unhealthy levels. However, by modifying the technique and choosing oils high in polyunsaturates (see *A Healthy Storecupboard*, page 90), a certain amount of fried food can be included in a healthy diet.

Shallow-frying: The amount of oil needed can obviously be kept to a minimum by using a non-stick pan. If you don't have a non-stick pan, try and reduce the amount of oil specified in the recipe. Start off by heating, say, just a tablespoon of oil along with a splash of liquid. If the contents of the pan later start to stick or look dry, you can add a little more. Usually, though, the food starts to release its juices and these act as an additional lubricant. Use a pan just big enough to take the food without overcrowding. If the pan is unnecessarily large, you'll have to use more oil.

Stir-frying: Preferable to shallow-frying, stir-frying requires very little oil and the food cooks quickly, thus sealing in natural juices and reducing vitamin loss. A wok produces the best results as the conical shape means that the food constantly falls back into the hottest part of the pan as it is being stirred. However, a large, high-sided frying pan will produce reasonable results. For successful stir-frying, follow these simple techniques:

▓ Cut the ingredients into small uniformly-sized pieces so that the food cooks evenly and quickly.

▓ Make sure the wok or pan is very hot before you add any oil – the oil should sizzle as soon as you add it.

▓ Have all your ingredients prepared, ready to add when the oil is at the right temperature. Those that require longer cooking go in first.

Wet-frying: This is a useful technique if you need to drastically reduce your fat intake. Bring to the boil 3–4 tablespoons of fat-free liquid (water, stock, wine or cooking liquid from steamed food) in a non-stick pan. Reduce the heat to medium-low, then add chopped vegetables, poultry or meat. Stir-fry for 2–15 minutes, depending on the ingredients, size, and degree of cooking required. Add a little more liquid if necessary.

Dry-frying: Meat containing 'hidden' fat, and watery vegetables such as onions and mushrooms, can be dry-fried carefully without any additional liquid or fat in a non-stick pan over low heat. They may even start to brown nicely.

GRILLING

Grilling brings out the best in good-quality meat, poultry and fish, and robust vegetables such as peppers, aubergines and onions. The direct dry heat of the grill quickly seals in juices, producing delicious flavours and succulent texture.

Compared with frying, grilling is a healthier cooking method, since it requires little, if any, additional fat. A small amount may be needed to prevent drying, or to lubricate the pan if you are using a ridged stove-top grill. For additional flavour and moisture, and for tender meat, marinate the food for an hour or two before grilling.

Food intended for grilling should be reasonably flat and compact in shape to allow the heat to penetrate and to enable the food to cook evenly. Bulky or irregularly shaped items, such as chicken quarters, are better cut into smaller pieces. Vegetables need to be halved or thickly sliced. Grilling is not suitable for tough cuts of meat, as the intense heat will toughen the fibres even more.

Thin tail fillets of oily fish, such as trout or salmon, are excellent for grilling. Place them skin-side up on a rack and cook very close to the heat, without turning, for 4–7 minutes depending on thickness. The skin protects the flesh and stops it from drying out, while the natural oils and juices make the fish wonderfully succulent.

White fish fillets are a little trickier since they can easily overcook and dry out.

Brush the skin with oil, and cook skin-side up, about 17.5 cm from the heat source. Turn carefully when the flesh looks nearly opaque – this should take 5–7 minutes depending on thickness – then brush again with oil and cook for another minute or two. Any juices that have dripped into the pan below can be poured over the fillets or used to make a sauce.

If you want to cook a whole fish – a trout or mackerel, for example – make two or three diagonal slashes in the thickest part of the flesh to allow the heat to penetrate more quickly. Grilling is usually done under a radiant source of heat in a grill pan, with or without a rack. Thin, evenly shaped pieces of meat or fish, or thickly sliced dense-fleshed vegetables, can be grilled on top of the stove, using a ridged cast-iron or non-stick grill pan. The ridges sear the food, creating attractive stripes, while the fat drains away between the ridges.

Top of the range are grills set into the work surface. They work rather like an indoor barbecue, with the heat source coming from below a built-in rack. They need an efficient ventilation system to avoid cooking smells.

ROASTING

As long as the food does not sit in fat, roasting is a healthy way of cooking whole poultry and larger joints of meat. Place the joint or bird on a rack over a roasting tin so that the fat drips into the tin. Drain off the fat before using the juices for gravy.

Large whole fish are delicious roasted in a sealed foil or greaseproof parcel with a splash of wine, citrus juice or stock. Add herbs, spices, or slivers of vegetables or citrus peel for extra flavour.

Roasting is an excellent way of cooking gutsy Mediterranean-style vegetables such as aubergines, sweet peppers, courgettes, whole heads of garlic and red onions. They produce wonderfully succulent juices and are delicious served hot, cold or at room temperature. Slice elongated vegetables in half lengthways, and round ones round the circumference. Place in a large roasting tin with plenty of space between them. If you use a non-stick tin, you may get away without adding any oil, though absorbent types such as aubergines and courgettes may need a light dab. To create that mouthwatering charred look, the vegetables need to be subjected to intense heat. Preheat the oven to the highest possible temperature before starting to cook.

STEWING AND BRAISING

Slow cooking over gentle heat in a moist environment transforms tougher cuts of meat and older birds. From a health point of view, the technique is ideal – fewer vitamins are lost and fat can be kept to a minimum. It is not essential to brown the meat before adding liquid, though some cooks claim that doing so produces a better flavour. If you want to brown the meat, use a separate non-stick pan and drain off any fatty liquid before adding the meat to the pot. Otherwise, skip the browning and simply pop the meat into the pot with a few vegetables, herbs, seasonings and an appropriate amount of water, wine or stock. Stews need more liquid, braises very little.

Allow plenty of time for cooking, and for cooling. Any fat from the meat can then accumulate on the surface and be blotted off before finishing the dish.

special diets

HIGH-FIBRE DIET

FIBRE CONTENT OF VARIOUS FOODS

- Bran provides 40 g fibre per 100 g portion

- Dried apricots 18 g per 100 g

- Prunes 13 g per 100 g

- Brown bread 6 g per 100 g

- Walnuts 6 g per 100 g

- Peas 5 g per 100 g

- Cooked wholemeal spaghetti 4 g per 100 g

- Cooked white spaghetti 2 g per 100 g

- Cooked brown rice 2 g per 100 g

- Cooked white rice 1 g per 100 g

A high-fibre diet provides up to 30 grams of fibre a day (most people eat about 12 grams daily and ideally should aim to eat 18 grams). Fibre is important because, although it provides little in the way of energy or nutrients, it aids the digestion and absorption of other foods. A high-fibre diet helps to prevent constipation, diverticular disease, irritable bowel syndrome and may even protect against bowel cancer. In addition, soluble fibre can reduce cholesterol levels.

WHAT IS FIBRE?

Dietary fibre – which is now referred to as non-starch polysaccharides (NSP) – is the term used to describe indigestible fibrous plant substances found in a number of foods (see below for examples). These substances are divided into two main groups: soluble and insoluble.

SOLUBLE AND INSOLUBLE FIBRE

Soluble fibre is important for the function of the stomach and upper intestines, where it absorbs fats and sugars to slow the rate at which they pass into the circulation. It also encourages the muscular contractions that propel digested food forwards. Insoluble fibre is more important in the large bowel, where it absorbs water, bacteria and toxins, bulks up the faeces and hastens stool excretion. Once fibre reaches the large bowel, enzymes released by bacteria start to ferment soluble fibre to release gases, while insoluble fibre is excreted largely unchanged.

All plant foods contain both soluble and insoluble fibre, though some sources are richer in one type than another.

SOURCES OF SOLUBLE AND INSOLUBLE FIBRE

Type of fibre	Plant source	Examples
SOLUBLE	Oats	Porridge, muesli
	Barley	Pearl barley
	Rye	Rye bread, crispbread
	Fruit	Figs, apricots, tomatoes, apples
	Vegetables	Carrots, potatoes, courgettes
	Pulses	Baked beans, kidney beans
INSOLUBLE	Wheat	Wholemeal bread, cereals
	Maize	Sweetcorn, corn bread
	Rice	Brown rice
	Pasta	Wholemeal pasta, spinach pasta
	Fruit	Rhubarb, blackberries, strawberries
	Leafy vegetables	Cabbage, spinach, lettuce
	Pulses	Peas, lentils, chick peas

FIBRE-RICH FOODS

To follow a high-fibre diet, you should eat more unrefined complex carbohydrates such as wholemeal bread, cereals, nuts, grains, root vegetables, pulses, sweetcorn and fruits. Foods containing 3 grams of fibre per 100 grams or more are a useful source of fibre, and foods with 6 or more grams are considered high fibre. Breakfast cereals containing bran offer one of the highest concentrations of dietary fibre. (For more on the fibre content of various foods, see charts in *How to Achieve a Balanced Diet*, page 39.)

FIBRE AND MOVEMENT

If the diet is lacking in fibre, very little bulk will reach the lower bowel. Instead of the small muscular contractions needed to move bulky stools downwards, the intestinal walls have to squeeze tightly to propel the smaller pellets on their way. This may trigger prolonged muscle spasm and pain in some people with irritable bowel syndrome (IBS). There is no consistent link between symptoms of IBS and fibre intake however, and it is unlikely that lack of fibre is the sole cause, but a fibre-rich diet is of all-round benefit.

RELIEVING CONSTIPATION

Changing to a high-fibre diet is one of the best ways to relieve constipation. You need to increase fibre intake gradually, however, as a sudden intake can cause feelings of bloating and distension in some people. This effect normally disappears after two or three weeks. When increasing fibre intake it is also important to ensure a good fluid intake. Drink at least 2 to 3 litres of fluids per day to help bulk the fibre up so it can do its job.

VARIETY, THE KEY

It is also important to eat as many different sources of fibre as possible. New research suggests that bowel bacteria quickly adapts to the types of roughage in your diet. If you mainly eat fibre of one type (eg bran), bowel bacteria will respond within a week or two by increasing their output of the enzymes needed to ferment this. The fibre reaching your colon will then be broken down more quickly so some benefits are lost.

OTHER EFFECTS

Foods rich in fibre are also good sources of many vitamins and minerals, particularly if you aim to increase your intake of fruit, vegetables and salad ingredients to at least five servings per day. The only point to be aware of is that a high-fibre diet can reduce absorption of calcium and iron in the bowel. It is therefore important to boost your calcium intake – for example by drinking an extra 600 ml (1 pint) semi-skimmed or skimmed milk per day – and to maximise iron absorption by ensuring your vitamin C intake is high – eat more citrus fruit, berries and kiwi fruit.

GLUTEN-FREE DIET

Gluten is a protein found in several cereals including wheat, rye, barley and oats. Gluten sensitivity causes a condition known as coeliac disease – also known as gluten-sensitive enteropathy. It is occasionally associated with an extremely itchy rash known as dermatitis herpetiformis. Interestingly, however, those with skin symptoms tend not to develop the abdominal symptoms of coeliac disease.

People with coeliac disease or dermatitis herpetiformis need to follow a gluten-free diet. This produces a rapid improvement within a few weeks so that weight is regained and symptoms resolve. The gluten-free diet must be followed for life which may prove difficult in the long term, because it means that many staple foods, like bread and pasta, must be replaced with gluten-free versions, some of which are available on prescription from a doctor. Labels on bought products also have to be 06 checked carefully to look for hidden gluten in items such as soups, stock cubes and dessert mixes – wheat flour is commonly used as a thickener and filler in many processed foods.

OTHER BENEFITS

In addition to coeliacs, increasing numbers of people seem to be finding that eliminating wheat or gluten from their diet can help cure a host of diverse health

WATCHPOINT
Check all medicines are gluten-free.

AVOID ANY FOOD LABELLED AS CONTAINING:

- Flour starch
- Wheat flour
- Wheat starch
- Food starch
- Edible starch
- Modified starch
- Cereal filler
- Cereal binder
- Cereal protein
- Malt
- Rye
- Vegetable protein
- Rusk
- Barley
- Oats

A GLUTEN-FREE DIET ALLOWS YOU TO EAT:

- Plenty of fruit, vegetables, and salad stuff, including potatoes
- Nuts and seeds
- Unprocessed meat, poultry or offal
- Plain (uncoated) fish
- Eggs, cheese, milk, yogurts (except muesli yogurt)
- Soya bran, rice bran
- Rice, tapioca, sago, arrowroot, buckwheat, millet, maize, corn and corn flour
- Special gluten-free bread, crispbread and pasta
- Gluten-free flour, soya flour, potato flour, pea flour, rice flour
- Sugar, jam, marmalade, honey, jelly
- Gluten-free biscuits, cakes
- Gluten-free breakfast cereals
- Tea, coffee, fruit juice
- Herbs, spices, vinegar, salt, pepper
- Milk, cream, butter, margarine and oils
- Wine, non-barley beer, spirits etc

FORBIDDEN FOODS INCLUDE:
- Ordinary (gluten-containing) bread
- Crispbread
- Pasta
- Ordinary flour, rye flour, barley flour
- Wheat bran
- Pastry
- Ordinary biscuits and cakes
- Breakfast cereals containing wheat or oats
- Barley, oatmeal, semolina
- Tinned and refined foods using wheat flour as a thickener
- Meat pies, beefburgers, sausages, tinned and other processed meats
- Foods in breadcrumbs such as fishcakes and Scotch eggs
- Foods in batter such as fish and sausages
- Potato croquettes
- Fruit pies
- Muesli yogurt
- Beer and stout made from barley
- Barley water and some night-time drinks
- Most stock cubes, gravy mixes etc

COOKING TIPS:
- Use sago or tapioca instead of semolina
- Use puffed rice cakes instead of biscuits or crackers
- Use cornflour for thickening gravies and sauces

VITAL VITAMINS AND MINERALS

People with coeliac disease have reduced absorption of vitamins and minerals from their diet – especially when a gluten-free diet is not being adhered to. This can lead to iron-deficiency anaemia or anaemia due to folic acid deficiency. It is important to ensure a varied intake of food including plenty of fresh fruit and vegetables. A vitamin and mineral supplement providing around 100% of the recommended daily amount (RDA) of as many micronutrients as possible is also a good idea.

For good health, the EC guidelines recommend the following daily intake of vitamins and minerals:

Vitamin A	800 µg	Biotin	150 mg
Vitamin B1	14 mg	Calcium	800 mg
Vitamin B2	1.6 mg	Folate	200 µg
Vitamin B3	18 mg	Iodine	150 µg
Vitamin B5	6 mg	Iron	14 mg
Vitamin B6	2 mg	Magnesium	300 mg
Vitamin B12	1 µg	Phosphorus	800 mg
Vitamin C	60 mg	Zinc	15 mg
Vitamin D	5 µg		
Vitamin E	10 mg		

(For further information on sources of vitamins and minerals, see *The Role of Essential Nutrients*, pages 21-36.)

LOW-FAT DIET

Dietary fats are an important part of a healthy diet, providing energy and essential fatty acids, as well as aiding the absorption of the fat-soluble vitamins A, D, E and K. However, most people eat too much fat, which in turn supplies excess energy leading to high body weight and obesity. Ideally, dietary fats should provide a maximum of 33% of our daily energy intake. In the western world, however, fats contribute over 40% of daily calories, which is far too high.

Cutting back and following a low-fat diet is one of the most important dietary changes most people can make to improve their future health.

DIETARY SOURCES OF ESSENTIAL FATTY ACIDS

◼ Omega-6 – found in safflower, grapeseed and sunflower oils, evening primrose oil, soft polyunsaturated margarine, seeds and nuts.

◼ Omega-3 – found in fish oils, plus vegetable oils, seeds and nuts.

FAT MAKE-UP

◼ Saturated fats – they carry a full set of hydrogen atoms and tend to be solid at room temperature. Found in solid fats such as butter and the fat in meat. Most are of animal origin – this is also the type of fat stored in the human body. Coconut is one of the few plant sources of saturated fat.

◼ Monounsaturated fats – these are deficient in only one pair of hydrogen atoms and tend to be liquid at room temperature. Best sources are olive oil, groundnut oil, nuts, olives and avocados.

◼ Polyunsaturated fats – these are deficient in two or more hydrogen atoms and also tend to be liquid at room temperature. They include the essential fatty acids, omega-6 and omega-3, derived from linoleic and alpha-linolenic acids respectively. Sources include nuts and seeds.

Most dietary fats contain a blend of saturates, monounsaturates and polyunsaturates in varying proportions. In general, saturated fats tend to be solid at room temperature while monounsaturated and polyunsaturated fats tend to be liquid – ie oils.

BALANCING THE FATS

A healthy low-fat diet should supply all the fats you need – of the right types – without providing any to excess. The average western diet currently contains excess saturated fat and excess omega-6 essential fatty acids. In contrast, the average diet provides too few omega-3 essential fatty acids. For a healthy balance, omega-6 intake should be no more than four or five times that of omega-3, and ideally should be equivalent.

A diet providing excess saturated fats has been linked with an increased risk of hardening and furring up of the arteries, leading to coronary heart disease and strokes. This is especially harmful if the diet is also low in antioxidants, such as vitamins C and E. This is because antioxidants help to protect circulating fats from chemical attack (oxidation) which triggers the furring up process.

Too great an intake of omega-6 essential fatty acids is associated with an increased risk of chronic inflammatory diseases, such as asthma, auto-immune diseases and some tumours. On the other hand, lack of essential fatty acids has been linked with a wide range of ailments from dry, itchy or inflamed skin to hormonal problems such as acne, prostate problems and attention deficit hyperactivity disorder.

IMPROVING HEALTH

As well as generally cutting back on fats when following a low-fat diet, it is important to include more of the beneficial essential fatty acids, monounsaturated fats and omega-3 in your diet. Eating omega-3 fish oils at least twice a week is beneficial and can lower the risk of coronary heart disease within six months. After 2 years, those on a high fish diet are almost a third less likely to die from heart disease than those not eating much fish. This is probably due to a thinning effect on the blood which reduces the chance of blood clots.

Similarly, monounsaturated fats, such as olive oil and rapeseed oil, help to maintain a healthy balance of circulating fats and can protect against coronary heart disease.

REDUCING FAT INTAKE

The simplest way to cut back on dietary fats is to avoid obviously fatty foods (eg doughnuts, chips, crisps, chocolate) as much as possible, and to choose reduced-fat versions of foods, such as dairy foods, which provide other important nutrients such as calcium.

▨ Steam, boil, grill or poach food rather than deep-frying.

▨ Always use fats and oils sparingly; measure quantities given in recipes rather than guessing to avoid adding unnecessary fat.

▨ Use skimmed or semi-skimmed, rather than wholemilk, products.

▨ Use low-fat versions of as many foods as possible eg mayonnaise, yogurts, salad dressings, reduced-fat cheese, reduced-fat monounsaturated spreads etc.

▨ Trim all visible fat from meat; choose extra-lean cuts.

For more information on cutting down fat, see A Guide to Nutrition, page 66.

HOW TO FOLLOW A HEALTHY LOW-FAT DIET

▨ Obtain at least half your daily calories from complex carbohydrates such as wholegrain bread, wholemeal pasta, brown rice, cereals, baked potatoes etc – but don't smother them in fat-filled sauces or spreads.

▨ Use monounsaturated fats (eg olive or rapeseed oil) for stir-frying.

▨ Decrease the amount of red meat you eat to only once or twice per week. Have more vegetarian meals instead.

▨ Eat as few processed foods as possible to reduce your intake of hidden fats.

▨ Increase the amount of pulses, nuts and seeds you eat as these are a rich source of essential fatty acids.

▨ Eat oily fish at least twice a week.

NUT-FREE DIET

For most people, nuts are a healthy and nutritious source of protein and energy. An estimated 1.3% of the population however have a nut allergy which in some cases can be life-threatening. The commonest nut allergy is to peanuts, which are also known as groundnuts. Many people with hypersensitivity to peanuts are also sensitive to walnuts, almonds, pistachios, hazelnuts and cashews. Some also react to Brazil nuts, although sensitivity to these can occur on its own. Peanuts are classed as oily beans, and around one in 20 people with a sensitivity will also have problems when eating peas and beans such as soya.

Nut hypersensitivity is becoming more common, possibly because of the increased commercial use of peanut oil and protein in prepared foods.

CHILDREN AT RISK

One child in 75 tests positive for a nut allergy. Those most at risk are young boys who also suffer from other atopic conditions such as asthma and eczema. Up to one in 500 children will have a sudden, severe reaction to nuts but less than one in a million will have a fatal reaction.

HOW DOES THE ALLERGY OCCUR?

Nut allergy occurs when the immune system recognises a foreign protein in the nut as harmful and makes a type of antibody (IgE) aimed against it. This anti-nut antibody attaches itself to mast cells in the skin, lining of the stomach and respiratory tract and, when the foreign protein of the nut is encountered, this triggers a sudden release of powerful chemicals such as histamine.

One of the first symptoms that may occur after eating a peanut-containing food is a warning tingling sensation in the mouth. This may be rapidly followed by redness, swelling of the throat, lips and around the eyes (angioedema), and spasm of respiratory muscles so wheeziness or severe breathing problems occur. In the skin, histamine release causes an itchy, raised rash (urticaria or hives) while involvement of the intestines may lead to vomiting, abdominal pain and occasionally, diarrhoea. In severe cases, low blood pressure leads to sudden collapse, known as anaphylactic shock, which obviously requires urgent medical treatment.

COPING WITH THE ALLERGY

The main way to deal with a nut allergy is to follow a nut-free diet. This basically involves careful inspection of food product labels to avoid those containing nuts or nut products.

Unfortunately, prepared dishes may contain nuts which are not listed as an ingredient, especially if they include sauces or pastes. Also, manufacturers cannot guarantee that cross-contamination of production lines will not occur where more than one product is made in batches using the same equipment. As a result, many products are labelled as 'May contain nuts' when in fact they don't, which can severely limit food choices for those affected.

Try to buy products which have all their ingredients clearly listed.

FOODS TO AVOID

■ Those containing peanut oil – also known as groundnut or arachis oil – nut extracts and nut flavouring.

■ Foods labelled as containing vegetable or blended oil or hydrolysed vegetable protein which may well contain some peanut extracts.

■ Many biscuits, cakes, spreads, cereals, dips and sauces, ice-creams, mincemeat and sweets.

■ Many vegetarian meals such as nut loaf, vegeburgers, sausages etc.

■ Some curry sauces.

■ Some Chinese dishes, especially Kung Po.

■ Marzipan and other ground almond products which may contain up to 50% peanut.

■ Some skin creams, cosmetics, ointments and shampoos.

NB Young children under the age of 4–5 should not be given whole nuts because of the risk of inhaling.

Alternatively, contact the manufacturer. Ingredients in products do often change, so constant checking of labels – even old favourites – is important.

If someone else is preparing food for you, give them plenty of notice about your nut allergy and the foods you can and cannot eat.

KEEPING A BALANCE

As nuts are an excellent source of beneficial essential fatty acids, it is important to eat oily fish (eg salmon, mackerel, herrings, sardines) regularly to provide these. Alternatively, take omega-3 or evening prim-rose oil supplements.

If symptoms of allergy occur, medical advice should always be sought without delay. If someone collapses, ring 999 for an ambulance. Those with severe nut allergy are advised to carry antihistamine syrup/tablets and an adrenaline injection with them at all times to be used if symptoms start.

A woman who is pregnant may wish to avoid eating peanuts and peanut products if she or her partner has a personal or family history of allergies. This may help to reduce the chance of the developing baby becoming sensitised against nut proteins.

LOW-CHOLESTEROL DIET

Cholesterol is used to carry essential fatty acids round the bloodstream and comes in low density (LDL) or high density (HDL) forms. Most cholesterol travelling in the bloodstream is made in the liver from dietary fats – relatively little comes from pre-formed cholesterol found in certain foods such as egg yolk, coconut and prawns. Nevertheless, a low-cholesterol diet may occasionally be advised for people who have abnormally high circulating levels of LDL cholesterol – high levels of LDL cause blocked arteries, which significantly increases the risk of coronary heart disease.

Unlike LDL, the HDL form of cholesterol actually protects against coronary heart disease, which is why HDL is sometimes referred to as 'good' cholesterol and LDL as 'bad'. A total cholesterol level that is above 6.5 millimoles per litre is regarded as high and should be reduced (see chart below for cholesterol levels).

WHAT TO EAT

A low-cholesterol diet involves reducing total fat intake – especially saturated fat which encourages the liver to produce LDL cholesterol – and avoiding foods that are naturally high in pre-formed cholesterol. You'll need to cut your intake of saturated fat to under 10% of calories consumed in a day (for a woman who eats 1940 calories a day, this means under 21 grams of saturated fat per day) and the total fat should come to no more than 33% of calories a day. Oily fish such as salmon, mackerel, herring and trout are good to include in your diet as they are low in saturated fats but high in omega-3 fatty acids which thin the blood, making it less likely to clot.

A high-fibre intake is also encouraged. Research suggests that eating 3 grams or more of soluble oat fibre (roughly equal to two large bowls of porridge) per day can lower total blood cholesterol levels by up to 0.16 millimoles per litre by absorbing fats in the gut. This slows their absorption so the body can handle them more easily. This is a small, but significant change.

Fruit, vegetables and salad ingredients rich in antioxidants, such as vitamin C and E can also help to prevent clogging of the arteries.

GUIDE TO CHOLESTEROL LEVELS

Total Blood Cholesterol Level

Desirable	< 5.2 mmol/l
Borderline	5.2 – 6.4 mmol/l
Abnormal	6.5 – 7.8 mmol/l
High	> 7.8 mmol/l

Slightly stricter criteria apply to men under the age of 30 and for those with coronary heart disease.

THE EXERCISE FACTOR

Exercise is also very important as it lowers harmful blood cholesterol levels, lowers blood pressure, reduces hardening and furring up of the arteries and also improves the circulation of blood to the heart through the small, collateral arteries. The risk of coronary heart disease is therefore twice as high in inactive males as in those who are physically active.

Perhaps the most striking example of how exercise affects blood fats was shown by Sir Ranulph Fiennes and Dr Michael Stroud during their epic, unassisted journey across the Antarctic in 1992. They needed to eat a high-fat diet to provide as much energy as possible without increasing the weight of their rations. Despite eating over 5500 calories a day, and twice as much fat as recommended, they burned most of it off. Their total blood cholesterol levels did not rise, but interestingly, their level of beneficial HDL cholesterol, which protects against coronary heart disease, went up whilst their level of harmful LDL cholesterol went down.

FOODS TO AVOID ON A LOW-CHOLESTEROL DIET

- Butter, lard, suet, cooking fats, margarines, vegetable oils

- Egg yolk, salad cream, mayonnaise

- Whole milk, cream, wholemilk yogurt

- Duck, goose, offal, sausages, pâté, luncheon meat, salami

- Fish roe, prawns, shrimps

- Sweet biscuits, cakes, pastries and pies

- Avocado pear

- Coconut oil

- Tinned and packet desserts

- Lemon curd

- Toffee, butterscotch

- Nuts, crisps

- Ice-cream

- Chocolate and chocolate products

LOW-CALORIE DIET

HEALTH PROBLEMS LINKED WITH BEING OVERWEIGHT

- High blood pressure

- Abnormal blood cholesterol levels

- Hardening and furring up of the arteries

- Heart attack

- Stroke

- Diabetes

- Gall stones

- Constipation

- Diverticular disease

- Indigestion and heartburn

- Back pain

- Osteoarthritis

- Varicose veins

- Haemorrhoids

A kilocalorie, or calorie as it is commonly referred to, is a measurement of energy found in food. Weight is put on when you consume more calories than you burn off. If excess energy is consumed over a prolonged period of time, it will be converted into saturated fat for storage in the body's fat stores, leading to high body weight and obesity. Unfortunately, this is an increasingly important medical problem, and it is estimated that by the year 2005 as many as 1 in 5 men and 1 in 4 women in the UK will be obese.

CHANGING ENERGY REQUIREMENTS
Most excess weight is gained after the age of 35 as so-called 'middle age spread'. Weight is put on more easily in later years because of changes in both the body and lifestyle. The most significant change is loss of lean muscle tissue, which is mostly replaced with fat. Resting metabolism also slows by around 5% every ten years after the age of 25. As a result, the daily need for calories goes down. By the time a woman is 75, she needs around 300 calories less per day than when she was 18, and 130 calories less per day than when she was 50. The difference is even greater in men (see chart below).

ESTIMATED ENERGY REQUIREMENTS FOR MEN AND WOMEN

Age	Cals per day Women	Men	Age	Cals per day Women	Men
15-18	2110	2755	60-64	1900	2380
19-50	1940	2550	65-74	1900	2330
51-59	1900	2550	75 +	1810	2100

HEALTH PROBLEMS
Obesity is linked with a number of health problems including high blood pressure, coronary heart disease, stroke and diabetes. Those who are overweight are one-and-a-half times more likely to have a heart attack than someone who maintains a healthy weight. Where excess weight is stored in the body is also important. If you are overweight and also store fat round your middle (apple shaped), you are twice as likely to develop coronary heart disease – especially if this runs in your family. Getting down to the healthy weight range for your height can reduce your risk of a heart attack by as much as 35–55%.

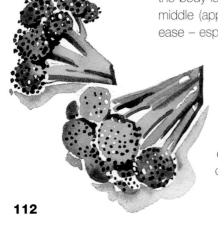

DO I NEED TO LOSE WEIGHT?
Your weight in proportion to your height can be assessed by using the scale known as the Body Mass Index (BMI). This is explained on page 64, but for an instant guide as to whether you are overweight, look at the chart opposite.

WORKING OUT YOUR CORRECT WEIGHT LEVEL

The following table gives the healthy BMI weight range for men and women according to individual heights. If your weight falls above the range given for your height, you are overweight.

Height		Optimum Healthy Weight Range			
		Men		Women	
Metres	Feet	Kg	Stones	Kg	Stones
1.47	4'10"			43 – 53	6 st 10 lb – 8 st 6 lb
1.50	4'11"			45 – 56	7 st 1 lb – 8 st 11 lb
1.52	5ft			43 – 55	6 st 11 lb – 8 st 9 lb
1.55	5'1"			45 – 57	7 st 1 lb – 8 st 13 lb
1.57	5'2"			46 – 59	7 st 3 lb – 9 st 4 lb
1.60	5'3"			48 – 61	7 st 8 lb – 9 st 8 lb
1.63	5'4"			50 – 63	7 st 12 lb – 9 st 13 lb
1.65	5'5"			51 – 65	8 stone – 10 st 3 lb
1.68	5'6"	56 – 70	8 st 12 lb – 11 stone	53 – 67	8 st 5 lb – 10 st 7 lb
1.70	5'7"	58 – 72	9 st 1 lb – 11 st 4 lb	54 – 69	8 st 7 lb – 10 st 12 lb
1.73	5'8"	60 – 75	9 st 6 lb – 11 st 10 lb	56 – 71	8 st 11 lb – 11 st 2 lb
1.75	5'9"	61 – 76	9 st 9 lb – 12 stone	57 – 73	8 st 13 lb – 11 st 7 lb
1.78	5'10"	63 – 79	9 st 13 lb – 12 st 6 lb	59 – 75	9 st 4 lb – 11 st 11 lb
1.80	5'11"	65 – 81	10 st 3 lb – 12 st 9 lb	61 – 77	9 st 8 lb – 12 st 1 lb
1.83	6 ft	67 – 83	10 st 7 lb – 13 st 1 lb	63 – 80	9 st 13 lb – 12 st 8 lb
1.85	6'1"	69 – 85	10 st 11 lb – 13 st 5 lb		
1.88	6'2"	71 – 88	11 st 2 lb – 13 st 12 lb		
1.90	6'3"	72 – 90	11 st 5 lb – 14 st 2 lb		
1.93	6'4"	75 – 93	11 st 10 lb – 14 st 8 lb		

CALORIES IN FOOD

Food provides different amounts of energy depending on its chemical structure:

◼ carbohydrates provide about 4 calories per gram

◼ protein provides about 4 calories per gram

◼ fat is the most energy-rich food available, giving 9 calories per gram

LOSING WEIGHT

The best way to lose weight is slowly and steadily at a rate of around 450 g (1 lb) per week. Trying to lose weight faster than this usually results in weight being quickly regained once eating habits return to their old unhealthy ways.

Having decided on your daily reduced calorie intake (1500 calories a day for an average woman, for instance, is a sensible goal), the best plan is to simply follow a healthy, well-balanced diet that is low in fat and high in fibre. Fill up on starchy foods, fruit and vegetables while avoiding excessive fat, sugar and salt. This will help you to lose weight naturally and slowly as your body cannot convert carbohydrates into body fat as easily as it converts dietary fat to flab.

Foods rich in carbohydrates and roughage also curb your appetite more quickly than foods rich in fat, so you tend to eat less overall. This type of diet will encourage healthy eating habits that can continue after you have reached your desired weight.

It is also important to increase your level of physical activity so you become fitter and burn up more energy, too.

(For more information on cutting calories, see *Weight Management* page 64).

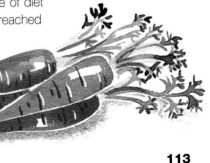

DAIRY PRODUCE-FREE DIET

Milk contains special milk proteins such as casein and a milk sugar, lactose, that can trigger allergic symptoms in some people. Milk protein allergy is mainly found in children and has been linked with diarrhoea and eczema. Most children grow out of the problem, however, and it is unusual to find milk protein sensitivity in adults.

**AVOID FOODS
LABELLED AS
CONTAINING:**

- Milk
- Butter
- Margarine
- Cheese
- Yogurt
- Cream
- Casein
- Hydrolysed casein
- Caseinates
- Whey
- Whey syrup sweetener
- Milk solids
- Non-fat milk solids
- Skimmed milk powder
- Lactose

LACTOSE INTOLERANCE

Lactose intolerance is far more common and is believed to be caused by deficiency of a metabolic enzyme known as lactase, which is needed to digest milk lactose before it can be absorbed. Lactase enzyme is released from the lining of the small intestine and acts on a molecule of lactose to break it down into two sugars, glucose and galactose, which are immediately absorbed into the bloodstream. People suffering from lactase deficiency will suffer unpleasant symptoms that can include:

- bloating and wind
- audible bowel sounds (borborygmi)
- abdominal pain
- diarrhoea

Lactase deficiency can be present from birth (primary lactase deficiency) or can result temporarily after a bout of gastroenteritis (secondary lactase deficiency). It is therefore usual to advise that children with diarrhoea should avoid milk until symptoms have improved.

DEALING WITH THE PROBLEM

The treatment of lactase deficiency involves following a dairy-produce or lactose-free diet in which soya or low-lactose milk products are used in place of cow's milk products.

LACTOSE CONTENT OF DIFFERENT MILKS

Type of milk	Lactose (g) per glass
Sheep's milk	9.9 g (avoid)
Skimmed cow's milk	9.8 g (avoid)
Full-fat cow's milk	9.3 g (avoid)
Goat's milk	8.6 g (avoid)
Low-lactose cow's milk	0.5 g
Soya milk	0

NB Yogurt made from cow's milk has a low lactose content as bacterial fermentation breaks the lactose down.

TOTAL MILK-FREE DIET

Some people may be advised to follow a total milk-free diet in which all foods containing milk need to be avoided, including cheese, yogurt and cream. Milk powder is found in many manufactured foods so you will need to check all labels carefully when buying ready-made products. Other points to bear in mind are:

■ Dairy substances may be found in foods such as breads, cereals, pancakes, potato croquettes, tinned sauces, burgers, luncheon meats, corned beef, sausages and fruit pies, so it is important to check all labels.

A variety of soy-based products are available to replace baby milk formula, butter, margarines and low-fat spreads.

■ Children under the age of 1 should not be given sheep or goat's milk as a substitute for dairy milk. These milks are not nutritionally complete and some children are also allergic to them.

■ If avoiding dairy products you will need to ensure an adequate intake of vitamins A, D and the mineral calcium from alternative sources (see below), including supplements.

ALTERNATIVE SOURCES OF CALCIUM

Good dietary sources of calcium other than dairy milk are:

■ Calcium-enriched soya milk

■ Eggs

■ Green leafy vegetables, eg broccoli, spinach

■ Whitebait and tinned salmon and sardines which include soft bones

■ Nuts eg almonds, brazils, hazelnuts

■ White and brown bread – in the UK, white and brown flour are fortified with calcium by law, but wholemeal flour is not

■ Seeds eg sesame, tahini

■ Dried or fresh figs

■ Pulses such as chick peas, beans, lentils, soya beans and products (eg tofu)

■ Oranges

■ Prawns, cockles, mussels

DIABETIC DIET

Blood glucose levels are controlled by several hormones such as insulin and glucagon. These normally keep blood glucose levels within a narrow range, despite wide variations in dietary intake. When resting blood glucose levels rise above a certain level, diabetes mellitus is diagnosed. A raised blood sugar level occurs when the body's ability to control glucose levels is impaired. This usually results from decreased production of insulin hormone in the pancreas gland (Type I diabetes) or from reduced sensitivity of body cells to the effects of insulin hormone (Type II diabetes).

CONTROLLING GLUCOSE LEVELS

Good control of blood glucose levels is important to reduce the long-term risk of high blood pressure, hardening and furring up of the arteries, coronary heart disease, stroke, kidney and eye problems. Type II diabetes can usually be controlled by diet alone, or diet plus tablets that help to lower blood sugar levels. Type I diabetes usually requires insulin replacement therapy. Unfortunately, insulin cannot be taken by mouth as it is broken down by stomach juices before it is absorbed. Insulin replacement therapy must therefore be given by injection between 1 and 4 times a day.

WHAT IS A DIABETIC DIET?

A diabetic diet is essentially similar to the healthy low-fat, high-fibre diet that everyone should be eating and it is unnecessary to eat special diabetic foods. It is important to obtain individual nutritional advice from a dietician however, who will show you how to tailor your food intake to your needs. The main principles of a diabetic diet are to:

■ Eat plenty of unrefined starchy carbohydrates that have a low to moderate glycaemic index

■ Increase fibre intake from wholemeal bread, wholegrain cereals, pulses, fruit and vegetables

■ Avoid overindulgence in sugar and food with a high sugar content such as sweets, honey, sweet biscuits, fizzy drinks and sweet alcoholic drinks

■ Eat regular meals and eat similar amounts of starchy foods each day

■ Avoid excess fried and fatty food and excess salt to help protect against high blood pressure

■ Eat meat, eggs, cheese, fish or pulses at least twice a day for protein

■ Maintain a healthy weight

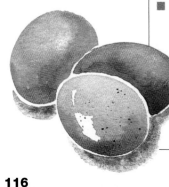

IMPORTANCE OF CARBOHYDRATES

Dietary carbohydrates provide the main source of energy and should ideally provide at least half your daily energy intake. Some forms of carbohydrate are quickly absorbed from the intestines to cause rapid changes in blood sugar levels, while other forms of carbohydrate are absorbed more steadily to help maintain more stable blood sugar levels. The way different foods affect blood glucose levels is known as their glycaemic index (GI). People with diabetes should, in general, aim to eat foods with a low to moderate GI. If eating foods with a high GI, these should be combined with foods of a lower GI to help even out fluctuations in blood glucose levels.

GUIDE TO GLYCAEMIC INDEX LEVELS IN FOODS

The following chart shows the glycaemic index of a variety of foods compared with glucose which has the highest glycaemic index of 100.

FOOD	GI	FOOD	GI
Glucose	100	Porridge oats	54
Baked potatoes	98	Crisps	51
Parsnips	97	Cake	50
Carrots	92	Grapes	44
Brown rice	82	Wholemeal pasta	42
Cornflakes	80	Baked beans	40
Weetabix	75	Oranges	40
Wholemeal bread	72	Apples	39
Chocolate bar	68	Ice cream	36
Shredded wheat	67	Milk	32
Raisins	64	Peaches	29
Bananas	62	Kidney beans	29
Chocolate biscuit	59	Grapefruit	26

HYPOGLYCAEMIA

If too much insulin is given, or not enough food is eaten, blood sugar levels will become too low – a problem known as hypoglycaemia.

A hypoglycaemic attack causes symptoms of light-headedness, dizziness, paleness, sweating, irritability, trembling, drowsiness or confusion. This needs to be treated urgently by giving sugar before it leads to loss of consciousness. Blood sugar levels therefore need to be constantly measured and meals eaten regularly.

GESTATIONAL DIABETES

Gestational diabetes occurs when the pancreas gland does not make enough insulin hormone to cope with the extra demands of pregnancy. Women with gestational diabetes are able to have a successful pregnancy as long as blood sugar levels are well controlled to prevent complications such as an unusually large or small baby or pre-term labour. Gestational diabetes is usually mild and can be controlled by a careful diet.

Sometimes, regular insulin injections are needed. In true gestational diabetes, blood sugar levels return to normal soon after delivery. Gestational diabetes is a sign that the pancreas cannot cope with extra strain, and three out of four women who experience it go on to develop Type II diabetes in later life. By adopting a low-fat, low-sugar, healthy diet and maintaining a healthy weight, this risk can be reduced.

RECIPES

menu suggestions

Here are some ideas for those on special diets. Each recipe also states whether or not it is particularly suitable for special diets, or you can refer to the listings which begin on page 383.

Low-fat menus

SERVES 6

Tomato, celery and apple soup
(page 145)
Seafood stew with fennel *(page 174)*
Melon and grape salad in chilli syrup
(page 329)

SERVES 4

Steamed scallops with spinach and
noodles *(page 129)*
Pork kebabs with mustard marinade
(page 199) served with a rocket or
watercress salad
Summer puddings *(page 318)*

SERVES 4

Iced beetroot soup *(page 150)*
Tarragon sole parcels *(page 159)*
served with vegetables
Passionfruit, grape and banana
smoothie *(page 323)*

Gluten-free menus

SERVES 4

Char-grilled summer vegetable
kebabs *(page 235)*
Spiced mackerel *(page 162)*
served with Stuffed yellow peppers
(page 229)
Coconut squares *(page 349)*

SERVES 4

Avocado dip with skewered
vegetables *(page 123)*
Steamed monkfish wrapped in
spinach *(page 161)*
served with Pea and mint risotto
(page 228)
Orange syrup cake *(page 342)*

Low-calorie menus

SERVES 8

Mushroom pâté *(page 122)*
Aromatic chicken parcels *(page 185)*
served with Red rice, spinach and
bean pilaff *(page 268)*
Passionfruit and strawberry terrine
(page 326)

SERVES 4

Miso fish soup *(page 142)*
Mixed vegetable curry *(page 220)*
served with rice
Blueberry and oatmeal flummery
(page 322)

Low-cholesterol menus

SERVES 6

Tomato and red pepper terrine
(page 124)
Caribbean ratatouille *(page 220)*
served with rice
Blackberry granita *(page 332)*

SERVES 4

Warm split pea dip *(page 122)*
Grilled chicken and sweet potato
salad *(page 295)* with green salad
Warm salad of summer fruit
(page 327)

Nut-free menu

SERVES 4

Pan-fried prawns with rye croûtons
(page 128)
Glazed calves' liver with sweet potato
and Swiss chard mash
(page 218)
Honeyed apricots *(page 315)*

High-fibre menus

SERVES 4

Broad bean and Pecorino salad
(page 302)
Chilli beef *(page 217)* or Gammon with
lentils *(page 205)*
Dried fruit salad with honey ginger
yogurt *(page 330)*

SERVES 4

Chilli chick pea cakes *(page 252)*
Simmered chicken with apple and
lentils *(page 186)* served with mashed
potato or wholemeal rolls
Fresh mango (one per person)

Diabetic menus

SERVES 6

Iced asparagus and shallot soup
(page 149)
Lemon-braised pork chops with
cumin and mushrooms *(page 203)*
served with vegetables
Raspberry cheesecakes *(page 317)*

SERVES 4

Fruit and prawn salad *(page 130)*
Chicken and artichoke filo pie
(page 184) served with vegetables
Quick apricot fool *(page 313)*

Dairy produce-free menu

SERVES 4

Vietnamese noodle soup with
teriyaki chicken *(page 247)*
Stir-fried prawns with pak choi
(page 177) with rice
Ginger-glazed pineapple
(half quantity) *(page 324)*

starters

400 g (14 oz) can chick peas, drained

2 tbsp tahini paste

2 tbsp olive oil

juice of 1 large lemon

2 garlic cloves, peeled and crushed

2 tbsp hot water

salt and freshly ground black pepper

wholemeal toast or wholemeal pitta bread, to serve

QUICK HUMMUS

SERVES 4 • PREPARATION: 15 MINUTES

1 Place the drained chick peas in a blender or food processor with the tahini paste, olive oil, lemon juice, crushed garlic cloves and hot water. Season with salt and pepper, then blend until smooth.

2 Serve with wholemeal toast or wholemeal pitta bread.

NUTRITIONAL ANALYSIS (per portion)	
Energy	210 cals
Protein	8.5 g
Carbohydrate	16.0 g
(of which sugars)	0.5 g
Fat	13.0 g
(of which saturates)	2.0 g
Fibre	5.0 g

SUITABLE FOR:
NUT-FREE, LOW-CHOLESTEROL, DAIRY PRODUCE-FREE AND DIABETIC DIETS.

---

225 g (8 oz) yellow split peas

1 bay leaf

125 g (4 oz) onion, peeled and chopped

3 garlic cloves, peeled and chopped

4 tbsp olive oil

salt and freshly ground black pepper

2 tbsp lemon juice

olive oil, for drizzling

ground paprika, to garnish

wholemeal pitta bread, to serve

WARM SPLIT PEA DIP

SERVES 4 • PREPARATION: 15 MINUTES • COOKING TIME: 55 MINUTES

1 Put the split peas into a large pan with 1.1 litres (2 pints) water. Bring to the boil and skim off any foam from the surface. Add the bay leaf, onion and garlic, cover and simmer for 50–55 minutes or until the peas have softened and absorbed the water to form a coarse purée.

2 Discard the bay leaf and beat the purée with the olive oil until smooth. Season very well and add the lemon juice.

3 Turn the dip into a serving dish and, while still warm, drizzle with olive oil. Serve warm or at room temperature, garnished with paprika, and accompanied by wholemeal pitta bread.

NUTRITIONAL ANALYSIS (per portion)	
Energy	295 cals
Protein	13.0 g
Carbohydrate	35.0 g
(of which sugars)	3.0 g
Fat	12.5 g
(of which saturates)	2.0 g
Fibre	4.0 g

SUITABLE FOR:
NUT-FREE, LOW-CHOLESTEROL, DAIRY PRODUCE-FREE AND DIABETIC DIETS.

---

2 tbsp olive oil

350 g (12 oz) brown-cap mushrooms, wiped and finely chopped

2 sticks celery, trimmed and finely chopped

1 garlic clove, peeled and crushed

1 tbsp lemon juice

200 g (7 oz) tub reduced-fat soft cheese

2 anchovies or 1 tsp anchovy paste

salt and freshly ground black pepper

toast or ficelle, to serve

slivers of lime and flat-leaf parsley, to garnish

MUSHROOM PÂTÉ

SERVES 8 • PREPARATION: 15 MINUTES • COOKING TIME: 15 MINUTES

1 Heat the oil in a frying pan and add the mushrooms, celery and garlic. Fry gently for about 10 minutes or until soft and all the liquid has evaporated. Stir in the lemon juice.

2 Allow the mushrooms to cool slightly and then place with the remaining ingredients in a blender or food processor. Blend the pâté until smooth. Adjust the seasoning, if necessary.

3 Serve the pâté on small squares of toast or slices of baked ficelle (narrow French bread) and garnish with lime and parsley.

NUTRITIONAL ANALYSIS (per portion)	
Energy	60 cals
Protein	2.5 g
Carbohydrate	1.0 g
(of which sugars)	1.0 g
Fat	6.0 g
(of which saturates)	2.0 g
Fibre	0.5 g

SUITABLE FOR:
NUT-FREE, LOW-CALORIE AND DIABETIC DIETS.

2 ripe avocados

25 g (1 oz) watercress, chopped

1 green chilli, deseeded and finely chopped

juice of 1 lime

1 tsp ground coriander

2 sun-dried tomatoes, chopped

salt and freshly ground black pepper

150 ml (¼ pint) low-fat natural yogurt

2 spring onions, trimmed and finely sliced

SKEWERED VEGETABLES

1 tbsp extra-virgin olive oil

225 g (8 oz) baby courgettes, thickly sliced

125 g (4 oz) baby corn, halved

225 g (8 oz) cherry tomatoes

AVOCADO DIP WITH SKEWERED VEGETABLES

SERVES 4 • PREPARATION: 15 MINUTES • COOKING TIME: 10 MINUTES

1 To make the dip, halve the avocados, remove the stones, then peel away the skins. Put the flesh in a bowl and mash with a fork.

2 Put the watercress, chopped chilli, lime juice, coriander and sun-dried tomatoes in a blender or food processor and work until very finely chopped. Season to taste with salt and pepper, then stir into the avocado with the yogurt and spring onions. Cover and chill until required.

3 Put the oil in a roasting tin, add the courgettes and corn and toss to coat in oil; season. Roast at 200°C (400°F) Mark 6 for 8–10 minutes or until just tender; transfer to kitchen paper and cool.

4 Thread a slice of courgette, piece of corn and a cherry tomato on to bamboo skewers and arrange on a platter. Pile the avocado dip into a small bowl and serve with the skewered vegetables.

NUTRITIONAL ANALYSIS (per portion)	
Energy	230 cals
Protein	6.0 g
Carbohydrate	8.0 g
(of which sugars)	7.0 g
Fat	20.0 g
(of which saturates)	4.0 g
Fibre	4.0 g

SUITABLE FOR:
GLUTEN-FREE, NUT-FREE AND DIABETIC DIETS.

CRAB AND ORANGE SALAD

SERVES 2 • PREPARATION: 25 MINUTES

1 orange
salt and freshly ground black pepper
½ tsp Dijon mustard
2 tsp wine vinegar
4 tbsp olive oil
2 small dressed crabs, each with about 100 g (3½ oz) crab meat (see Note)
2 tsp chopped, fresh flat-leaf parsley
toasted focaccia, black olives and lemon slices, to serve

1 For the orange vinaigrette, grate the rind and squeeze the juice of the orange. Place the rind and 3 tbsp orange juice in a small bowl with salt and pepper, the Dijon mustard and wine vinegar. Whisk together until thoroughly combined, then whisk in the olive oil.

2 Place the white crab meat in a small bowl and moisten with some of the vinaigrette; adjust the seasoning if necessary. Take a 6.5 cm (2½ inch) pastry cutter and place on a serving plate. Spoon half the brown crab meat into the base, then top with half the white. Sprinkle with the chopped fresh parsley and a little extra vinaigrette. Carefully remove the pastry cutter to leave a neat round of crab. Repeat on another plate with remaining crab.

3 Drizzle a little extra dressing around the crab and serve with fingers of toasted focaccia, olives and lemon slices.

NOTE: If you can't find dressed crab, use the same weight of frozen crab meat. Defrost at cool room temperature.

NUTRITIONAL ANALYSIS (per portion)	
Energy	350 cals
Protein	21.0 g
Carbohydrate	7.0 g
(of which sugars)	7.0 g
Fat	27.0 g
(of which saturates)	4.0 g
Fibre	1.5 g

SUITABLE FOR:
NUT-FREE AND DIABETIC DIETS.

TOMATO AND RED PEPPER TERRINE

SERVES 6 • PREPARATION: 40 MINUTES, PLUS CHILLING • COOKING TIME: 10 MINUTES

1 kg (2¼ lb) red peppers, halved and deseeded
6 tsp pesto sauce
8 tbsp extra-virgin olive oil
1 kg (2¼ lb) ripe tomatoes, skinned, quartered and deseeded
salt and freshly ground black pepper
20 large basil leaves
4 tsp balsamic vinegar

1 Line a 900 ml (1½ pint) non-stick loaf tin with cling film. Put the peppers, cut-side down on a foil-lined grill rack and place under a hot grill for about 10 minutes until the skins are charred. Transfer to a bowl, cover and cool. Remove the skins.

2 Whisk 2 tsp pesto with 4 tsp olive oil. Cover the base of the lined terrine mould with a layer of the red peppers. Arrange a layer of tomatoes on top, then season well and drizzle with a little of the pesto mixture. Scatter a little roughly torn basil over. Continue layering until all the ingredients have been used, ending with a layer of red peppers.

3 Cover the top with cling film and press down with a heavy weight, approximately 2 kg (4½ lb). Leave overnight.

4 Unmould the terrine and cut into thick slices. Drizzle the remaining oil around each portion; finish with a drizzle of the remaining pesto and the balsamic vinegar.

NUTRITIONAL ANALYSIS (per portion)	
Energy	240 cals
Protein	3.0 g
Carbohydrate	16.0 g
(of which sugars)	15.0 g
Fat	19.5 g
(of which saturates)	3.0 g
Fibre	4.5 g

SUITABLE FOR:
LOW-CHOLESTEROL,
DAIRY PRODUCE-FREE AND
DIABETIC DIETS.

3.2-3.4 kg (7-7½ lb)
medium-sized leeks

salt and freshly ground
black pepper

3 tbsp lemon juice

120 ml (4 fl oz) olive oil

4 tbsp capers, rinsed

2 tsp caraway seeds,
toasted and lightly
crushed

grated lemon rind and
finely sliced spring onion
tops, to garnish

*NOTE: Use a wooden
board and weights or a
second tin filled with full
cans to weight down the
terrine – this will extract
liquid from the leeks.
Drain the terrine regularly.*

LEEK TERRINE

*SERVES 8 • PREPARATION: 30 MINUTES, PLUS
CHILLING • COOKING TIME: 45 MINUTES*

1 Remove the root base, the tough green ends
and outer leaves from the leeks – you may have to
cut very long leeks into about 23 cm (9 inch)
lengths to fit into the terrine. Wash well.

2 Bring a large saucepan or casserole of salted
water to the boil. Add half the leeks and cook for
about 20 minutes or until well cooked. Drain and
plunge into ice-cold water. Repeat with remaining
leeks, then drain well. Place on wire racks for at
least 10 minutes to remove excess water. Pat dry.

3 To assemble the terrine, line a 900 g (2 lb) loaf
tin with a double layer of cling film. Trim the leeks
to fit and arrange a layer in the base so they fit
tightly and the white ends are facing the same
way; season. Cover with another layer of leeks so
the green ends are on top of the white ends.
Repeat until the leeks are slightly higher than the
top of the tin. Cover with cling film and weigh
down. Place in a roasting tin and chill overnight.

4 To make the dressing, place the lemon juice
and seasoning in a small pan, then whisk in the oil,
capers and caraway seeds.

5 Turn the terrine out and carefully remove cling
film. Slice, using a sharp knife in a gentle sawing
action, then arrange on plates. Warm the dressing
gently, spoon around the terrine and garnish.

NUTRITIONAL ANALYSIS	
(per portion)	
Energy	170 cals
Protein	6.5 g
Carbohydrate	12.0 g
(of which sugars)	9.0 g
Fat	13.5 g
(of which saturates)	2.0 g
Fibre	9.0 g

SUITABLE FOR:
HIGH-FIBRE, GLUTEN-FREE,
NUT-FREE, LOW-CHOLESTEROL,
DAIRY PRODUCE-FREE AND
DIABETIC DIETS.

3 ripe mangoes
1 passionfruit
4 tbsp grapeseed oil
3 tbsp lemon juice
salt and freshly ground
black pepper
5 tsp chopped fresh mint
50-75 g (2-3 oz) Parma
ham

PARMA HAM WITH MINT AND MANGO RELISH

SERVES 6 • PREPARATION: 15 MINUTES

1 Peel the mangoes, using a potato peeler, then cut down either side of the central stone; cut away as much of the remaining flesh as possible. Halve the passionfruit and scoop out the pulp.

2 In a blender or food processor, purée the flesh of one mango with the pulp of the passionfruit. With the motor running, slowly add the oil and lemon juice. Season with salt and pepper, then fold in the fresh mint.

3 Thickly slice the remaining mangoes and arrange on serving plates with the Parma ham. Divide the mint and mango relish among individual dishes or ramekins to accompany, and serve.

NUTRITIONAL ANALYSIS (per portion)	
Energy	155 cals
Protein	2.0 g
Carbohydrate	12.0 g
(of which sugars)	11.5 g
Fat	9.5 g
(of which saturates)	2.0 g
Fibre	2.0 g

SUITABLE FOR:
GLUTEN-FREE, NUT-FREE, LOW-CHOLESTEROL, LOW-CALORIE, DAIRY PRODUCE-FREE AND DIABETIC DIETS.

2 red peppers, halved and deseeded
1 small red onion, peeled and halved
3 tbsp olive oil
2 tbsp sun-dried tomato paste
1 tbsp balsamic vinegar
salt and freshly ground black pepper
8 sardines, about 450 g (1 lb) total weight, thawed if frozen
1 mild red chilli, deseeded and finely chopped
1 large garlic clove, peeled and crushed
½ tsp ground paprika
coarse sea salt, to sprinkle
flat-leaf parsley, to garnish

SPICED SARDINES WITH PEPPER SAMBAL

SERVES 4 • PREPARATION: 20 MINUTES • COOKING TIME: ABOUT 35 MINUTES

1 Put the peppers, cut-side down on a foil-lined grill rack and place under a hot grill for about 10 minutes until the skins are charred. Transfer to a polythene bag and leave for 20 minutes. Peel away the skins from the peppers.

2 Put the peppers in a food processor with ½ onion, 2 tbsp oil, the tomato paste, vinegar and seasoning. Blend until smooth, then transfer to a small saucepan. Cook over a gentle heat, stirring frequently, for 15 minutes until thick and pulpy.

3 Meanwhile, score the sardines two to three times diagonally on each side. Season with salt and pepper, then arrange on a lightly oiled, foil-lined grill rack. Finely chop the remaining onion half with the remaining olive oil, chilli, garlic and paprika. Spread half the mixture over the sardines.

4 Place the sardines under a moderate grill for 5 minutes. Turn them over and spread with the remaining onion mixture. Grill for a further 3–5 minutes until cooked through and just beginning to char. Sprinkle with salt and parsley and serve with the pepper sambal.

NUTRITIONAL ANALYSIS (per portion)	
Energy	300 cals
Protein	24.5 g
Carbohydrate	8.0 g
(of which sugars)	7.0 g
Fat	19.0 g
(of which saturates)	4.5 g
Fibre	2.0 g

SUITABLE FOR:
GLUTEN-FREE, NUT-FREE, LOW-CHOLESTEROL, DAIRY PRODUCE-FREE AND DIABETIC DIETS.

225 g (8 oz) floury potatoes, such as King Edward's, boiled and mashed with a little milk

3 tbsp milk

5 tbsp self-raising flour, sieved

4 large eggs, separated

3 tbsp soured cream

salt, pepper and pinch of cayenne pepper

vegetable oil, for frying

300 ml (½ pint) half-fat crème fraîche

275-350 g (10-12 oz) smoked salmon

fresh dill and lemon wedges, to garnish

PICKLED VEGETABLES

75 ml (3 fl oz) white wine vinegar

2 tbsp caster sugar

225 g (8 oz) cucumber, halved, deseeded and cut into thin strips

75 g (3 oz) radishes, cut into thin strips

1 spring onion, trimmed and cut into thin strips

1 tsp mustard seeds

1 tbsp chopped fresh dill

SMOKED SALMON AND POTATO BLINIS

SERVES 6 • PREPARATION: 30 MINUTES • COOKING TIME: 30 MINUTES

1 To make the blinis, place the mashed potato in a bowl, then beat in 3 tbsp milk with the flour, egg yolks, cream and seasoning. In a separate bowl, whisk the egg whites until they just hold their shape; fold into the potato mixture.

2 To cook the blinis, lightly oil a non-stick frying pan and place over a high heat for 2–3 minutes. Add 1–2 tbsp batter and spread to a circle 9 cm (3½ inches) wide. Lower the heat and cook for 1–2 minutes or until bubbles appear. Flip the blinis over and cook for about 1 minute. Remove from the pan and keep warm, interleaved with greaseproof paper. Repeat with remaining batter.

3 For the vegetables, place the vinegar and sugar in a saucepan and bring to the boil. Bubble for 2 minutes, then leave to cool. Stir in the cucumber, radishes, spring onion, mustard seeds and dill.

4 Top each blini (one per person) with some crème fraîche, salmon and pickled vegetables. Garnish with dill and lemon wedges, and serve.

NUTRITIONAL ANALYSIS (per portion)	
Energy	372 cals
Protein	20.0 g
Carbohydrate	24.0 g
(of which sugars)	8.0 g
Fat	31.0 g
(of which saturates)	16.0 g
Fibre	1.0 g

SUITABLE FOR:

NUT-FREE *(provided oil is sunflower or something similar – not groundnut)* AND DIABETIC DIETS.

225 g (8 oz) salmon fillet, skinned and chilled

mixed salad leaves, such as rocket, lamb's lettuce or frisée

50 g (2 oz) cucumber, peeled, deseeded and finely chopped

1 bunch spring onions, trimmed and roughly chopped

1 large green chilli, deseeded and finely chopped

pared lime rind, to garnish

MARINADE

grated rind and juice of 3 limes

4 tbsp olive oil

2 tomatoes, skinned, deseeded and diced

4 tbsp chopped fresh coriander

2 tsp caster sugar

salt and freshly ground black pepper

MARINATED SALMON SALAD WITH LIME AND CORIANDER

SERVES 4 • PREPARATION: 20 MINUTES, PLUS CHILLING

1 To make the marinade, combine the grated lime rind and juice, oil, tomatoes, coriander, caster sugar and seasoning in a small bowl. Cover and set aside.

2 Using a sharp knife, cut the salmon fillet on the diagonal into wafer thin slices. Place in a large, non-metallic shallow dish, pour over the marinade, then cover and chill for up to 3 hours or until the salmon is pink and opaque.

3 To serve, arrange the mixed salad leaves on individual serving plates, then top with the salmon slices and the marinade juices. Arrange the chopped cucumber, spring onions and chilli on top of the salmon, then garnish with pared lime rind. Serve at once.

NUTRITIONAL ANALYSIS (per portion)	
Energy	235 cals
Protein	13.5 g
Carbohydrate	4.0 g
(of which sugars)	4.0 g
Fat	18.0 g
(of which saturates)	3.0 g
Fibre	1.0 g

SUITABLE FOR:
GLUTEN-FREE, NUT-FREE, LOW-CHOLESTEROL, DAIRY PRODUCE-FREE AND DIABETIC DIETS.

350 g (12 oz) large whole raw prawns

salt and freshly ground black pepper

100 g (3½ oz) rye bread

3 tbsp olive oil

3 garlic cloves, peeled and crushed

leaves from 4 sprigs of tarragon

2 tbsp runny honey

2 tbsp lemon juice

lamb's lettuce, to serve

tarragon sprigs, to garnish

PAN-FRIED PRAWNS WITH RYE CROÛTONS

SERVES 4 • PREPARATION: 15 MINUTES • COOKING TIME: ABOUT 6 MINUTES

1 Remove the heads and shells from the prawns, leaving the tails attached. Pat dry on kitchen paper and season lightly. Slice the rye bread, then cut into small cubes.

2 Heat 1 tbsp oil in a non-stick frying pan. Add the rye bread and fry on both sides for about 3 minutes until golden and crisp. Remove with a slotted spoon and drain on kitchen paper.

3 Heat another 1 tbsp oil in the frying pan. Add the prawns and cook for 1 minute until the prawns have coloured on the underside. Turn the prawns and cook for a further minute. Drain; keep warm.

4 Heat the remaining oil and fry the garlic and tarragon for 1 minute. Stir in the honey, lemon juice and a little seasoning and warm through.

5 Arrange a bed of lamb's lettuce on 4 individual serving plates. Pile the prawns and croûtons on top, then spoon over the cooking juices. Serve warm, scattered with extra tarragon.

NUTRITIONAL ANALYSIS (per portion)	
Energy	230 cals
Protein	17.5 g
Carbohydrate	20.5 g
(of which sugars)	9.5 g
Fat	9.0 g
(of which saturates)	1.5 g
Fibre	1.0 g

SUITABLE FOR:
NUT-FREE AND DAIRY PRODUCE-FREE DIETS.

12 medium scallops

salt and freshly ground black pepper

300 ml (½ pint) fish stock

3 tbsp lime juice

1½ tsp caster sugar

3 tbsp Thai fish sauce

2.5 cm (1 inch) piece fresh root ginger, peeled and grated

75 g (3 oz) fresh rice noodles

4 spring onions, trimmed and sliced

100 g (3½ oz) baby spinach

1 tbsp sesame oil

lime rind shreds, to garnish

STEAMED SCALLOPS WITH SPINACH AND NOODLES

SERVES 4 • PREPARATION: 15 MINUTES • COOKING TIME: ABOUT 8 MINUTES

1 Lightly season the scallops with salt and pepper. Put the fish stock, lime juice, sugar, fish sauce and ginger in a wok. Place a lightly oiled steaming rack over the wok and bring the stock to the boil (see Note).

2 Place the scallops on the rack, cover the wok with a lid and steam the scallops gently for about 5 minutes until cooked through. Test by piercing a scallop; the flesh should have turned opaque through to the centre. Remove the scallops and keep warm.

3 Add the rice noodles to the stock and cook very gently for 2 minutes. Stir in the spring onions and spinach and cook for 1 minute until the spinach has wilted.

4 Pile the noodles and vegetables on to warmed serving plates or into bowls and arrange the scallops on top. Spoon over the remaining cooking liquid and drizzle the scallops with sesame oil. Serve scattered with lime shreds.

NUTRITIONAL ANALYSIS
(per portion)

Energy	170 cals
Protein	14.0 g
Carbohydrate	18.0 g
(of which sugars)	1.0 g
Fat	5.0 g
(of which saturates)	1.0 g
Fibre	1.0 g

SUITABLE FOR:

GLUTEN-FREE, LOW-FAT, NUT-FREE, LOW-CALORIE, DAIRY PRODUCE-FREE AND DIABETIC DIETS.

NOTE: If you don't have a wok with a steamer, use a frying pan or large saucepan and rest the scallops on a vegetable steamer or small wire rack. Make a tent of foil over the scallops if the pan doesn't have a lid.

1 firm ripe papaya
1 pink grapefruit
1 small firm ripe mango
1 large firm ripe banana
12 large cooked prawns,
shell on
orange rind shreds, to
garnish

DRESSING
1½ tbsp lemon juice
1 tsp rice wine vinegar
1 tbsp caster sugar
1 tbsp dark soy sauce
¼ tsp crushed red chillies
2 tbsp groundnut oil
pinch of salt

FRUIT AND PRAWN SALAD

SERVES 4 • PREPARATION: 15 MINUTES •
COOKING TIME: 2 MINUTES

1 To make the dressing, place the lemon juice, vinegar, sugar, soy sauce and chillies in a small saucepan and heat gently to dissolve the sugar. Remove from the heat and whisk in the oil and salt. Leave to cool.

2 For the salad, peel and halve the papaya, then scoop out the seeds and thinly slice the flesh. Peel the grapefruit, removing all of the white pith, and cut out the segments free from the membranes. Peel the mango, cut the flesh away from the stone, then cut into slices. Peel and slice the banana. Peel the prawns, leaving on the tail end shells.

3 Arrange the fruits on a large serving platter and spoon over the dressing. Arrange the prawns on top of the salad and garnish with orange shreds. Serve immediately.

NUTRITIONAL ANALYSIS (per portion)	
Energy	195 cals
Protein	15.0 g
Carbohydrate	20.0 g
(of which sugars)	16.0 g
Fat	6.0 g
(of which saturates)	1.0 g
Fibre	2.5 g

SUITABLE FOR:
GLUTEN-FREE, DAIRY PRODUCE-
FREE AND DIABETIC DIETS.

2 garlic cloves, peeled and crushed

450 g (1 lb) large raw prawns, peeled and de-veined

6 tbsp olive oil

rind and juice of 1 lemon and 1 lime

1 red chilli, deseeded and finely chopped

175 g (6 oz) fennel, trimmed and finely sliced

6 tbsp chopped fresh mint

salt and freshly ground black pepper

1 ripe ogen melon, about 450 g (1 lb) total weight, peeled and cut into large chunks

finely sliced red chilli, pared lime rind, lime halves and fresh mint sprigs, to garnish

MELON AND PRAWNS WITH MINT DRESSING

SERVES 6 • PREPARATION: 15 MINUTES, PLUS MARINATING AND CHILLING • COOKING TIME: 10 MINUTES

1 Mix the garlic with the prawns, 1 tbsp oil and the lemon and lime rind. Leave to marinate for 6–8 hours, or preferably overnight.

2 Heat 1 tbsp oil in a wok or frying pan. Add the chilli and fennel and fry for 5 minutes. Add the marinated prawns and continue cooking for a further 3–4 minutes. Transfer to a bowl and chill.

3 To make the dressing, mix the remaining olive oil with the lemon and lime juices, then stir in the mint and season. Toss the prawns with the melon chunks and pour over the dressing. Garnish with chilli, lime rind, lime halves and mint sprigs.

NUTRITIONAL ANALYSIS (per portion)	
Energy	200 cals
Protein	17.5 g
Carbohydrate	5.0 g
(of which sugars)	5.0 g
Fat	12.5 g
(of which saturates)	2.0 g
Fibre	1.0 g

SUITABLE FOR:
GLUTEN-FREE, NUT-FREE, DAIRY PRODUCE-FREE AND DIABETIC DIETS.

---

3 large shallots, peeled and finely chopped

3 tbsp olive oil

4 garlic cloves, peeled and crushed

1.1 kg (2½ lb) ripe plum tomatoes, skinned, deseeded and roughly chopped

2 sticks celery, preferably with leaves, chopped

300 ml (½ pint) white wine

4 tsp balsamic vinegar

2 tbsp harissa (see Note)

2 bay leaves

2 kg (4½ lb) live mussels

4 tbsp chopped flat-leaf parsley

wholemeal bread, to serve

MUSSELS WITH TOMATO AND HARISSA

SERVES 8 • PREPARATION: 30 MINUTES • COOKING TIME: 50 MINUTES

1 Heat the olive oil in a very large saucepan, add the chopped shallots and cook gently for 5–10 minutes or until soft and transparent. Add the crushed garlic, cook for 2–3 minutes, then add the chopped tomatoes and celery, white wine, balsamic vinegar, harissa and bay leaves. Bring to the boil and bubble gently for 20–30 minutes or until reduced by half.

2 Scrub the mussels and pull any 'beards' from the shells. Tap any open mussels, discarding those that do not close when you do so. Wash the mussels in two or three changes of clean water. Add the mussels to the saucepan, cover with a tight-fitting lid, bring to the boil and cook for 5–7 minutes or until the mussels have opened – discard any that don't open during cooking.

3 Spoon the mussels, along with some of the cooking liquid, into deep soup bowls for serving. Sprinkle generously with chopped parsley and serve with chunks of warm bread.

NUTRITIONAL ANALYSIS (per portion)	
Energy	155 cals
Protein	14.0 g
Carbohydrate	5.0 g
(of which sugars)	5.0 g
Fat	6.0 g
(of which saturates)	1.0 g
Fibre	1.5 g

SUITABLE FOR:
LOW-CALORIE, DAIRY PRODUCE-FREE AND DIABETIC DIETS.

NOTE: Harissa is a North African chilli paste which adds heat to a number of savoury dishes. If you can't find harissa, fry two large, finely chopped red chillies with the shallots at step 1.

700 g (1½ lb) trimmed baby leeks

salt and freshly ground black pepper

juice of 1 lemon

½ tsp Dijon mustard

6 tbsp olive oil

900 g (2 lb) live mussels

1 bay leaf

6 peppercorns

120 ml (4 fl oz) white wine

4 tbsp roughly chopped fresh chervil or parsley

2 tbsp chopped fresh chives

orange wedges, to garnish

NOTE: The leeks absorb a lot of water while cooking; drain several times on kitchen paper or the moisture will dilute the flavour of the dressing.

MUSSEL AND LEEK SALAD

SERVES 4 • PREPARATION: 10 MINUTES, PLUS DRAINING • COOKING TIME: 20 MINUTES

1 Cook the leeks in boiling, salted water until just tender, then drain and plunge immediately into ice-cold water. Drain and dry well (see Note).

2 Place 2 tbsp lemon juice in a bowl; season with salt and pepper and add the Dijon mustard. Whisk together, then whisk in the olive oil. Toss the leeks with a little of the dressing, season, cover and chill. Reserve the remaining dressing.

3 Scrub the mussels and pull any 'beards' from the shells. Tap any open mussels, discarding those that do not close when you do so. Wash the mussels in two or three changes of clean water. Place in a large pan, add the bay leaf, peppercorns and white wine. Cover, bring to the boil over a moderate heat and cook for 5–7 minutes or until the mussels open, shaking the pan occasionally; discard any that do not open. Drain, returning the mussels to the pan.

4 Mix the herbs into the reserved dressing. Pour the dressing over the mussels, then spoon over the leeks. Serve garnished with orange wedges.

NUTRITIONAL ANALYSIS
(per portion)

Energy	255 cals
Protein	14.5 g
Carbohydrate	5.0 g
(of which sugars)	4.0 g
Fat	19.0 g
(of which saturates)	3.0 g
Fibre	4.0 g

SUITABLE FOR:
GLUTEN-FREE, NUT-FREE, DAIRY PRODUCE-FREE AND DIABETIC DIETS.

1.1-1.4 kg (2½-3 lb) mixed peppers, halved and deseeded

2 x 50 g (2 oz) cans anchovy fillets

milk, for soaking

50 ml (2 fl oz) olive oil

2 tsp chopped fresh thyme or 1 tsp dried

3 garlic cloves, peeled and crushed

salt and freshly ground black pepper

3 tbsp chopped fresh basil

3 tbsp chopped fresh mint

basil and mint leaves, to garnish

toasted ciabatta, to serve

ROASTED RED PEPPER AND ANCHOVY COMPOTE

SERVES 6-8 • PREPARATION: 10 MINUTES • COOKING TIME: 1 HOUR, PLUS COOLING

1 Place the peppers in a roasting tin and cook at 200°C (400°F) Mark 6 for 45 minutes. When cool, skin and cut into large cubes.

2 Meanwhile, cover the anchovies with milk and soak for 10 minutes.

3 Heat the oil in a large, non-stick frying pan. Add the peppers, thyme and crushed garlic, then cook gently for 5–10 minutes. Drain the anchovies, discarding the milk, then pat dry with kitchen paper. Add to the peppers and cook for 5 minutes; season with salt and pepper. Cool, cover and refrigerate.

4 Stir in the chopped basil and mint. Garnish and serve with toasted ciabatta.

NUTRITIONAL ANALYSIS (per portion)	
Energy	145 cals
Protein	5.0 g
Carbohydrate	11.0 g
(of which sugars)	11.0 g
Fat	8.0 g
(of which saturates)	0.5 g
Fibre	3.0 g

SUITABLE FOR:

NUT-FREE, LOW-CHOLESTEROL, LOW-CALORIE, DAIRY PRODUCE-FREE AND DIABETIC DIETS.

---

4 tbsp olive oil, plus oil for brushing

4 garlic cloves, peeled and finely chopped

2 x 400 g (14 oz) cans chopped plum tomatoes

150 ml (¼ pint) white wine

2 sprigs thyme

1 tbsp sun-dried tomato paste

1 tsp caster sugar

salt and freshly ground black pepper

4 long, thin aubergines

6 tbsp Greek yogurt

strips of roasted red pepper and rocket leaves, to serve

AUBERGINE TIMBALES

SERVES 6 • PREPARATION: 30 MINUTES • COOKING TIME: 1½ HOURS, PLUS COOLING

1 Heat the olive oil in a large saucepan, add the garlic and fry for 30 seconds. Add the plum tomatoes, wine, thyme sprigs, sun-dried tomato paste, caster sugar and seasoning. Bring to the boil and simmer, uncovered, for 45 minutes or until thick, stirring occasionally. Discard the thyme and set aside to cool.

2 Trim the aubergine tops and slice off six thin rounds. Cut the remainder lengthways into 5 mm (¼ in) thick slices. Brush both sides with olive oil and grill for 4–5 minutes until brown.

3 Lightly oil six 175 ml (6 fl oz) ramekins. Place an aubergine round in the base and use strips of aubergine to line the sides.

4 Spoon 1 tbsp yogurt into each mould, then add 3 tbsp of the tomato mixture. Trim the excess aubergine and cover the tops with foil.

5 Place the moulds in a roasting tin half-filled with hot water. Cook at 180°C (350°F) Mark 4 for about 30–35 minutes. Serve with strips of roasted red pepper and rocket leaves.

NUTRITIONAL ANALYSIS (per portion)	
Energy	145 cals
Protein	3.5 g
Carbohydrate	10.0 g
(of which sugars)	9.5 g
Fat	10.0 g
(of which saturates)	2.0 g
Fibre	3.0 g

SUITABLE FOR:

GLUTEN-FREE, NUT-FREE, LOW-CHOLESTEROL, LOW-CALORIE AND DIABETIC DIETS.

450 g (1 lb) young spinach leaves

2 tbsp extra-virgin olive oil

75 g (3 oz) shallots, peeled and finely chopped

4 garlic cloves, peeled and finely chopped

450 g (1 lb) small, bite-size field mushrooms

75 g (3 oz) very roughly chopped mixed basil and flat-leaf parsley

salt and freshly ground black pepper

12 thin slices ciabatta bread, toasted

shavings of Parmesan cheese, to serve

HOT GARLIC MUSHROOMS WITH WILTED SPINACH

SERVES 6 • PREPARATION: 15 MINUTES • COOKING TIME: ABOUT 25 MINUTES

1 Wash and dry the spinach. Heat 1 tbsp olive oil in a large, non-stick saucepan and add the shallots and garlic. Cook for 7–8 minutes or until golden brown and soft.

2 Add the mushrooms and fry over a high heat for 5–6 minutes or until the mushrooms are soft and all the liquid has evaporated. Transfer from the pan to a large heatproof bowl and keep warm.

3 Heat the remaining olive oil in the saucepan and add half the spinach and mixed herbs. Cook over a high heat until the leaves are beginning to wilt. Add to the mushrooms and repeat with the remaining spinach and herbs.

4 Toss the mushroom and garlic mixture with all the spinach and herbs, then season well. Divide among the hot ciabatta toast, top with shavings of Parmesan and serve.

NUTRITIONAL ANALYSIS (per portion)	
Energy	140 cals
Protein	6.5 g
Carbohydrate	17.5 g
(of which sugars)	3.0 g
Fat	5.0 g
(of which saturates)	1.0 g
Fibre	3.0 g

SUITABLE FOR:
LOW-FAT, NUT-FREE, LOW-CHOLESTEROL, LOW-CALORIE AND DIABETIC DIETS.

50 g (2 oz) shelled walnuts

4 garlic cloves, peeled and crushed

1 tbsp chopped fresh thyme

1 tsp caster sugar

2 tsp grainy mustard

3 tbsp lemon juice

9 tbsp extra-virgin olive oil

salt and freshly ground black pepper

4 globe artichokes, stalks trimmed

NOTE: This is a delicious way to serve artichokes, but If you're worried about the fat content, try replacing the aioli with a ready-made low-fat dressing.

ARTICHOKES WITH WALNUT, THYME AND GARLIC AIOLI

SERVES 4 • PREPARATION: 10 MINUTES • COOKING TIME: 40 MINUTES

1 Toast the walnuts, then chop fairly finely. Beat together the garlic, thyme, sugar, mustard and 1 tbsp lemon juice in a small bowl, seasoning with salt and pepper. Gradually whisk in the oil in a thin trickle, whisking well until thickened. Whisk in 3 tbsp cold water. Stir in half the walnuts.

2 Bring a large saucepan of salted water to the boil with the remaining lemon juice. Add the artichokes, cover and cook gently for 35–40 minutes until a leaf can be pulled easily from the artichokes. Drain thoroughly.

3 Halve the artichokes and, using a teaspoon, scoop out the smallest leaves from the centre of each half; also remove the fibrous choke which covers the artichoke hearts.

4 Transfer to serving plates and scatter with the remaining walnuts and a little seasoning. Pour the aioli into the centre of the artichokes to serve.

NUTRITIONAL ANALYSIS (per portion)	
Energy	325 cals
Protein	3.5 g
Carbohydrate	3.0 g
(of which sugars)	2.0 g
Fat	33.5 g
(of which saturates)	4.0 g
Fibre	0.5 g

SUITABLE FOR:
GLUTEN-FREE, DAIRY PRODUCE-FREE AND DIABETIC DIETS.

125 g (4 oz) couscous

1 small red onion, peeled and thinly sliced

1 aubergine, halved and cut into 5 mm (¼ inch) slices

1 courgette, halved and cut into 5 mm (¼ inch) slices

1 large red or yellow pepper, deseeded and thinly sliced

2 sprigs rosemary

3 tbsp olive oil, plus extra for brushing

1 tbsp lemon juice

2 tbsp chopped fresh mint

3 tbsp chopped flat-leaf parsley

1 tsp salt and freshly ground black pepper

fresh tomato sauce, to serve

COUSCOUS WITH ROASTED VEGETABLES

SERVES 6 • PREPARATION: 20 MINUTES, PLUS CHILLING • COOKING TIME: 50 MINUTES

1 Lightly oil six ovenproof 200 ml (7 fl oz) capacity moulds, then set aside. Place the couscous in a large bowl, pour over 450 ml (¾ pint) boiling water and leave to soak for 30 minutes.

2 Meanwhile, place the vegetables and rosemary in a large roasting tin and drizzle the oil over the top. Cook at 200°C (400°F) Mark 6 for 30–35 minutes, turning occasionally.

3 Discard the rosemary, then mix the vegetables with the soaked couscous and stir in the lemon juice, mint, parsley and plenty of seasoning.

4 Divide the couscous mixture between the moulds, ensuring the couscous is well packed down. Cover with foil, place on a baking sheet and cook at 180°C (350°F) Mark 4 for 15 minutes. Leave to cool and chill for at least 2 hours before unmoulding and serving with tomato sauce.

NUTRITIONAL ANALYSIS (per portion)	
Energy	125 cals
Protein	2.5 g
Carbohydrate	15.0 g
(of which sugars)	4.0 g
Fat	6.0 g
(of which saturates)	1.0 g
Fibre	2.0 g

SUITABLE FOR:
NUT-FREE, LOW-CHOLESTEROL, LOW-CALORIE, DAIRY PRODUCE-FREE AND DIABETIC DIETS.

6 slices hard goat's cheese

150 ml (¼ pint) good-quality olive oil

25 g (1 oz) fresh basil, leaves removed, stalks reserved

1 tsp mixed peppercorns, crushed

175 ml (6 fl oz) balsamic vinegar

6 slices Parma ham, 140 g (4½ oz) total weight, cut in half

1 tbsp soft brown sugar

6 slices ciabatta, cut at an angle

1 small garlic clove, peeled and crushed

salt and freshly ground black pepper

lemon juice (optional)

125 g (4 oz) rocket or watercress sprigs

basil sprigs, to garnish

PEPPERCORN-CRUSTED GOAT'S CHEESE SALAD

SERVES 6 • PREPARATION: 20 MINUTES, PLUS MARINATING • COOKING TIME: 15 MINUTES

1 Place the cheese in a bowl, pour the oil over and add the basil stalks. Cover and leave in a cool place to marinate for 12 hours.

2 Remove the cheese from the oil and dust with peppercorns. Strain and reserve the oil.

3 To make balsamic dressing, place the vinegar in a saucepan, bring to the boil and bubble for 4–5 minutes or until syrupy. Set aside to cool.

4 Place the Parma ham on a non-stick baking sheet, sprinkle with sugar and grill until crisp; set aside. Brush the ciabatta with a little reserved oil and toast on one side. Set aside.

5 To make the basil dressing, place the basil leaves, garlic and remaining oil in a food processor and process until smooth. Season and add lemon juice to taste. Set aside.

6 Place the cheese on the untoasted side of the ciabatta and place under a moderate grill until just melting. Divide the rocket and ham among 6 individual serving plates, top with the ciabatta, drizzle with the dressings, garnish and serve.

NUTRITIONAL ANALYSIS (per portion)	
Energy	300 cals
Protein	6.5 g
Carbohydrate	19.0 g
(of which sugars)	5.0 g
Fat	19.0 g
(of which saturates)	5.0 g
Fibre	1.0 g

SUITABLE FOR:
NUT-FREE AND DIABETIC DIETS.

1 garlic clove, peeled

½ tsp sea salt

1 tsp powdered English mustard

2 tbsp balsamic vinegar

2 tbsp walnut or hazelnut oil

3 tbsp olive oil

freshly ground black pepper

125 g (4 oz) blue cheese, such as Roquefort, Gorgonzola or Stilton

2 large pears

1 bunch watercress, about 175 g (6 oz), or mixed green salad leaves such as rocket, endive and frisée

150 g (5 oz) sprouted beans

WATERCRESS, PEAR AND BLUE CHEESE SALAD

SERVES 4 • PREPARATION TIME: 20 MINUTES

1 Using a pestle and mortar, or with the back of a strong knife on a chopping board, crush the garlic with the salt until it is creamy. Add the mustard and work into the paste. Whisk into the balsamic vinegar and oils and season to taste with ground black pepper.

2 Roughly crumble the cheese. Quarter or halve the pears (peel, if wished) and brush with a little of the dressing to prevent discolouration.

3 Mix together the watercress, sprouted beans and pears in a large bowl and drizzle with 3 tbsp dressing (see Note). Add the cheese and toss the salad. Serve immediately.

NUTRITIONAL ANALYSIS (per portion)	
Energy	245 cals
Protein	9.0 g
Carbohydrate	5.0 g
(of which sugars)	4.5 g
Fat	24.0 g
(of which saturates)	8.0 g
Fibre	2.0 g

SUITABLE FOR:
GLUTEN-FREE AND DIABETIC DIETS.

NOTE: Store the remaining dressing in a screw-top jar in the refrigerator for up to two weeks.

Watercress... a healthy salad choice

Low in calories as well as being packed with vitamins and minerals, watercress has a delicious tangy flavour that combines well with strong-tasting cheeses. It contains large amounts of vitamin C and beta-carotene, as well as vitamin E – all powerful antioxidants that protect against cancer by mopping up free radicals.

1 small charantais or cantaloupe melon

1 small ogen or galia melon

½ large honeydew melon

350 g (12 oz) watermelon

DRESSING
2 tbsp caster sugar

1 tbsp chopped preserved stem ginger in syrup, drained

2 tbsp orange juice

2 tsp lemon juice

CHILLED MELON AND GINGER SALAD

SERVES 6 • PREPARATION: 15 MINUTES, PLUS CHILLING • COOKING TIME: 10 MINUTES

1 To make the dressing, place the sugar and ginger in a small saucepan with 120 ml (4 fl oz) water. Heat gently to dissolve the sugar, then bring to the boil and simmer for 10 minutes.

2 Transfer to a bowl and stir in the orange and lemon juices. Set aside to cool.

3 Peel each melon and discard the seeds. Cut the flesh into thin wedges and mix together in a large bowl.

4 Pour over the cooled dressing, stir well, cover and chill for 1 hour before serving.

NUTRITIONAL ANALYSIS (per portion)	
Energy	86 cals
Protein	1.5 g
Carbohydrate	20.5 g
(of which sugars)	20.5 g
Fat	0.5 g
(of which saturates)	0.1 g
Fibre	1.5 g

SUITABLE FOR:
GLUTEN-FREE, LOW-FAT, NUT-FREE, LOW-CHOLESTEROL, LOW-CALORIE, DAIRY PRODUCE-FREE AND DIABETIC DIETS.

450 g (1 lb) aubergines

2 garlic cloves

700 g (1½ lb) green or red peppers, halved and deseeded

4 tbsp olive oil

salt and freshly ground black pepper

3 large green chillies

½ tsp caraway seeds

2 tbsp lemon juice

1 tbsp small capers (optional)

25 g (1 oz) marinated fresh anchovies or canned (optional), roughly chopped

2 tbsp chopped fresh mint

warm toast, to serve

NOTE: Served Tunisian style, with the 'little dishes' given below, this salad makes an unusual start to a meal.

TUNISIAN 'MECHOUIA' SALAD

SERVES 6 • PREPARATION: 20 MINUTES • COOKING TIME: 1 HOUR

1 Place the whole aubergines in a roasting tin and cook at 220°C (425°F) Mark 7 for 20 minutes. Add the unpeeled garlic, pepper halves and 2 tbsp oil; season with salt. Cook for a further 30 minutes. Cool, then skin and roughly chop peppers, garlic and aubergines.

2 Return the vegetables to the roasting tin. Deseed and chop 1 chilli and add to the roasting tin with the remaining whole chillies. Add the caraway seeds, lemon juice, capers and anchovies (if using). Season with salt and pepper, then mix well and cook, uncovered, for 10–15 minutes until the liquid has evaporated.

3 Cool the vegetables, then transfer to a serving dish. Sprinkle with chopped mint and serve at room temperature with warm toast and the Mixed Little Dishes given below.

NUTRITIONAL ANALYSIS (per portion)	
Energy	105 cals
Protein	2.5 g
Carbohydrate	9.0 g
(of which sugars)	8.5 g
Fat	9.0 g
(of which saturates)	1.0 g
Fibre	3.5 g

SUITABLE FOR:
GLUTEN-FREE, NUT-FREE, LOW-CHOLESTEROL, LOW-CALORIE, DAIRY PRODUCE-FREE AND DIABETIC DIETS.

PICKLED VEGETABLES

1 cucumber

4 sticks celery, trimmed and cut into chunks

125 g (4 oz) baby carrots, trimmed and peeled

125 g (4 oz) radishes, trimmed

2 tsp salt

4 tbsp sugar

4 tbsp white wine vinegar

1 tbsp pink peppercorns, drained and rinsed

salt and freshly ground black pepper

BABY VEGETABLE SALAD

225 g (8 oz) baby turnips, halved or sliced

225 g (8 oz) baby fennel, trimmed and sliced

2 tbsp harissa

4 tbsp olive oil

MIXED LITTLE DISHES

SERVES 6 • PREPARATION: 20 MINUTES, PLUS MARINATING AND CHILLING

1 To make the pickled vegetables, halve, deseed and thickly slice the cucumber, then mix with the celery, carrots and radishes. Sprinkle the salt over the vegetables and leave for 2 hours. Rinse with cold water; drain. Sprinkle with the sugar, white wine vinegar, pink peppercorns, salt and black pepper. Cover and chill overnight.

2 To make the baby vegetable salad, put the turnips and fennel in a serving bowl and toss together. Mix the harissa with the olive oil: spoon over the vegetables.

3 Serve both dishes with the Tunisian 'Mechouia' Salad given above.

NUTRITIONAL ANALYSIS (per portion)	
Energy	135 cals
Protein	1.5 g
Carbohydrate	19.5 g
(of which sugars)	19.5 g
Fat	7.2 g
(of which saturates)	1.0 g
Fibre	3.0 g

SUITABLE FOR:
GLUTEN-FREE, NUT-FREE, LOW-CHOLESTEROL, LOW-CALORIE, DAIRY PRODUCE-FREE AND DIABETIC DIETS.

450 g (1 lb) asparagus

2 oranges, peel and pith removed, and thinly sliced

50 g (2 oz) pecans or walnuts, toasted and roughly chopped

125 g (4 oz) frisée or other salad leaves

2 tbsp fresh tarragon sprigs

DRESSING

2 tsp Dijon mustard

2 tbsp sherry vinegar

4 tbsp olive oil

2 tbsp orange juice

salt and freshly ground black pepper

ZESTY ORANGE AND ASPARAGUS SALAD

SERVES 4 • PREPARATION: 10 MINUTES • COOKING TIME: 6 MINUTES

1 To make the dressing, whisk together the mustard, vinegar, oil and orange juice, then season with salt and pepper. Set aside.

2 Remove the tough woody ends of the asparagus and pare a little of the tough outer skin from the base. Tie in a bundle and place upright in a tall pan (hold in place with scrunched-up foil, if necessary). Pour in enough boiling water to come about three-quarters of the way up the stems. The heads should be above the water level.

3 Cover with foil and boil gently for 6 minutes or until just tender.

4 Drain the asparagus and toss in the dressing while still hot. Toss together the oranges, pecans, salad leaves and tarragon and divide between 4 individual serving plates. Top with the asparagus and dressing and serve immediately.

NUTRITIONAL ANALYSIS (per portion)	
Energy	250 cals
Protein	6.0 g
Carbohydrate	11.0 g
(of which sugars)	10.5 g
Fat	20.5 g
(of which saturates)	2.5 g
Fibre	4.0 g

SUITABLE FOR:

GLUTEN-FREE, LOW-CHOLESTEROL, DAIRY PRODUCE-FREE AND DIABETIC DIETS.

4 red peppers

400 g (14 oz) cherry tomatoes

2 tbsp chilli oil

salt and freshly ground black pepper

basil leaves, to garnish

DRESSING

1 tbsp soft brown sugar

2 tbsp balsamic vinegar

3 tbsp olive oil

1 small red chilli, deseeded and chopped

WARM PEPPER AND TOMATO SALAD WITH BALSAMIC DRESSING

SERVES 4 • PREPARATION: 15 MINUTES • COOKING TIME: 50 MINUTES

1 Cut the peppers in half lengthways. Remove the seeds, but leave the stalks intact. Lay the peppers in a lightly oiled baking tray and fill each half with the cherry tomatoes. Drizzle each with a little chilli oil and season with salt and pepper.

2 Roast the peppers in the oven at 180°C (350°F) Mark 4 for 45–50 minutes until lightly browned.

3 Meanwhile, make the dressing. Place the sugar and vinegar in a bowl and whisk until the sugar has dissolved. Gradually whisk in the olive oil, then stir in the chilli. Season to taste.

4 Transfer the peppers to individual serving dishes and pour over the roasting juices. Drizzle with the dressing, garnish with basil leaves and serve.

NUTRITIONAL ANALYSIS (per portion)	
Energy	215 cals
Protein	2.5 g
Carbohydrate	19.5 g
(of which sugars)	2.0 g
Fat	15.0 g
(of which saturates)	2.0 g
Fibre	4.0 g

SUITABLE FOR:

GLUTEN-FREE, NUT-FREE, LOW-CHOLESTEROL, DAIRY PRODUCE-FREE AND DIABETIC DIETS.

Red pepper ... all good

Weight for weight, an uncooked pepper provides over twice the vitamin C of an orange. Red peppers are an excellent source of beta-carotene, containing twenty-five times more than yellow ones. They also contain bioflavonoids which, together with beta-carotene and vitamin C, are powerful cancer-fighting antioxidants. Useful amounts of vitamin E, B vitamins and potassium are also found in peppers.

soups

1 litre (1¾ pints) fish stock

2 tsp grated fresh root ginger

1 tbsp mirin

4 spring onions, trimmed and finely sliced

1 red chilli, deseeded and finely sliced

125 g (4 oz) shiitake mushrooms, finely sliced

125 g (4 oz) daikon (Japanese radish), cut into fine strips, or pared

50 g (2 oz) carrot, cut into fine strips

50 g (2 oz) miso paste

225 g (8 oz) lemon sole or plaice fillet, skinned and cut into strips

Japanese soy sauce

MISO FISH SOUP

SERVES 4 • PREPARATION: 25 MINUTES •
COOKING TIME: 15 MINUTES

1 Bring the stock to the boil in a saucepan. Add the ginger and mirin and bring back to the boil. Add the vegetables, reduce the heat to very low and cook gently for 2–3 minutes or until the vegetables are tender.

2 Stir the miso into the soup and add the strips of fish. Cook over a very low heat for 2–3 minutes or until the fish is cooked through. Avoid stirring the soup at this stage as the fish may break up.

3 Season the soup with soy sauce, spoon into individual bowls and serve at once.

NUTRITIONAL ANALYSIS (per portion)	
Energy	90 cals
Protein	13.0 g
Carbohydrate	5.0 g
(of which sugars)	2.0 g
Fat	2.0 g
(of which saturates)	0.2 g
Fibre	1.1 g

SUITABLE FOR:
GLUTEN-FREE, LOW-FAT, NUT-FREE, LOW-CHOLESTEROL, LOW-CALORIE, DAIRY PRODUCE-FREE AND DIABETIC DIETS.

900 g (2 lb) mixed fish fillets and shellfish, such as whiting, John Dory, red mullet, live mussels and cooked prawns

a pinch of saffron strands

3 tbsp olive oil

1 onion, peeled and sliced

1 leek, trimmed and sliced

2 sticks celery, trimmed and sliced

2 garlic cloves, peeled and crushed

397 g can chopped tomatoes, or 225 g (8 oz) fresh tomatoes, skinned, deseeded and chopped

1 strip of pared orange rind

1 tbsp sun-dried tomato paste

½ tsp fennel seeds

1.1 litres (2 pints) fish stock

salt and freshly ground black pepper

3 tbsp chopped mixed fresh parsley and thyme

French bread, to serve

BOUILLABAISSE

SERVES 4 • PREPARATION: 15 MINUTES • COOKING TIME: 45 MINUTES

1 Cut the fish into bite-sized pieces and peel the prawns. Clean the mussels.

2 Place the saffron in a bowl and pour over 150 ml (¼ pint) boiling water.

3 Heat the oil in a large pan, add the onion, leek, celery and garlic and cook for about 5 minutes or until beginning to soften. Add the tomatoes, orange rind, tomato paste and fennel seeds; cook for 1–2 minutes.

4 Add the fish stock with the saffron and its liquid, then season with salt and pepper to taste. Bring to the boil and simmer for about 30 minutes, then adjust seasoning if necessary.

5 Add the fish and mussels (not the prawns) and cook for about 5–6 minutes until the fish is just cooked and the mussels have opened (discard any closed ones). Stir in the herbs and prawns, then serve with French bread.

NUTRITIONAL ANALYSIS (per portion)	
Energy	285 cals
Protein	44.5 g
Carbohydrate	6.0 g
(of which sugars)	5.0 g
Fat	10.0 g
(of which saturates)	1.5 g
Fibre	1.5 g

SUITABLE FOR:
NUT-FREE, DAIRY PRODUCE-FREE AND DIABETIC DIETS.

NOTE: If you use mainly white varieties of fish rather than the oily type, it will help to keep the calorie count lower.

15 g (½ oz) dried porcini or shiitake mushrooms

2 tbsp oil

225 g (8 oz) fillet steak, cut into thin strips

1.1 litres (2 pints) beef stock

Thai fish sauce

1 large red chilli, deseeded and finely chopped

1 stick lemon grass, trimmed and thinly sliced

2.5 cm (1 inch) piece fresh root ginger, peeled and finely chopped

6 spring onions, halved lengthways and cut into 2.5 cm (1 inch) lengths

1 garlic clove, peeled and crushed

¼ tsp caster sugar

50 g (2 oz) medium egg noodles

125 g (4 oz) spinach leaves, roughly chopped

4 tbsp chopped fresh coriander

freshly ground black pepper

SPICED BEEF AND NOODLE SOUP

SERVES 4 • PREPARATION: 10 MINUTES, PLUS SOAKING • COOKING TIME: 10 MINUTES

1 Break the dried mushrooms into pieces and leave to soak in 150 ml (¼ pint) boiling water for 15 minutes.

2 Heat the oil in a large saucepan, brown the meat in two batches and set aside. Pour the stock into the pan with 2 tbsp Thai fish sauce, the mushrooms and their soaking liquid, chilli, lemon grass, ginger, spring onions, garlic and sugar. Bring to the boil.

3 Break the noodles up slightly and add to the pan, then stir gently until they begin to separate. Simmer for 4–5 minutes or until the noodles are just tender, stirring occasionally.

4 Stir in the spinach, coriander and reserved steak. Adjust the seasoning, adding a little more Thai fish sauce if necessary. Serve in warmed bowls.

NUTRITIONAL ANALYSIS (per portion)	
Energy	190 cals
Protein	15.5 g
Carbohydrate	12.0 g
(of which sugars)	1.0 g
Fat	10.0 g
(of which saturates)	2.0 g
Fibre	1.0 g

SUITABLE FOR:
NUT-FREE, LOW-CHOLESTEROL, DAIRY PRODUCE-FREE AND DIABETIC DIETS.

NOTE: Fillet steak is extremely lean and tender and, although expensive, there's no waste. The tail end tapers, making it cheaper and suitable for recipes where meat is cut into strips, as in this one.

125 g (4 oz) green or yellow split peas, soaked overnight in double their volume of cold water

25 g (1 oz) butter

225 g (8 oz) onion, peeled and chopped

1 tbsp ground coriander

40 g (1½ oz) pearl barley

2 litres (3½ pints) ham or turkey stock

1 bay leaf

1 stick celery

fresh thyme sprig

225 g (8 oz) potatoes, peeled and cut into chunks

400 g (14 oz) carrots, peeled and cut into chunks

salt and freshly ground black pepper

150 g (5 oz) cooked turkey, cut into chunks

150 g (5 oz) piece cooked ham, cut into chunks

150 g (5 oz) baby spinach

fresh coriander sprigs and freshly ground black pepper, to garnish

50 g (2 oz) grated Parmesan, (optional)

TURKEY, HAM AND SPINACH BROTH WITH SPLIT PEAS

SERVES 6 • PREPARATION: 20 MINUTES, PLUS OVERNIGHT SOAKING • COOKING TIME: 1 HOUR 15 MINUTES

1 Drain the split peas and place in a saucepan with cold water to cover. Bring to the boil and simmer for 10 minutes. Drain the peas and discard the liquid.

2 Meanwhile, melt the butter in a saucepan, add the onion and cook for 5 minutes or until soft but not coloured. Add the ground coriander and cook for 30 seconds.

3 Add the split peas, pearl barley and stock. Tie the bay leaf, celery and thyme sprig together and add to the pan. Bring to the boil and simmer for 40 minutes or until the peas and barley are tender. Add the potatoes and cook for 5 minutes; add the carrots and cook for 5–10 minutes. Season well with salt and pepper.

4 Add the turkey, ham and spinach and bring back to the boil. Simmer for 2–3 minutes. Garnish with coriander and pepper and serve with grated Parmesan cheese, if you wish.

NUTRITIONAL ANALYSIS (per portion)	
Energy	300 cals
Protein	23.0 g
Carbohydrate	30.5 g
(of which sugars)	6.0 g
Fat	14.0 g
(of which saturates)	6.5 g
Fibre	4.0 g

SUITABLE FOR:

GLUTEN-FREE, NUT-FREE, LOW-CHOLESTEROL AND DIABETIC DIETS.

ROASTED GARLIC AND SWEET POTATO SOUP

1 whole garlic bulb
25 g (1 oz) butter
350 g (12 oz) onions, peeled and finely diced
125 g (4 oz) celery, trimmed and finely diced
125 g (4 oz) carrots, peeled and finely diced
900 g (2 lb) sweet potatoes or pumpkin, peeled and diced
few sprigs fresh thyme or large pinch dried
300 ml (½ pint) dry white wine
600 ml (1 pint) good chicken stock
300 ml (½ pint) skimmed milk
salt and freshly ground black pepper
thyme sprigs, to garnish

SERVES 6 • PREPARATION: 20 MINUTES • COOKING TIME: ABOUT 1 HOUR

1 Halve the garlic bulb horizontally. Place the root half (which stays whole) in an ovenproof dish and roast at 200°C (400°F) Mark 6 for 30 minutes.

2 Melt the butter in a large saucepan, add the onions, celery and carrots and fry gently until soft and golden. Stir in the sweet potatoes and thyme and cook for a further 1–2 minutes.

3 Add the white wine, stock and roasted garlic bulb. Bring to the boil, then cover and simmer gently for about 30 minutes or until all the vegetables are very soft.

4 Remove the garlic bulb and slip out the cloves that will now be very soft. Allow the soup mixture to cool slightly before puréeing with the garlic in a blender or food processor. Return the soup to the pan and stir in the milk. Reheat gently and adjust the seasoning. Add a little milk or extra stock to thin the soup further, if necessary.

5 To serve, garnish the soup with thyme sprigs.

NUTRITIONAL ANALYSIS (per portion)	
Energy	249 cals
Protein	5.0 g
Carbohydrate	41.0 g
(of which sugars)	16.0 g
Fat	5.0 g
(of which saturates)	3.0 g
Fibre	5.0 g

SUITABLE FOR:
GLUTEN-FREE, NUT-FREE, LOW-CHOLESTEROL AND DIABETIC DIETS.

TOMATO, CELERY AND APPLE SOUP

25 g (1 oz) butter
275 g (10 oz) onions, peeled and roughly chopped
1 head green celery, about 400 g (14 oz), trimmed and roughly chopped
400 g (14 oz) cooking apples
2 garlic cloves, peeled and crushed
2 x 400 g (14 oz) cans plum tomatoes
300 ml (½ pint) apple juice
450 ml (¾ pint) vegetable stock
pinch of sugar
salt and freshly ground black pepper
basil leaves and Greek yogurt, to garnish

SERVES 6 • PREPARATION: 15 MINUTES • COOKING TIME: 50 MINUTES

1 Melt the butter in a large, heavy-based saucepan. Add the onions and celery and cook for 10 minutes, stirring occasionally, until the onion is soft and golden. Meanwhile, peel, core and roughly chop the cooking apples.

2 Add the crushed garlic and apples to the pan and cook for a further 5 minutes, then stir in the tomatoes, apple juice and vegetable stock. Bring to the boil and simmer, uncovered, for 30 minutes.

3 Cool the soup slightly, then purée in batches in a blender or food processor until smooth. Pass the purée through a fine sieve.

4 Return the soup to the wiped-out pan. Bring back to the boil, add a pinch of sugar and adjust the seasoning. Garnish with a small swirl of yogurt, top with basil and serve.

NUTRITIONAL ANALYSIS (per portion)	
Energy	115 cals
Protein	3.0 g
Carbohydrate	19.0 g
(of which sugars)	18.0 g
Fat	4.0 g
(of which saturates)	2.5 g
Fibre	3.0 g

SUITABLE FOR:
GLUTEN-FREE, LOW-FAT, LOW-CHOLESTEROL, LOW-CALORIE AND DIABETIC DIETS.

NOTE: For a richer-tasting soup, replace the apple juice with the same quantity of medium cider.

75 g (3 oz) green lentils

2 tbsp oil

175-200 g (6-7 oz) chorizo sausage or peppered salami, cut into cubes

350 g (12 oz) onions, peeled and roughly chopped

225 g (8 oz) carrots, peeled and roughly chopped

225 g (8 oz) parsnips, peeled and roughly chopped

1 tsp ground cumin

1.7 litres (3 pints) vegetable stock

2 bay leaves

a few thyme sprigs

salt and freshly ground black pepper

CARROT, PARSNIP AND LENTIL SOUP

SERVES 6 • PREPARATION: 20 MINUTES, PLUS SOAKING • COOKING TIME: 55 MINUTES

1 Soak the lentils in double their volume of cold water for 6 hours or overnight.

2 Heat the oil in a large pan, add the chorizo sausage and cook, stirring, for 5 minutes or until golden. Remove with a slotted spoon and set aside. Add the onions to the pan and cook for 10 minutes or until soft and golden.

3 Add the carrots, parsnips, cumin and drained lentils and cook, stirring, for 5 minutes. Stir in the stock, bay leaves and thyme. Bring to the boil and simmer for 30 minutes or until the vegetables are tender.

4 Cool slightly, remove the herbs and purée the soup in batches in a blender or food processor.

5 Return the soup to the wiped-out pan, bring back to the boil and correct the seasoning. Serve with the reserved chorizo.

NUTRITIONAL ANALYSIS (per portion)	
Energy	275 cals
Protein	11.0 g
Carbohydrate	18.0 g
(of which sugars)	8.0 g
Fat	18.0 g
(of which saturates)	14.0 g
Fibre	4.5 g

SUITABLE FOR:
NUT-FREE, DAIRY PRODUCE-FREE AND DIABETIC DIETS.

NOTE: Cubes of ciabatta bread, tossed in a little oil and baked in the oven until crisp, make a tasty garnish, combining well with the chorizo.

SPINACH AND RICE SOUP

SERVES 4 • PREPARATION: 10 MINUTES •
COOKING TIME: 30 MINUTES

4 tbsp extra-virgin olive oil

1 onion, peeled and finely chopped

2 garlic cloves, peeled and crushed

2 tsp chopped fresh thyme or large pinch dried

2 tsp chopped fresh rosemary or large pinch dried

grated rind of ½ lemon

2 tsp ground coriander

¼ tsp cayenne pepper

125 g (4 oz) arborio (risotto) rice

1.1 litres (2 pints) vegetable stock

225 g (8 oz) fresh or frozen spinach (see Note)

4 tbsp pesto sauce

salt and ground black pepper

extra-virgin olive oil, to serve

freshly grated Parmesan cheese, to garnish (optional)

1 Heat half the oil in a saucepan, add the onion, garlic, herbs, lemon rind and spices, then fry gently for 5 minutes.

2 Add the remaining oil along with the rice and cook, stirring, for 1 minute. Add the stock, bring to the boil and simmer gently for 20 minutes or until the rice is tender.

3 Meanwhile, shred the spinach, then stir into the soup with the pesto sauce. Cook for 2 minutes, then season with salt and pepper to taste.

4 Serve drizzled with a little oil, and topped with Parmesan cheese, if wished.

NUTRITIONAL ANALYSIS (per portion)	
Energy	305 cals
Protein	5.5 g
Carbohydrate	28 g
(of which sugars)	2.0 g
Fat	17.0 g
(of which saturates)	2.5 g
Fibre	1.5 g

SUITABLE FOR:
GLUTEN-FREE, LOW-CHOLESTEROL AND DIABETIC DIETS.

Spinach... greens are good for you

Spinach is one of the most nutrient-rich vegetables, containing vast amounts of beta-carotene, folic acid and potassium. It is also a rich source of two lesser-known carotenes, thought specifically to protect the retina from oxidative damage.

COURGETTE, ORANGE AND PASTA SOUP

SERVES 4 • PREPARATION: 20 MINUTES •
COOKING TIME: 50 MINUTES

2 tbsp olive oil

125 g (4 oz) onion, peeled and finely diced

1 garlic clove, peeled and finely chopped

125 g (4 oz) leek, trimmed and finely chopped

2 tsp chopped fresh thyme

450 ml (¾ pint) good vegetable stock

450 ml (¾ pint) tomato juice

4 very ripe tomatoes, skinned and finely chopped

225 g (8 oz) courgettes, finely diced

50 g (2 oz) pastina (small soup pasta)

pared rind of 1 orange

salt and freshly ground black pepper

125 g (4 oz) baby leaf spinach

2 tbsp chopped fresh basil

pinch of sugar, if necessary

1 Heat the oil in a large saucepan and add the onion, garlic, leek and thyme. Cook for a good 10 minutes until very soft and golden brown. Add the stock, tomato juice and tomatoes, then cover and simmer for 30 minutes.

2 Add the diced courgettes to the soup with the pastina and orange rind. Season well with salt and pepper. Simmer the soup, uncovered, very gently for about 10–15 minutes or until the pasta and vegetables are very tender.

3 Adjust the seasoning, remove the orange rind and stir in the spinach and basil to wilt. Add a pinch of sugar if the tomatoes are very acidic, then serve.

NUTRITIONAL ANALYSIS (per portion)	
Energy	165 cals
Protein	6.5 g
Carbohydrate	21.0 g
(of which sugars)	10.0 g
Fat	7.0 g
(of which saturates)	1.0 g
Fibre	4.0 g

SUITABLE FOR:
NUT-FREE, LOW-CHOLESTEROL, DAIRY PRODUCE-FREE AND DIABETIC DIETS.

2 tbsp olive oil

2 leeks, trimmed and thinly sliced

2 sticks celery, trimmed and thinly sliced

2 garlic cloves, peeled and crushed

1 large potato, peeled and diced

1 tbsp chopped fresh thyme

1.1 litres (2 pints) vegetable stock

225 g (8 oz) fresh or frozen peas

400 g (14 oz) can flageolet beans

mint sprigs, to garnish

MINT CREAM
2 tbsp chopped fresh mint

120 ml (4 fl oz) half-fat crème fraîche

salt and freshly ground black pepper

CREAMY PEA AND FLAGEOLET SOUP

*SERVES 6 • PREPARATION: 20 MINUTES •
COOKING TIME: 35 MINUTES*

1 To make the mint cream, put the mint in a bowl, pour on 1 tbsp boiling water and set aside until cool. Drain the mint and mix with the crème fraîche. Season with salt and pepper to taste. Cover and set aside.

2 Heat the oil in a large saucepan, add the leeks, celery and garlic and fry gently for 5 minutes until softened. Stir in the potato and thyme and fry for a further 5 minutes. Add the stock and bring to the boil. Cover and simmer for 15 minutes.

3 Stir in the peas and flageolet beans together with their liquid. Return to the boil and cook, covered, for a further 10 minutes.

4 Allow to cool slightly, then purée the soup in a blender or food processor until very smooth.

5 Return the soup to the pan and heat through gently. Adjust the seasoning and serve topped with a swirl of mint cream and garnished with mint sprigs.

NUTRITIONAL ANALYSIS	
(per portion)	
Energy	215 cals
Protein	9.0 g
Carbohydrate	23.0 g
(of which sugars)	5.0 g
Fat	10.0 g
(of which saturates)	4.0 g
Fibre	7.0 g

SUITABLE FOR:
HIGH-FIBRE, GLUTEN-FREE,
NUT-FREE AND DIABETIC DIETS.

900 g (2 lb) very ripe cherry tomatoes

1 cucumber, peeled, halved lengthways and deseeded

1 garlic clove, peeled and chopped

1 red chilli, deseeded and finely chopped

2 spring onions, trimmed and finely chopped

4 tbsp extra-virgin olive oil

1 tbsp red wine vinegar

1 tbsp caster sugar

salt and freshly ground black pepper

extra paprika and handful of wild rocket, to garnish

HOT SPICY GAZPACHO

SERVES 4 • PREPARATION: 20 MINUTES • COOKING TIME: 5 MINUTES

1 Put the tomatoes, cucumber, garlic, chilli, spring onions, olive oil, vinegar and sugar in a food processor and blend until smooth. Heat gently in a saucepan until warm, then season to taste.

2 To serve, spoon the warm soup into soup bowls, sprinkle over a little paprika and garnish each serving with a rocket leaf.

NUTRITIONAL ANALYSIS (per portion)	
Energy	165 cals
Protein	2.5 g
Carbohydrate	12.5 g
(of which sugars)	12.5 g
Fat	12.0 g
(of which saturates)	2.0 g
Fibre	3.0 g

SUITABLE FOR:

GLUTEN-FREE, NUT-FREE, LOW-CHOLESTEROL, DAIRY PRODUCE-FREE AND DIABETIC DIETS.

1.1 kg (2½ lb) asparagus

3 tbsp oil

4 large shallots, peeled and finely chopped

200 g (7 oz) leeks, trimmed, cleaned and finely chopped

salt and freshly ground black pepper

chervil sprigs, to garnish

ICED ASPARAGUS AND SHALLOT SOUP

SERVES 6 • PREPARATION: 15 MINUTES, PLUS CHILLING • COOKING TIME: 35 MINUTES

1 Using a sharp knife, trim the tough stalk ends of the asparagus and remove the bitter outer bracts (this will yield around 700 g (1½ lb)). Cut the tips off the asparagus and set aside. Thinly pare the stalks with a vegetable parer and chop into 2.5 cm (1 inch) pieces.

2 Heat the oil in a large saucepan, add the shallots and cook gently for 2–3 minutes. Add the leeks and continue to cook for about 10 minutes, until soft. Add the chopped asparagus and 900 ml (1½ pints) water; season and bring to the boil.

3 Simmer gently, uncovered, for 10–20 minutes or until the asparagus is very soft. Cool a little.

4 Pour the soup into a food processor or blender and process until very smooth. If using a food processor, push through a fine sieve (see Note).

5 Halve the reserved asparagus tips lengthways if they are large and cook in boiling, salted water for 2–3 minutes or until just tender, then drain and refresh with cold water. Add the asparagus tips to the soup, cover and chill for at least 4 hours, preferably overnight.

6 Mix approximately 450–600 ml (¾–1 pint) iced water into the soup; season well. Serve in chilled soup bowls, garnished with chervil.

NOTE: The easiest way to push the asparagus purée through a sieve is with the base of a ladle.

NUTRITIONAL ANALYSIS (per portion)	
Energy	95 cals
Protein	6.0 g
Carbohydrate	5.5 g
(of which sugars)	5.0 g
Fat	7.0 g
(of which saturates)	1.0 g
Fibre	4.0 g

SUITABLE FOR:

GLUTEN-FREE, NUT-FREE, LOW-CHOLESTEROL, LOW-CALORIE, DAIRY PRODUCE-FREE AND DIABETIC DIETS.

250 g (9 oz) cooked
beetroot, roughly
chopped

3 sharp eating apples,
peeled, cored and
quartered

5 tbsp creamed
horseradish

425 ml (14 fl oz) can beef
consommé

300 ml (½ pint) vegetable
stock

2 tbsp lemon juice, plus 2
tsp

salt and freshly ground
black pepper

4 tbsp crème fraîche

crushed ice cubes

50 g (2 oz) cucumber,
diced

2 tbsp chopped fresh
chives

ICED BEETROOT SOUP

SERVES 4 • PREPARATION: 20 MINUTES, PLUS CHILLING

1 In a blender, process the beetroot and two of the apples in batches to form a smooth purée. Add 3 tbsp horseradish, the consommé and stock, then process again. Add 2 tbsp lemon juice and season well. Chill for at least 1 hour.

2 Mix the crème fraîche with the remaining creamed horseradish. Dice the remaining apple and mix with 2 tsp lemon juice.

3 To serve, ladle the chilled soup into chilled glasses or soup bowls, garnish with a little crushed ice, the crème fraîche mixture, cucumber, apple and chives.

NUTRITIONAL ANALYSIS (per portion)	
Energy	110 cals
Protein	4.0 g
Carbohydrate	20.0 g
(of which sugars)	17.0 g
Fat	5.0 g
(of which saturates)	2.0 g
Fibre	2.5 g

SUITABLE FOR:
LOW-FAT, NUT-FREE,
LOW-CHOLESTEROL, LOW-
CALORIE AND DIABETIC DIETS.

fish and shellfish

50 g (2 oz) couscous

salt and freshly ground black pepper

75 g (3 oz) pecorino or Parmesan cheese, grated

4 long, skinless cod fillets, each about 175 g (6 oz)

plain flour

1 large egg, beaten

a little oil for frying

COD WITH PECORINO CRUST

SERVES 4 • PREPARATION: 30 MINUTES, PLUS STANDING AND CHILLING • COOKING TIME: 15 MINUTES

1 Soak the couscous in 75 ml (3 fl oz) boiling water for 10–15 minutes or until the liquid is absorbed. Season with salt and pepper, then spread on a tray; leave uncovered for 15 minutes to dry out a little. Place the couscous in a bowl and stir in the cheese.

2 Season the fish. Dip each fillet in flour, beaten egg, then the couscous mixture. Twist each fillet, as if into a knot, and place on a baking sheet. Cover lightly and chill for 1 hour.

3 Grease a grill pan and place the fish under a moderately hot grill for 12–14 minutes or until cooked through.

NUTRITIONAL ANALYSIS (per portion)	
Energy	300 cals
Protein	42.5 g
Carbohydrate	10.0 g
(of which sugars)	0.1 g
Fat	9.0 g
(of which saturates)	4.5 g
Fibre	0.2 g

SUITABLE FOR:
LOW-CALORIE AND DIABETIC DIETS.

---

1 tbsp hoisin sauce

4 tbsp light soy sauce

4 tbsp dry vermouth

4 tbsp orange juice

½ tsp Chinese five-spice powder

½ tsp ground cumin

1 garlic clove, peeled and crushed

4 thick cod fillets or steaks, each about 150 g (5 oz)

2 bulbs fennel, about 700 g (1½ lb)

1 tbsp vegetable oil

2 tsp sesame seeds

fennel tops, to garnish

COD STEAKS WITH FENNEL

SERVES 4 • PREPARATION: 10 MINUTES, PLUS MARINATING • COOKING TIME: 30 MINUTES

1 To make the marinade, combine the first 7 ingredients. Place the cod in a shallow, non-metallic dish and pour over the marinade. Cover and leave in a cool place for at least 1 hour.

2 Thinly slice the fennel, reserving the tops. Remove the fish, reserving the marinade and place under a hot grill, or on a lightly oiled hot griddle, for 4 minutes, then turn over and cook for 3–4 minutes or until cooked.

3 Heat the oil in a sauté pan and cook the fennel briskly for 5–7 minutes or until brown and beginning to soften. Add the marinade, bring to the boil and bubble until reduced and sticky. Place the fish on a bed of fennel, spoon round any pan juices and sprinkle over the sesame seeds. Garnish with fennel tops.

NUTRITIONAL ANALYSIS (per portion)	
Energy	175 cals
Protein	29.0 g
Carbohydrate	5.0 g
(of which sugars)	5.0 g
Fat	4.0 g
(of which saturates)	0.5 g
Fibre	3.0 g

SUITABLE FOR:
GLUTEN-FREE, LOW-FAT, NUT-FREE, LOW-CHOLESTEROL, LOW-CALORIE, DAIRY PRODUCE-FREE AND DIABETIC DIETS.

2 tsp ground cumin

4 tbsp olive oil

6 thick cod fillets, each about 150 g (5 oz)

coarse sea salt

crushed mixed peppercorns

coriander, to garnish

BEAN SALSA
1 avocado

396 g can borlotti beans or 420 g can pinto beans, drained and rinsed

225 g (8 oz) plum tomatoes, skinned, deseeded and diced

1 small red onion, peeled and very finely chopped

4 tbsp chopped fresh coriander

grated rind of 1 lime and juice of 2

salt and freshly ground black pepper

3 tbsp olive oil

SPICY COD WITH BEAN SALSA

SERVES 6 • PREPARATION: 20 MINUTES, PLUS CHILLING • COOKING TIME: 15 MINUTES

1 Mix the cumin and oil together in a small bowl, then brush over the cod fillets. Cover and set aside in a cool place.

2 To make the salsa, halve the avocado and remove the stone, then peel and dice the flesh. Place the avocado in a bowl, add the remaining ingredients, seasoning with salt and pepper, and mix together. Cover and chill.

3 Preheat the grill with the grill pan in place. Grind sea salt and crushed peppercorns over the cod fillets and grill on one side only for approximately 10–12 minutes or until cooked through to the centre (see Note).

4 Serve the grilled cod with the bean salsa, garnished with coriander sprigs.

NUTRITIONAL ANALYSIS	
(per portion)	
Energy	315 cals
Protein	33.5 g
Carbohydrate	12.0 g
(of which sugars)	3.0 g
Fat	20.0 g
(of which saturates)	3.0 g
Fibre	5.0 g

SUITABLE FOR:
GLUTEN-FREE, NUT-FREE, LOW-CALORIE, DAIRY PRODUCE-FREE AND DIABETIC DIETS.

NOTE: The cooking time of the cod will depend on the thickness of the individual fillets, not on the total weight.

1 red chilli, deseeded and finely chopped

2 tsp dark soy sauce

grated rind and juice of 1 lime

¼ tsp ground allspice or 6 allspice berries, crushed (see Note)

50 g (2 oz) light soft brown (muscovado) sugar

4 thick cod fillets, with skin, each about 175 g (6 oz)

lime wedges, to garnish

GRILLED COD WITH SWEET CHILLI GLAZE

SERVES 4 • PREPARATION: 10 MINUTES • COOKING TIME: 5 MINUTES

1 Stir the chilli, soy sauce, lime rind and juice, allspice and sugar together.

2 Grill the cod for about 1 minute on the flesh side. Turn skin-side up and grill for 1 minute. Remove from the heat and spoon the chilli glaze over. Return to the grill for a further 2–3 minutes until the skin is crisp and golden. Garnish with lime wedges and serve at once.

NUTRITIONAL ANALYSIS (per portion)	
Energy	190 cals
Protein	32.0 g
Carbohydrate	13.0 g
(of which sugars)	13.0 g
Fat	1.0 g
(of which saturates)	0.2 g
Fibre	0.0 g

SUITABLE FOR:
GLUTEN-FREE, LOW-FAT, NUT-FREE, LOW-CHOLESTEROL, LOW-CALORIE, DAIRY PRODUCE-FREE AND DIABETIC DIETS.

4 thick cod fillets, each about 175 g (6 oz)

grated rind of 1 lime

1 tbsp chilli oil

coriander sprigs, to serve

STIR-FRIED VEGETABLES

1 tbsp sesame oil

1 red chilli, deseeded and finely chopped

2 garlic cloves, peeled and chopped

8 spring onions, trimmed and finely sliced

125 g (4 oz) shiitake mushrooms, sliced

225 g (8 oz) carrots, peeled and cut into fine strips

300 g (10 oz) pak choi, roughly chopped

2 tbsp soy sauce

MARINATED COD WITH STIR-FRIED VEGETABLES

SERVES 4 • PREPARATION: 20 MINUTES, PLUS MARINATING • COOKING TIME: ABOUT 6 MINUTES

1 Put the cod fillets into a shallow, non-metallic dish. Mix the lime rind with the chilli oil and rub over the fillets. Cover and marinate in a cool place for 30 minutes.

2 Heat the sesame oil in a large frying pan, add the chilli, garlic, spring onions, mushrooms and carrots and stir-fry for 2–3 minutes or until the vegetables are beginning to soften. Add the pak choi and stir-fry for a further 1–2 minutes. Add the soy sauce and cook for a further minute. Adjust the seasoning and set aside.

3 To cook the fish, place the cod fillets under a moderately hot grill for 2–3 minutes, turn and cook for another 2–3 minutes, or until the fish is cooked through; the flesh should be opaque and feel firm to the touch.

4 Transfer the fish to 4 individual serving plates, pile the stir-fried vegetables on top and garnish with coriander sprigs. Serve at once.

NUTRITIONAL ANALYSIS (per portion)	
Energy	235 cals
Protein	35.0 g
Carbohydrate	7.5 g
(of which sugars)	7.0 g
Fat	7.5 g
(of which saturates)	1.0 g
Fibre	3.5 g

SUITABLE FOR:
GLUTEN-FREE, NUT-FREE, LOW-CHOLESTEROL, LOW-CALORIE, DAIRY PRODUCE-FREE AND DIABETIC DIETS.

Right: Marinated Cod with Stir-fried Vegetables

225 g (8 oz) shallots

50 g (2 oz) butter

1 tsp caster sugar

350 g (12 oz) young leeks, trimmed and finely sliced on the diagonal

salt and freshly ground black pepper

4 fish fillets, such as plaice, each about 125 g (4 oz), skinned

2 tbsp oil

100 ml (3½ fl oz) medium dry white wine

300 ml (½ pint) fish stock

125 g (4 oz) cherry tomatoes, halved or quartered

75 g (3 oz) stoned black olives

flat-leaf parsley and slices of lemon, to garnish

NOTE: Keep the heat high under the frying pan so the juices don't escape from the fish.

PROVENÇAL FISH FILLETS

SERVES 4 • PREPARATION: 20 MINUTES • COOKING TIME: 30 MINUTES

1 Place the shallots in a pan of water, bring to the boil and cook for 5 minutes. Drain and plunge into cold water. Trim the ends, peel off the skins and dry well.

2 Heat 25 g (1 oz) butter in a frying pan, add the shallots and sugar and cook over a low heat for 5 minutes or until golden. Add the leeks and cook for 4-5 minutes until just soft. Set aside.

3 Season the fish with salt and ground black pepper. Heat the oil and remaining butter in the pan. Fry the fish for 3 minutes on each side or until golden (see Note). Remove from the pan with a slotted spoon and keep warm.

4 Pour the wine into the pan, bring to the boil and bubble until the liquid is reduced by half. Add the stock, return to the boil and bubble for 10 minutes or until syrupy. Add the tomatoes and olives and bubble for 1 minute, then return the shallots and leeks to the pan to warm through; season. Garnish with parsley and slices of lemon and serve.

NUTRITIONAL ANALYSIS (per portion)	
Energy	300 cals
Protein	22.0 g
Carbohydrate	9.5 g
(of which sugars)	7.5 g
Fat	20.0 g
(of which saturates)	7.0 g
Fibre	4.0 g

SUITABLE FOR:
GLUTEN-FREE, NUT-FREE, LOW-CALORIE AND DIABETIC DIETS.

White fish... a plus for slimmers

White fish, like plaice and haddock, is almost fat-free. A 100 g (3½ oz) portion contains less than 1 g fat and only 81 cals. It is a good source of B12, and contains iodine and selenium.

---

8 plaice fillets, about 550 g (1¼ lb)

5 tbsp tapenade (black olive paste)

150 ml (¼ pint) dry white wine

fried garlic slices and fresh basil leaves, to garnish

DRESSING

4 tbsp olive oil

rind of ½ lemon

4 tbsp lemon juice

2 tbsp capers

salt and freshly ground black pepper

1 large or 2 small tomatoes, deseeded and diced

25 g (1 oz) stoned black olives, finely sliced

PLAICE WITH TOMATO AND CAPER DRESSING

SERVES 4 • PREPARATION: 15 MINUTES • COOKING TIME: 10 MINUTES

1 Skin the plaice, if necessary, then spread the tapenade over the smoother side and roll up.

2 Place the fish in a small, flameproof casserole and pour the wine around it. Bring gently to the boil, cover, reduce the heat and simmer for 8–10 minutes until just cooked. Using a slotted spoon, remove the fish and place in a warmed serving dish. Reserve the cooking liquor.

3 To make the dressing, whisk 4 tbsp of the reserved cooking liquor with the oil, lemon rind and juice, capers and salt and pepper to taste. Add the tomatoes and olives.

4 Spoon the dressing over the fish. Serve garnished with fried garlic slices and basil leaves.

NUTRITIONAL ANALYSIS (per portion)	
Energy	340 cals
Protein	25.0 g
Carbohydrate	1.0 g
(of which sugars)	1.0 g
Fat	20.0 g
(of which saturates)	3.0 g
Fibre	1.0 g

SUITABLE FOR:
GLUTEN-FREE, NUT-FREE, LOW-CHOLESTEROL, LOW-CALORIE, DAIRY PRODUCE-FREE AND DIABETIC DIETS.

75 g (3 oz) fresh breadcrumbs

250 g (9 oz) undyed smoked haddock or fresh haddock

150 ml (¼ pint) semi-skimmed milk

250 g (9 oz) potatoes

salt and freshly ground black pepper

225 g (8 oz) washed spinach

1 egg, beaten

lemon wedges, to serve

fresh chives, to garnish

CHIVE SAUCE
400 ml (12 fl oz) half-fat crème fraîche (see Note)

grated rind and juice of 1 lemon

4 tbsp chopped fresh chives

NOTE: Per 100 ml (3½ fl oz), full-fat crème fraîche has 40 g fat/380 cals; half-fat crème fraîche, 15 g fat/165 cals.

HADDOCK FISHCAKES WITH CHIVE SAUCE

MAKES 8 • PREPARATION: 30 MINUTES • COOKING TIME: 45 MINUTES

1 Lightly toast the breadcrumbs. Place the fish in a large, shallow pan, add the milk and bring to the boil. Cover and simmer for 10 minutes. Remove the fish from the pan, reserving the milk. Flake the fish flesh, discarding bones and skin; set aside.

2 Meanwhile, peel the potatoes and cut into even-sized pieces. Boil in salted water for 15–20 minutes until soft. Drain well, return to a low heat for 2–3 minutes to dry, then mash and beat in the reserved milk.

3 Cook the spinach in a pan for 2–3 minutes until just wilted. Squeeze to remove the liquid, chop, then mix with the potato and fish. Season.

4 On a lightly floured surface, shape the mixture into 8 cakes. Brush with beaten egg, then coat in breadcrumbs. Place on a non-stick baking sheet.

5 Cook at 200°C (400°F) Mark 6 for 20–25 minutes or until hot to the centre.

6 Meanwhile, make the sauce. Gently heat the crème fraîche with the lemon rind in a pan. Add the chives, seasoning and a little lemon juice.

7 Serve the fishcakes with the sauce and lemon wedges, garnished with chives.

NUTRITIONAL ANALYSIS (per portion)	
Energy	380 cals
Protein	11.5 g
Carbohydrate	16.0 g
(of which sugars)	4.0 g
Fat	28.0 g
(of which saturates)	17.0 g
Fibre	1.0 g

SUITABLE FOR:
NUT-FREE, LOW-CALORIE AND DIABETIC DIETS.

4 tbsp polenta

15 g (½ oz) melted butter

4 large plaice fillets, skin on

1-2 tbsp finely grated Parmesan cheese

25 g (1 oz) stoned black olives, finely chopped

TOMATO AND CHILLI SAUCE

450 g (1 lb) very ripe tomatoes, preferably on the vine, roughly chopped (see Note)

175 g (6 oz) shallots, peeled and finely chopped

2 garlic cloves, peeled and crushed

1 red chilli, split and deseeded

salt and freshly ground black pepper

1 tsp caster sugar or runny honey

2 tbsp chopped fresh basil

2 large tomatoes, skinned, deseeded and diced

POLENTA PLAICE WITH TOMATO AND CHILLI SAUCE

SERVES 4 • PREPARATION: 15 MINUTES • COOKING TIME: ABOUT 25 MINUTES

1 To make the tomato and chilli sauce, place the first 4 ingredients in a small saucepan and bring to the boil. Reduce the heat to a slow simmer and cook for 15–20 minutes or until the consistency of soft chutney. Remove the chilli, then sieve the mixture into a bowl. Season with salt, pepper and sugar. Stir the basil and diced tomatoes into the sauce and set aside, until at room temperature.

2 For the polenta plaice, put the polenta in a small bowl and add 2 tbsp boiling water. Soak for 2–3 minutes, until water has only just been absorbed.

3 Use half the butter to brush over the base of a heatproof dish just large enough to hold the plaice in a single layer. Lay the plaice in the dish, skin-side up. Mix the polenta with the Parmesan cheese and olives and season.

4 Grill the fish for 3 minutes or until the skin begins to bubble and turn golden. Carefully turn the fish over with a fish slice.

5 Brush the remaining melted butter over the fish and crumble over the polenta mixture.

6 Return to the grill for a further 3–4 minutes or until the topping is crisp and golden. Serve with the tomato and chilli sauce.

NUTRITIONAL ANALYSIS (per portion)	
Energy	275 cals
Protein	29.0 g
Carbohydrate	21.0 g
(of which sugars)	9.0 g
Fat	8.0 g
(of which saturates)	3.0 g
Fibre	3.0 g

SUITABLE FOR:

GLUTEN-FREE, NUT-FREE, LOW-CALORIE AND DIABETIC DIETS.

NOTE: It's vital to use very soft ripe tomatoes in this recipe, to ensure enough flavour and natural juice for the finished sauce.

---

2 tbsp chopped fresh coriander

1 tbsp chopped fresh parsley

3 garlic cloves, peeled and crushed

1 tsp salt

1 tsp ground cumin

2 tsp ground paprika

pinch of cayenne pepper

1 tsp harissa or chilli sauce

50 ml (2 fl oz) olive oil

2 tbsp lemon juice

pinch of saffron strands

4 haddock, cod or turbot fillets, about 700 g (1½ lb)

lemon wedges and flat-leaf parsley, to garnish

AFRICAN SPICED FISH FILLETS

SERVES 4 • PREPARATION: 5 MINUTES, PLUS MARINATING • COOKING TIME: 6 MINUTES

1 Mix together all the ingredients except the fish. Place the fish in a non-metallic dish and pour the marinade over. Cover and leave in a cool place for 1 hour.

2 Place the fish on a foil-lined baking sheet and cook under a hot grill for 5–6 minutes or until golden and firm to touch.

3 Garnish with the lemon wedges and the flat-leaf parsley and serve immediately.

NUTRITIONAL ANALYSIS (per portion)	
Energy	220 cals
Protein	33.5 g
Carbohydrate	0.4 g
(of which sugars)	0.0 g
Fat	10.0 g
(of which saturates)	1.5 g
Fibre	0.0 g

SUITABLE FOR:

GLUTEN-FREE, NUT-FREE, LOW-CHOLESTEROL, LOW-CALORIE, DAIRY PRODUCE-FREE AND DIABETIC DIETS.

1 tbsp sunflower oil

125 g (4 oz) oyster mushrooms, finely sliced

4 spring onions, trimmed and finely sliced

grated rind and juice of 1 lime

salt and freshly ground black pepper

4 double fillets of lemon sole, each about 175 g (6 oz), skinned

4 sprigs tarragon, lightly crushed with a rolling pin

lime wedges, to serve

TARRAGON SOLE PARCELS

SERVES 4 • PREPARATION: 15 MINUTES • COOKING TIME: 15 MINUTES

1 Using non-stick baking parchment, cut out 4 circles, 30 cm (12 inches) in diameter. Fold each circle in half and set aside.

2 Heat the oil in a pan, add the mushrooms and sauté over a low heat for 3 minutes. Add the spring onions and continue to cook for 1 minute. Transfer to a bowl and stir in the lime rind. Season with salt and pepper and leave to cool completely.

3 Heat 2 baking sheets in the oven at 220°C (425°F) Mark 7 for 5 minutes.

4 Arrange the fish fillets, skinned-side uppermost, on a chopping board. Divide the cool mushroom mixture between the fillets. Fold each fillet in half and place on one side of the paper circle. Sprinkle with the lime juice and arrange a tarragon sprig on each fish. Season lightly.

5 Fold the free half of the paper circle over the fish to make a semi-circular parcel. Fold the edges of the paper over, twisting and pinching hard to seal. Place on the heated baking sheets, spacing them a little, and cook in the oven for 10 minutes.

6 Serve immediately with lime wedges.

NUTRITIONAL ANALYSIS
(per portion)

Energy	170 cals
Protein	30.5 g
Carbohydrate	0.3 g
(of which sugars)	0.3 g
Fat	5.0 g
(of which saturates)	0.7 g
Fibre	0.2 g

SUITABLE FOR:
GLUTEN-FREE, LOW-FAT, NUT-FREE, LOW-CHOLESTEROL, LOW-CALORIE, DAIRY PRODUCE-FREE AND DIABETIC DIETS.

Fish... full of goodness

As well as providing protein essential for the maintenance and repair of body cells, fish provides B vitamins and a wide variety of essential minerals. It is also one of the richest sources of iodine.

2 lemon sole, each about 350 g (12 oz), de-scaled

6 tbsp olive oil, plus extra for brushing

salt and freshly ground black pepper

finely grated rind of 2 lemons and 4 tsp lemon juice

100 g (3½ oz) olive or sun-dried tomato ciabatta crumbs

finely grated rind of 2 limes

75 g (3 oz) stoned black olives, roughly chopped

lemon and lime wedges and flowering thyme, to garnish

OLIVE-CRUSTED SOLE

SERVES 4 • PREPARATION: 35 MINUTES • COOKING TIME: 15 MINUTES

1 Slit each sole along the backbone on the white-skinned side. Ease the flesh back to make a pocket.

2 Line a baking sheet with foil and brush with oil. Place the sole on the baking sheet, cut sides uppermost. Season the fish with salt and pepper and sprinkle with the lemon juice.

3 Mix the ciabatta crumbs with 2 tbsp oil, the lemon and lime rinds and olives; season. Spoon the crumbs into the fish pockets.

4 Drizzle with the remaining oil and cook at 200°C (400°F) Mark 6 for 10–15 minutes, depending on the thickness of the sole. Serve, garnished with lemon and lime wedges and flowering thyme.

NUTRITIONAL ANALYSIS
(per portion)

Energy	520 cals
Protein	63.0 g
Carbohydrate	19.0 g
(of which sugars)	0.6 g
Fat	24.0 g
(of which saturates)	3.0 g
Fibre	1.1 g

SUITABLE FOR:

NUT-FREE, LOW-CHOLESTEROL, DAIRY PRODUCE-FREE AND DIABETIC DIETS.

---

4 halibut steaks, each about 175 g (6 oz)

1 tbsp olive oil

juice of ½ a lemon

salt and white pepper

rocket leaves, to garnish

DRESSING

½ garlic clove, peeled and crushed

1 green chilli, deseeded and finely chopped

1 red chilli, deseeded and finely chopped

450 g (1 lb) tomatoes, skinned, deseeded and chopped

1 tbsp rice wine vinegar

1 tsp light brown (muscovado) sugar

4-5 tbsp olive oil

GRILLED HALIBUT WITH HOT TOMATO DRESSING

SERVES 4 • PREPARATION: 15 MINUTES • COOKING TIME: 6 MINUTES

1 To make the dressing, put the garlic, chillies and tomatoes in a blender or food processor. Pulse for 20 seconds or until chopped. Add the vinegar and sugar and continue to pulse for a further 5 seconds. With the motor running, gradually add the olive oil. Season to taste with salt and pepper.

2 Place the halibut steaks on a lightly oiled baking sheet. Mix the olive oil and lemon together, season with salt and pepper, then brush over the fish. Grill for 2–3 minutes on each side.

3 Arrange the cooked fish on 4 individual serving plates and spoon a little dressing over the top. Serve garnished with rocket.

NUTRITIONAL ANALYSIS
(per portion)

Energy	310 cals
Protein	32.0 g
Carbohydrate	4.5 g
(of which sugars)	4.5 g
Fat	18.0 g
(of which saturates)	2.5 g
Fibre	1.0 g

SUITABLE FOR:

GLUTEN-FREE, NUT-FREE, LOW-CHOLESTEROL, LOW-CALORIE, DAIRY PRODUCE-FREE AND DIABETIC DIETS.

175 g (6 oz) large spinach leaves

2 tbsp white wine

1 tbsp lemon juice

2 shallots, peeled and finely chopped

4 monkfish fillets, each about 175 g (6 oz), trimmed

salt and freshly ground black pepper

VINAIGRETTE

3 tbsp chopped fresh mixed herbs, such as dill, tarragon and parsley

2 tsp Dijon mustard

1 tbsp sherry or white wine vinegar

3 tbsp sunflower oil

STEAMED MONKFISH WRAPPED IN SPINACH

SERVES 4 • PREPARATION: 30 MINUTES • COOKING TIME: 20 MINUTES

1 Blanch the spinach in a saucepan of boiling water for 30 seconds. Drain and refresh under running cold water, then pat dry on kitchen paper.

2 Put the wine, lemon juice and shallots in a small pan and cook over a very low heat for 3–4 minutes or until tender and liquid has evaporated. Cool.

3 With a sharp knife, cut out the tough stalks from the spinach. Arrange 3–4 leaves on a chopping board, so that they overlap. Put a spoonful of the cold shallot mixture across the leaves and place a monkfish fillet on top. Wrap the leaves around the monkfish. Repeat with the remaining fish fillets.

4 Arrange the fish on a steamer above simmering water. Lightly season with salt and pepper. Cover the pan with a tight-fitting lid and steam for 12–15 minutes or until the fish is opaque and feels firm.

5 Meanwhile, make the vinaigrette. Whisk the ingredients together; season to taste.

6 Lift the fish from the steamer and pat dry. Arrange on 4 individual serving plates, spoon the vinaigrette around the fish and serve immediately.

NUTRITIONAL ANALYSIS	
(per portion)	
Energy	220 cals
Protein	29.0 g
Carbohydrate	2.5 g
(of which sugars)	2 .0 g
Fat	9.5 g
(of which saturates)	1.5 g
Fibre	1.0 g

SUITABLE FOR:

GLUTEN-FREE, NUT-FREE, LOW-CHOLESTEROL, LOW-CALORIE, DAIRY PRODUCE-FREE AND DIABETIC DIETS.

225 g (8 oz) Japanese soba noodles (buckwheat noodles)

salt and freshly ground black pepper

8 spring onions, trimmed and finely sliced

225 g (8 oz) mangetout, trimmed and halved

4 seabass or cod fillets, each about 175 g (6 oz), skin on

1 tbsp chilli oil

coriander sprigs, to garnish

soy sauce, to serve

DRESSING
1 tbsp sesame oil

½ tsp wasabi paste

1 red chilli, deseeded and finely chopped

2 tsp pickled ginger, chopped

2 tbsp dark soy sauce

3 tbsp rice wine vinegar

JAPANESE NOODLES WITH GRILLED SEABASS

SERVES 4 • PREPARATION: 15 MINUTES, PLUS MARINATING • COOKING TIME: 15 MINUTES

1 Cook the soba noodles in boiling salted water for 6–7 minutes, then drain and tip into a large bowl.

2 Blanch the spring onions and mangetout in plenty of boiling water, then drain and refresh by running under cold water. Toss the cooled vegetables into the noodles. Whisk the dressing ingredients together, seasoning to taste with salt and pepper, and add to the noodles. Cover and leave to marinate for 15 minutes.

3 Slash the skin of the seabass fillets and brush with the chilli oil. Grill the fish for 3 minutes on each side until cooked through.

4 Divide the noodle salad between 4 individual serving plates and arrange the seabass fillets on top. Garnish with coriander and serve, handing soy sauce separately.

NUTRITIONAL ANALYSIS (per portion)	
Energy	470 cals
Protein	43.0 g
Carbohydrate	44.0 g
(of which sugars)	4.0 g
Fat	15.0 g
(of which saturates)	1.5 g
Fibre	3.0 g

SUITABLE FOR:
GLUTEN-FREE, NUT-FREE, LOW-CHOLESTEROL, LOW-CALORIE, DAIRY PRODUCE-FREE AND DIABETIC DIETS.

---

450 g (1 lb) small mackerel or sardines, filleted

lemon wedges, to serve

SPICE MARINADE
50 ml (2 fl oz) olive oil

4 tbsp lemon juice

3 garlic cloves, peeled and crushed

1 tsp cayenne pepper

1 tsp garam marsala

1 tsp ground coriander

1 tsp ground cumin

2 tsp ground paprika

3 tbsp finely chopped fresh coriander

salt and freshly ground black pepper

SPICED MACKEREL

SERVES 4 • PREPARATION: 5 MINUTES, PLUS MARINATING • COOKING TIME: 10 MINUTES

1 To make the marinade, put the olive oil and lemon juice in a bowl and mix in the garlic, cayenne pepper, garam marsala, ground coriander, cumin, paprika and fresh coriander. Season with plenty of salt and ground black pepper.

2 Open out the fish and press along the backbone to flatten. Coat the fish with the spice mixture, then cover and leave for 1 hour.

3 Grill the fish for 8–10 minutes or until cooked and crisp. Garnish the mackerel with lemon wedges and serve.

NUTRITIONAL ANALYSIS (per portion)	
Energy	328 cals
Protein	21.0 g
Carbohydrate	0.0 g
(of which sugars)	0.0 g
Fat	27.0 g
(of which saturates)	5.0 g
Fibre	0.0 g

SUITABLE FOR:
GLUTEN-FREE, NUT-FREE, LOW-CHOLESTEROL, LOW-CALORIE, DAIRY PRODUCE-FREE AND DIABETIC DIETS.

Oily fish... the healthy choice

Oily fish, such as sardines, mackerel and trout, should be eaten at least twice a week. They contain essential omega-3 fatty acids, thought to provide protection against heart disease. They are also one of the few dietary sources of vitamin D, vital for calcium absorption, and offer an excellent source of iodine, needed for normal growth.

HERB AND OAT HERRINGS

SERVES 4 • PREPARATION: 25 MINUTES • COOKING TIME: 5 MINUTES

4 tbsp pinhead oatmeal

1 tbsp chopped fresh parsley

1 tbsp chopped fresh chives

1 tbsp chopped fresh mint

salt

large pinch of cayenne pepper

4 filleted herrings, each about 150 g (5 oz)

1 tbsp olive oil

juice of ½ lemon

lemon wedges, to serve

1 Place the oatmeal, parsley, chives and mint in a bowl and mix together. Season lightly with salt and cayenne pepper.

2 Open out the fish and press along the backbone to flatten. Line the grill pan with foil and place the fish, flesh-side up, on the grill rack. Mix the olive oil and lemon juice together and brush over the fish.

3 Sprinkle the oatmeal mixture evenly over the herrings. Pat down lightly and grill for 5–6 minutes until the topping is golden and the fish cooked through. Serve at once with lemon wedges.

NUTRITIONAL ANALYSIS (per portion)	
Energy	370 cals
Protein	28.0 g
Carbohydrate	11.5 g
(of which sugars)	0.0 g
Fat	24.0 g
(of which saturates)	5.0 g
Fibre	1.0 g

SUITABLE FOR:

NUT-FREE, LOW-CHOLESTEROL, LOW-CALORIE, DAIRY PRODUCE-FREE AND DIABETIC DIETS.

2-3 tbsp olive oil

2 red onions, about 300 g (10 oz), peeled, halved and cut into petals

2 garlic cloves, peeled and crushed

2 red peppers, about 350 g (12 oz), halved, deseeded and cut into chunks

225 g (8 oz) courgettes, trimmed and cut into small chunks

salt and freshly ground black pepper

900 g (2 lb) sardines (about 16), cleaned

olive oil and lemon juice, to drizzle

small basil sprigs, to garnish

GRILLED SARDINES WITH MEDITERRANEAN VEGETABLES

SERVES 4 • PREPARATION: 15 MINUTES • COOKING TIME: 20 MINUTES

1 Heat the oil in a large non-stick frying pan, add the onions and fry for 2–3 minutes or until almost soft. Add the garlic and peppers and stir-fry for 5 minutes, then add the courgettes and stir-fry for 4–5 minutes or until almost soft. Keep warm.

2 Season the sardines and cook under a hot grill for 3–4 minutes on each side, or until cooked in the centre (see Note).

3 Drizzle the sardines with a little oil and lemon juice. Garnish with basil and serve with the vegetables.

NUTRITIONAL ANALYSIS (per portion)	
Energy	510 cals
Protein	44.0 g
Carbohydrate	13.0 g
(of which sugars)	11.0 g
Fat	30.0 g
(of which saturates)	7.5 g
Fibre	3.0 g

SUITABLE FOR:
GLUTEN-FREE, NUT-FREE, LOW-CHOLESTEROL, DAIRY PRODUCE-FREE AND DIABETIC DIETS.

NOTE: Sardines are also good barbecued, and Mediterranean flavours set them off to perfection.

150 g (5 oz) creamed coconut, crumbled

2 tsp cumin seeds

2 large red chillies, deseeded and roughly chopped

4 garlic cloves, peeled

salt and freshly ground black pepper

2 tbsp lemon juice

4 tbsp chopped fresh coriander

2 tbsp chopped fresh flat-leaf parsley

1 tbsp chopped fresh chives

6 salmon steaks, each about 225 g (8 oz), or a 900 g (2 lb) salmon tail joint

oil, for brushing

1 stick lemon grass, thinly sliced

banana leaves, to serve (optional)

lime halves, to serve

coriander sprigs, to garnish

NOTE: If barbecuing a salmon joint, use a barbecue fish grill to help you turn the salmon as it cooks.

SALMON WITH CORIANDER AND COCONUT

SERVES 6 • PREPARATION: 15 MINUTES • COOKING TIME: 10 MINUTES

1 Place the crumbled creamed coconut in a measuring jug and add 300 ml (½ pint) boiling water. Stir until evenly combined.

2 Place the cumin seeds in a small saucepan and cook for 10 seconds or until they turn a nutty brown colour. Place the cumin in a blender or food processor with half the chopped chillies, plus the garlic and ½ tsp salt. Blend for 1 minute. Add the lemon juice, chopped herbs and coconut milk. Work to a smooth paste.

3 Season the salmon steaks or joint with salt and pepper and brush lightly with oil.

4 Scatter the salmon with the remaining chilli and lemon grass, then cook under a hot grill or on a barbecue (see Note), allowing 4–5 minutes each side for steaks and 10 minutes each side for a joint, until just cooked through.

5 Warm the coriander and coconut sauce in a small pan or flameproof dish. Serve warm with the salmon, wrapped in banana leaves, if using, with limes to squeeze over. Garnish with coriander.

NUTRITIONAL ANALYSIS (per portion)	
Energy	579 cals
Protein	46.0 g
Carbohydrate	2.0 g
(of which sugars)	1.5 g
Fat	44.5 g
(of which saturates)	20.0 g
Fibre	0.0 g

SUITABLE FOR:
GLUTEN-FREE, NUT-FREE, DAIRY PRODUCE-FREE AND DIABETIC DIETS.

Right: Salmon with Coriander and Coconut

grated rind and juice of
2-3 large lemons

50 g (2 oz) couscous

salt and freshly ground
black pepper

4 skinless, boneless
salmon fillets, each about
175 g (6 oz)

25 g (1 oz) plain flour

1 egg, beaten

175 g (6 oz) stoned mixed
olives

2 anchovy fillets

5 tbsp olive oil

1 tbsp capers or caper
berries

2 tbsp chopped fresh flat-
leaf parsley

1 garlic clove, peeled and
sliced

450 g (1 lb) tomatoes,
preferably plum, chopped

grated lemon rind, to
garnish

COUSCOUS SALMON

*SERVES 4 • PREPARATION: ABOUT 1 HOUR,
PLUS CHILLING • COOKING TIME: 15 MINUTES*

1 Reserve 1 tbsp lemon juice, then make the rest
up to 175 ml (6 fl oz) by adding boiling water. Pour
over the couscous, then leave for 15 minutes or
until the grains have absorbed the liquid.

2 Stir in the lemon rind and season well. Spread
the couscous on a tray and place in a warm place
for about 20 minutes to dry out a little.

3 Season the salmon and dip each fillet into the
flour, then beaten egg and finally the couscous
mixture. Cover lightly; chill for 1 hour or overnight.

4 Place the olives, anchovies, 2 tbsp oil and the
reserved lemon juice in a food processor; blend
for about 5 seconds. Spoon the mixture into a
bowl, add capers, parsley and garlic; set aside.

5 Drizzle the tomatoes with 1 tbsp olive oil and
season well. Heat the remaining oil in a non-stick
frying pan, then fry the salmon for 4 minutes on
each side or until golden. Keep warm.

6 Fry the tomatoes, in the oil clinging to them, for
1–2 minutes. Add the olive mixture and warm for 1
minute. Serve with the salmon, garnished.

NUTRITIONAL ANALYSIS	
(per portion)	
Energy	580 cals
Protein	37.0 g
Carbohydrate	15.0 g
(of which sugars)	3.5 g
Fat	42.0 g
(of which saturates)	7.0 g
Fibre	2.5 g

SUITABLE FOR:
NUT-FREE, LOW-CHOLESTEROL,
DAIRY PRODUCE-FREE AND
DIABETIC DIETS.

*NOTE: The lemon
couscous forms a crispy
coating and helps keep
the salmon moist. The
coated fillets can be
stored in the freezer then
cooked from frozen for a
speedy supper.*

700 g (1½ lb) waxy potatoes, such as Desirée or Maris Bard, peeled and cut into chunks

350 g (12 oz) cooked salmon fillet, skinned

50 g (2 oz) smoked salmon trimmings, chopped

1 egg, beaten

2 tbsp chopped fresh chives

1 tbsp chopped fresh dill

salt and ground white pepper

2 tsp oil

dill sprigs, to garnish

DILL YOGURT

150 ml (¼ pint) low-fat natural yogurt

2 tbsp capers, rinsed and chopped

2 tbsp chopped fresh dill

salt and ground white pepper

SALMON ROSTI FISHCAKES

SERVES 4 • PREPARATION: 30 MINUTES • COOKING TIME: 20 MINUTES

1 To make the dill yogurt, mix the yogurt with the remaining ingredients and season to taste with salt and pepper. Chill until required.

2 Cut the potatoes into large chunks and par-boil in boiling salted water for 10–12 minutes. Drain and, when cool enough to handle, grate on the coarse side of a grater. Cool completely.

3 Place the salmon in a large bowl and break up into large flakes. Add the smoked salmon, egg chives and dill and mix well. Stir in the cold potato and season to taste with salt and pepper. Divide the mixture into 8 and shape to form cakes.

4 Heat the oil in a non-stick frying pan, add half the rosti and cook for 2–3 minutes, then turn and fry for 2–3 minutes on the other side. Drain on kitchen paper while frying the remaining rosti.

5 Serve 2 fishcakes per person, with a spoonful of the yogurt and garnished with sprigs of dill.

NUTRITIONAL ANALYSIS (per portion)	
Energy	375 cals
Protein	28.0 g
Carbohydrate	32.0 g
(of which sugars)	4.0 g
Fat	16.0 g
(of which saturates)	3.0 g
Fibre	2.0 g

SUITABLE FOR:

GLUTEN-FREE, NUT-FREE, LOW-CHOLESTEROL, LOW-CALORIE AND DIABETIC DIETS.

2.5 kg (5½ lb) whole salmon, cleaned and scaled

banana leaves, lime wedges, spring onion and carrot slices, to garnish

MARINADE

175 ml (6 fl oz) dark soy sauce

175 ml (6 fl oz) rice wine vinegar or dry sherry

6 garlic cloves, peeled and cut into wafer-thin slices

7.5 cm (3 inch) piece fresh root ginger, peeled and grated

3 tbsp runny honey

4 whole star anise, lightly crushed

ORIENTAL SALMON

SERVES 12 • PREPARATION: 20 MINUTES, PLUS MARINATING AND COOLING • COOKING TIME: 40 MINUTES

1 Clean the salmon well under cold running water. Make 3–4 diagonal slashes on either side of the fish and place it in a non-metallic dish.

2 To make the marinade, combine all the ingredients in a blender. Coat the salmon with the marinade. Cover and chill for at least 8 hours or overnight, turning occasionally.

3 Place the salmon on a large piece of foil in a roasting tin, spoon a little of the marinade over the top and loosely wrap the foil around the fish. Cook at 200°C (400°F) Mark 6 for 35–40 minutes or until the salmon is just cooked through (see Note).

4 Open the foil and place the fish under a hot grill for 6-8 minutes or until golden. Cool and chill the salmon until required.

5 Arrange the chilled salmon on a large platter on top of banana leaves. Serve, garnished with the lime wedges and spring onion and carrot slices.

NUTRITIONAL ANALYSIS (per portion)	
Energy	400 cals
Protein	43.0 g
Carbohydrate	6.0 g
(of which sugars)	5.0 g
Fat	23.0 g
(of which saturates)	4.0 g
Fibre	0.0 g

SUITABLE FOR:

GLUTEN-FREE, NUT-FREE, LOW-CHOLESTEROL, LOW-CALORIE, DAIRY PRODUCE-FREE AND DIABETIC DIETS.

NOTE: The cooking time will depend on the thickness of the fish rather than its weight – a fatter-fleshed fish will take more time than a lean one, even if they weigh the same.

4 trout, each about 375 g (13 oz), gutted and rinsed

juice of 1 lime

4 fresh dill sprigs

125 g (4 oz) red onion, peeled and finely sliced

4 bay leaves

salt and freshly ground black pepper

TARTARE YOGURT
150 ml (¼ pint) low-fat natural yogurt

1 tbsp capers, rinsed and roughly chopped

1 tbsp gherkins, rinsed and roughly chopped

1 shallot, peeled and finely chopped

1 hard-boiled egg, peeled and chopped

1 tbsp chopped fresh parsley

salt and freshly ground black pepper

WHOLE BARBECUED TROUT WITH TARTARE YOGURT

SERVES 4 • PREPARATION: 15 MINUTES • COOKING TIME: 15 MINUTES

1 Rinse the trout under cold running water. Trim off the fins and cut out the gills with a pair of scissors.

2 Place each trout on a large sheet of foil, sprinkle the lime juice, dill and red onion over each and place a bay leaf on top. Lightly season with salt and pepper. Loosely wrap the foil around each fish to form a parcel and set aside until ready to cook.

3 To make the tartare yogurt, mix the yogurt with the remaining ingredients and season to taste with salt and pepper. Transfer to a serving dish.

4 Cook the fish on the barbecue for 12–15 minutes, or heat 2 baking sheets in the oven at 220°C (425°F) Mark 7 for 5 minutes, then place the parcels on the baking sheets and cook in the oven for 12 minutes.

5 Serve either hot or cold, with the tartare yogurt.

NUTRITIONAL ANALYSIS (per portion)	
Energy	400 cals
Protein	62.0 g
Carbohydrate	6.5 g
(of which sugars)	5.5 g
Fat	13.5 g
(of which saturates)	1.0 g
Fibre	0.5 g

SUITABLE FOR:
GLUTEN-FREE, NUT-FREE, LOW-CHOLESTEROL, LOW-CALORIE AND DIABETIC DIETS.

---

2 tuna steaks, each about 200 g (7 oz)

olive oil, for basting

175 g (6 oz) thin French beans, trimmed

225 g (8 oz) tomatoes, cut into wedges

1 crisp lettuce heart, or a large handful of salad leaves, torn into pieces

1 red or mild onion, peeled and thinly sliced

½ cucumber, peeled and thinly sliced

4 hard-boiled eggs

50 g (2 oz) can anchovies, drained

handful of black olives

2 tbsp roughly torn flat-leaf parsley, to garnish

DRESSING
4 tbsp olive oil

1 tbsp white wine vinegar

1 garlic clove, peeled and crushed

salt and freshly ground black pepper

FRESH TUNA NIÇOISE

SERVES 4 • PREPARATION: 20 MINUTES • COOKING TIME: 15 MINUTES

1 Put the tuna steaks on the grill rack and brush with olive oil. Grill for about 7 minutes each side, until firm and cooked through. Cool, then cut into chunks.

2 Cook the French beans in a pan of boiling water for 2–3 minutes until barely tender. Drain and refresh under cold running water, then pat dry with a tea-towel.

3 Put all the vegetables in a large salad bowl and toss lightly to mix. Quarter the eggs and add to the salad with the tuna, anchovies and olives. Toss lightly to mix.

4 To make the dressing, place the olive oil in a small bowl and whisk in the vinegar, garlic and salt and pepper to taste. Pour over the salad and sprinkle with the torn flat-leaf parsley to garnish. Serve at once.

NUTRITIONAL ANALYSIS (per portion)	
Energy	430 cals
Protein	37.0 g
Carbohydrate	5.5 g
(of which sugars)	5.0 g
Fat	29.0 g
(of which saturates)	5.5 g
Fibre	2.5 g

SUITABLE FOR:
GLUTEN-FREE, NUT-FREE, LOW-CALORIE, DAIRY PRODUCE-FREE AND DIABETIC DIETS.

VARIATION:

In place of the fresh tuna, you could use one 200 g (7 oz) can tuna in oil, drained and flaked.

4 swordfish steaks, each about 175 g (6 oz)

olive oil, for brushing

BULGHAR WHEAT SALAD

125 g (4 oz) bulghar (cracked) wheat

grated rind and juice of 1 large lemon

4 spring onions, trimmed and finely sliced

125 g (4 oz) cherry tomatoes, halved

2 tbsp chopped fresh mint

50 g (2 oz) Kalamata olives, stoned

salt and freshly ground black pepper

GREMOLATA

2 garlic cloves

grated rind of 1 lemon

2 tbsp finely chopped fresh parsley

GREMOLATA SWORDFISH WITH LEMON AND MINT BULGHAR WHEAT

SERVES 4 • PREPARATION: 15 MINUTES •
COOKING TIME: 10 MINUTES, PLUS STANDING

1 To make the bulghar wheat salad, put the wheat in a sieve and rinse under cold running water. Transfer to a saucepan, cover with water and bring to the boil. Simmer for 3–4 minutes, then remove from the heat; stand for 15 minutes.

2 Drain the wheat well and pat dry with kitchen paper. Tip into a large bowl and add the remaining salad ingredients. Season to taste with salt and pepper, then toss together. Cover and chill.

3 To make the gremolata, blanch the garlic in boiling water for 3 minutes, then crush. Mix with the lemon rind and parsley, season to taste and set aside.

4 To cook the fish, lightly brush the swordfish steaks with olive oil, then grill for 2–3 minutes on each side, depending on thickness of the steaks.

5 To serve, divide the bulghar wheat salad between 4 individual serving plates, arrange the swordfish steaks on top and sprinkle with the gremolata. Serve immediately.

NUTRITIONAL ANALYSIS (per portion)	
Energy	344 cals
Protein	35.0 g
Carbohydrate	25.0 g
(of which sugars)	1.0 g
Fat	12.0 g
(of which saturates)	2.0 g
Fibre	1.0 g

SUITABLE FOR:

NUT-FREE, LOW-CHOLESTEROL, LOW-CALORIE, DAIRY PRODUCE-FREE AND DIABETIC DIETS.

3-4 tbsp olive oil

6 tuna steaks, each about 175 g (6 oz)

3 tbsp balsamic vinegar

450 g (1 lb) watermelon, thickly sliced

125 g (4 oz) baby spinach, prepared

125 g (4 oz) feta cheese, crumbled into large chunks

125 g (4 oz) red onion, peeled and finely chopped

75 g (3 oz) black olives, stoned and halved

crushed black pepper

TUNA WITH WATERMELON SALSA

SERVES 6 • PREPARATION: 20 MINUTES • COOKING TIME: 4 MINUTES

1 Heat 2 tbsp oil in a frying pan or griddle and, when very hot, add the tuna steaks. Fry on each side for 2 minutes (see Note). Turn the heat up and add the balsamic vinegar, then bubble until reduced by about half. Remove the tuna steaks and keep warm.

2 Arrange the watermelon slices and spinach on the serving plates, place the tuna steaks with their dressing on top and sprinkle the feta cheese, red onion and black olives over the tuna. Drizzle with the remaining olive oil and season with crushed black pepper.

NUTRITIONAL ANALYSIS (per portion)	
Energy	415 cals
Protein	46.0 g
Carbohydrate	7.0 g
(of which sugars)	7.0 g
Fat	19.5 g
(of which saturates)	6.0 g
Fibre	1.0 g

SUITABLE FOR:
GLUTEN-FREE, NUT-FREE, LOW-CALORIE AND DIABETIC DIETS.

NOTE: If you prefer your tuna medium to well done, increase the cooking time by 1 minute on each side.

---

4 red snapper fillets, each 175 g (6 oz)

1 tbsp sunflower oil

1 stick lemon grass, sliced

fresh coriander sprigs and lime wedges, to garnish

dark soy sauce, to serve

MARINADE

1 tsp ground ginger

1 tsp ground coriander

2 tsp runny honey

salt and freshly ground black pepper

1 red chilli, deseeded and chopped

1 garlic clove, peeled and crushed

2.5 cm (1 inch) piece fresh root ginger, grated

SALAD

225 g (8 oz) mangetout, trimmed

225 g (8 oz) courgettes, sliced

1 yellow pepper, deseeded and sliced

1 large bunch of spring onions, sliced

DRESSING

grated zest and juice of 2 limes

1 tbsp runny honey

1 red chilli, deseeded and finely chopped

1 tbsp Thai fish sauce

WARM THAI SNAPPER SALAD

SERVES 4 • PREPARATION: 30 MINUTES • COOKING TIME: 10 MINUTES

1 Remove any bones from the snapper fillets and set the fish aside.

2 To make the marinade, mix the ingredients together and rub over the surface of the fish. Chill until required.

3 Blanch the mangetout, courgette and yellow pepper in a saucepan of boiling salted water until just tender. Drain and refresh under cold running water, then pat dry with kitchen paper and turn into a large bowl. Add the spring onions and toss to mix well.

4 To make the dressing, mix all the ingredients together and season to taste. Tip on to the vegetables, toss together and leave to stand for 15 minutes.

5 Meanwhile, cook the fish. Mix together the oil and lemon grass and brush over the fish. Place under a moderately hot grill for 3–4 minutes until cooked through.

6 Pile the salad into the centre of 4 individual serving plates and top with fish. Garnish with coriander sprigs and lime wedges and serve hot or warm, accompanied with soy sauce.

NUTRITIONAL ANALYSIS (per portion)	
Energy	260 cals
Protein	39.0 g
Carbohydrate	15.0 g
(of which sugars)	14.0 g
Fat	6.0 g
(of which saturates)	1.0 g
Fibre	3.0 g

SUITABLE FOR:
GLUTEN-FREE, NUT-FREE, LOW-CHOLESTEROL, LOW-CALORIE, DAIRY PRODUCE-FREE AND DIABETIC DIETS.

Right: Warm Thai Snapper Salad

6 whole fish, such as red snapper, tilapia or rainbow trout, gutted, about 175-225 g (6-8 oz) each

salt and freshly ground black pepper

2 lemons, sliced

olive oil, for brushing

225 g (8 oz) packet vine leaves

lemon wedges, to serve

BARBECUED FISH WRAPPED IN VINE LEAVES

SERVES 6 • PREPARATION: 30 MINUTES • COOKING TIME: 14 MINUTES

1 Rinse the fish, pat dry and season inside with salt and pepper. Place 2-3 halved lemon slices in each cavity, then brush the fish with oil. Wrap each fish in vine leaves, tie with wet string and brush again with oil (see Note).

2 Cook the fish on a hot barbecue for 5–7 minutes on each side, depending on thickness. Serve with lemon wedges.

NUTRITIONAL ANALYSIS (per portion)	
Energy	195 cals
Protein	36.0 g
Carbohydrate	0.1 g
(of which sugars)	0.0 g
Fat	6.0 g
(of which saturates)	1.0 g
Fibre	0.0 g

SUITABLE FOR:
GLUTEN-FREE, NUT-FREE, LOW-CHOLESTEROL, LOW-CALORIE, DAIRY PRODUCE-FREE AND DIABETIC DIETS.

---

4 red mullet fillets, each about 125 g (4 oz), scaled and small bones removed

salt and freshly ground black pepper

1 tsp cumin seeds

4 tbsp olive oil

225 g (8 oz) onion, peeled, halved and cut into petals

2 garlic cloves, peeled and crushed

150 g (5 oz) couscous

50 g (2 oz) raisins

150 ml (¼ pint) orange juice

flat-leaf parsley, to garnish

SPICED RED MULLET WITH RAISIN COUSCOUS

SERVES 4 • PREPARATION: 5 MINUTES, PLUS 10 MINUTES SOAKING • COOKING TIME: 20 MINUTES

1 With a sharp knife, slash the skin side of the red mullet fillets two or three times. Season and press on the cumin seeds, then set aside.

2 Heat 2 tbsp oil in a large non-stick frying pan and fry the onion for 10 minutes or until brown and soft. Add the garlic and fry for 1 minute, then remove and set aside. Meanwhile, soak the couscous according to the packet instructions and cover.

3 Wipe out the pan and heat 2 tbsp oil. Fry the fish for about 3 minutes on each side. Remove and keep warm.

4 Add the raisins and orange juice to the pan, bring to the boil and bubble for 2–3 minutes or until lightly syrupy. Fork the onion through the soaked couscous and season. Serve the red mullet with the couscous and orange sauce, garnished with flat-leaf parsley.

NUTRITIONAL ANALYSIS (per portion)	
Energy	295 cals
Protein	10.0 g
Carbohydrate	36.0 g
(of which sugars)	15.0 g
Fat	13.0 g
(of which saturates)	1.5 g
Fibre	1.0 g

SUITABLE FOR:
NUT-FREE, LOW-CHOLESTEROL, LOW-CALORIE, DAIRY PRODUCE-FREE AND DIABETIC DIETS.

Couscous... grains of goodness

Soothing, simple and delicious, couscous is made from the dried granules of semolina flour and water. It is similar to bulghar wheat but has a lighter texture when cooked. Like all grains, couscous provides the complex carbohydrates necessary for maintaining energy levels. It also contains iron, calcium and B vitamins.

172

SEAFOOD SAFFRON PIE

SERVES 6 • PREPARATION: 45 MINUTES • COOKING TIME: 40 MINUTES

450 g (1 lb) large cooked prawns, peeled, shells reserved

1 slice of lemon

1 small onion, peeled and chopped

1 garlic clove, peeled and chopped

5 tbsp white wine

150 ml (¼ pint) skimmed milk

large pinch of saffron strands

1 tbsp sunflower oil

1 tbsp flour

225 g (8 oz) prepared squid pouches, sliced

225 g (8 oz) haddock fillet, skinned and cut into chunks

225 g (8 oz) cooked shelled mussels

3 tbsp chopped fresh coriander

salt and freshly ground black pepper

6 sheets filo pastry

1 tbsp olive oil

1 tsp sesame seeds

1 Put the prawn shells in a large saucepan with the lemon, onion, garlic, white wine and 300 ml (½ pint) water. Bring to the boil, cover and simmer for 15 minutes. Strain into a jug, discarding the shells.

2 To make the sauce, heat the milk and saffron in a pan to scalding point. Infuse for 15 minutes.

3 Mix the oil and flour together in a saucepan over a low heat and cook for 1 minute, stirring. Stir in the infused milk and reserved prawn stock. Bring to the boil, then simmer for 1 minute, stirring.

4 Add the squid and haddock to the sauce and continue to cook over a low heat for 3 minutes. Add the mussels, prawns and coriander and cook for a further minute or until very hot. Season to taste with salt and pepper. Transfer to a 30 x 18 cm (12 x 7 inch) gratin dish.

5 Brush each sheet of filo pastry with the olive oil, then crumple the pastry, to form folds, and arrange on top of the seafood. Sprinkle the top with sesame seeds. Bake at 190°C (375°F) Mark 5 for 20–25 minutes or until the filo is brown and the filling is piping hot. Serve immediately.

NUTRITIONAL ANALYSIS (per portion)	
Energy	210 cals
Protein	31.0 g
Carbohydrate	5.5 g
(of which sugars)	2.0 g
Fat	6.0 g
(of which saturates)	1.0 g
Fibre	0.5 g

SUITABLE FOR:
NUT-FREE AND LOW-CALORIE DIETS.

5 tbsp olive oil

3 garlic cloves, peeled and finely chopped

450 g (1 lb) prepared squid or octopus, sliced into rings

12-18 large raw prawns, peeled and de-veined

rind and juice of ½ lemon

2 tbsp chopped fresh flat-leaf parsley

salt and freshly ground black pepper

fresh herbs, such as thyme and basil, to garnish

SEAFOOD WITH GARLIC, PARSLEY AND LEMON

SERVES 6 • PREPARATION: 15 MINUTES • COOKING TIME: 10 MINUTES

1 Heat 4 tbsp oil in a frying pan, add the garlic and cook until slightly golden. Cook the squid quickly in batches, keeping it warm. Cook the prawns until they are just pink, then set aside with the squid; reserve any cooking juices.

2 Place the lemon rind and juice in a pan, adding any juices from the squid and prawns. Bring to the boil, then bubble for 3–4 minutes or until syrupy.

3 Return the squid and prawns to the pan with the remaining oil and parsley and toss together. Season and serve warm, garnished with herbs.

NUTRITIONAL ANALYSIS (per portion)	
Energy	195 cals
Protein	23.0 g
Carbohydrate	1.0 g
(of which sugars)	0.0 g
Fat	11.0 g
(of which saturates)	2.0 g
Fibre	0.0 g

SUITABLE FOR:

GLUTEN-FREE, NUT-FREE, LOW-CALORIE, DAIRY PRODUCE-FREE AND DIABETIC DIETS.

900 g (2 lb) live mussels

225 g (8 oz) prepared squid pouches and tentacles

900 ml (1½ pints) fish stock

75 ml (3 fl oz) Pernod

225 g (8 oz) large cooked prawns, peeled with shells reserved

2 tbsp chopped fresh parsley, stalks reserved

1 tbsp olive oil

1 fennel bulb, trimmed and finely sliced

1 tsp fennel seeds

1 tbsp finely chopped garlic

1 red chilli, deseeded and finely sliced

400 g (14 oz) can chopped plum tomatoes

400 g (14 oz) can pimientoes, drained and finely sliced

700 g (1½ lb) white fish fillets, such as cod, plaice, or orange roughy, skinned and cut into 2.5 cm (1 inch) chunks

1 tbsp chopped fresh basil

salt and freshly ground black pepper

SEAFOOD STEW WITH FENNEL

SERVES 6 • PREPARATION: 30 MINUTES • COOKING TIME: 45 MINUTES

1 Scrub the mussels and pull any 'beards' from the shells. Tap any open mussels, discarding those that do not close when you do so. Wash the mussels in 2–3 changes of clean water. Slice the squid into strips, leaving any tentacles whole.

2 Put the stock and Pernod in a large saucepan, add the prawn shells and parsley stalks and bring to the boil. Simmer for 15 minutes, then strain the stock into a clean pan; discard the shells.

3 Heat the oil in a large saucepan, add the fennel and cook over a medium heat until beginning to soften and turn golden.

4 Add the fennel seeds, garlic and chilli and cook for a further 2 minutes, stirring occasionally. Add the stock, tomatoes and pimientoes. Bring to the boil, then simmer gently for 15 minutes.

5 Add the white fish chunks and mussels to the pan and cook over a very low heat for 4 minutes. Stir in the squid and continue to cook gently for a further 1 minute. Remove and discard any mussels that have remained shut.

6 Add the prawns, chopped parsley and basil to the stew. Season to taste with salt and pepper, then cook gently for 2 minutes. Serve at once.

NUTRITIONAL ANALYSIS (per portion)	
Energy	260 cals
Protein	42.0 g
Carbohydrate	9.5 g
(of which sugars)	8.5 g
Fat	5.0 g
(of which saturates)	1.0 g
Fibre	2.0 g

SUITABLE FOR:

GLUTEN-FREE, LOW-FAT, NUT-FREE, LOW-CALORIE, DAIRY PRODUCE-FREE AND DIABETIC DIETS.

Right: Seafood Stew with Fennel

225 g (8 oz) raw king prawns, peeled and de-veined

550 g (1¼ lb) monkfish fillet, cut into 2.5 cm (1 inch) cubes

juice of ½ lime

1 garlic clove, peeled and crushed

2 tbsp chilli oil

2 tbsp teriyaki sauce

2 limes and 1 lemon, each cut into 8 wedges

sliced green chilli, spring onion curls and flat-leaf parsley, to garnish

SEAFOOD AND LIME KEBABS

SERVES 4 • PREPARATION: 25 MINUTES, PLUS MARINATING • COOKING TIME: 6 MINUTES

1 Place the king prawns and monkfish in a bowl. Combine the lime juice, garlic, chilli oil and teriyaki sauce and pour over the top. Stir well to coat and leave in a cool place for up to 1 hour.

2 Remove the seafood from the marinade and thread on to 8 skewers, interspersed with lime and lemon wedges.

3 Cook the kebabs under a grill or on a griddle for 3 minutes, turning once during cooking and brushing with the marinade. Garnish with green chilli, spring onion and parsley. Serve at once.

NUTRITIONAL ANALYSIS (per portion)	
Energy	200 cals
Protein	31.5 g
Carbohydrate	0.0 g
(of which sugars)	0.0 g
Fat	6.5 g
(of which saturates)	1.0 g
Fibre	0.0 g

SUITABLE FOR:

GLUTEN-FREE, NUT-FREE, LOW-CALORIE, DAIRY PRODUCE-FREE AND DIABETIC DIETS.

---

225 g (8 oz) sugarsnap peas, sliced diagonally

175 g (6 oz) baby courgettes, sliced diagonally

salt and freshly ground black pepper

2 tbsp olive oil

1 onion, peeled and finely chopped

¼ tsp saffron strands (optional)

225 g (8 oz) arborio (risotto) rice

1 garlic clove, peeled and crushed

225 g (8 oz) brown-cap mushrooms, quartered

juice and rind of 1 lemon

750 ml (1¼ pints) hot fish, chicken or vegetable stock

300 g (10 oz) cooked peeled prawns

3 tbsp finely chopped fresh chives

spring onion curls (see Note) and grated lemon rind, to garnish

PRAWN AND LEMON RISOTTO

SERVES 4 • PREPARATION: 15 MINUTES • COOKING TIME: 40 MINUTES

1 Place the sugarsnap peas and courgettes in a large pan of boiling salted water, then bring to the boil. Cook for 1–2 minutes, then drain and plunge into ice-cold water.

2 Heat the olive oil in a medium, non-stick saucepan, then add the onion and saffron strands, if using. Cook over a medium heat for 10 minutes or until soft. Add the rice, garlic and mushrooms and cook, stirring, for 1–2 minutes. Season with salt and pepper.

3 Add the grated lemon rind and about one-third of the stock. Simmer gently, stirring frequently, until most of the liquid has been absorbed. Add another one-third of the stock, then repeat the process.

4 Add the remaining stock. Cover, stirring, for 10 minutes or until the rice is tender and most of the stock has been absorbed. Add the prawns, drained vegetables, 1–2 tbsp lemon juice and the chives, then heat for 3–4 minutes. Garnish with spring onion curls and grated lemon rind to serve.

NUTRITIONAL ANALYSIS (per portion)	
Energy	370 cals
Protein	22.0 g
Carbohydrate	50.5 g
(of which sugars)	4.0 g
Fat	7.0 g
(of which saturates)	1.0 g
Fibre	2.0 g

SUITABLE FOR:

GLUTEN-FREE, NUT-FREE, LOW-CALORIE, DAIRY PRODUCE-FREE AND DIABETIC DIETS.

NOTE: To make spring onion curls, thinly slice the onions lengthways, soak in ice-cold water for 30 minutes, then drain.

225 g (8 oz) pak choi or Chinese mustard cabbage

2 tbsp vegetable oil

2 garlic cloves, peeled and thinly sliced

1 stick lemon grass, cut in half and bruised

2 kaffir lime leaves, torn into small pieces

1 small red onion, peeled and thinly sliced

1 hot red chilli, deseeded and thinly sliced

4 cm (1½ inch) piece fresh root ginger, peeled and cut into long thin shreds

1 tbsp coriander seeds, lightly crushed

450 g (1 lb) large raw prawns, peeled and de-veined (see Note)

175 g (6 oz) mangetout, trimmed and halved diagonally

2 tbsp Thai fish sauce

juice of 1 lime, or to taste

fried sliced red chilli, to garnish

STIR-FRIED PRAWNS WITH PAK CHOI

SERVES 4 • PREPARATION: 30 MINUTES • COOKING TIME: 6 MINUTES

1 Trim the pak choi or Chinese mustard cabbage, discarding damaged or discoloured leaves. Tear the leaves into manageable sized pieces.

2 Heat the oil in a wok or large frying pan. Add the garlic, lemon grass, lime leaves, onion, chilli, ginger and coriander, and stir-fry for 2 minutes.

3 Add the prawns, mangetout and pak choi or Chinese mustard cabbage and stir-fry for 2–3 minutes until the vegetables are cooked but still crisp and the prawns are pink and opaque.

4 Add the Thai fish sauce and lime juice, and heat through for 1 minute. Discard the lemon grass. Serve immediately while the vegetables are crisp, garnished with sliced red chilli.

NUTRITIONAL ANALYSIS (per portion)	
Energy	165 cals
Protein	22.0 g
Carbohydrate	4.0 g
(of which sugars)	3.5 g
Fat	6.0 g
(of which saturates)	1.0 g
Fibre	2.0 g

SUITABLE FOR:

GLUTEN-FREE, NUT-FREE, LOW-CALORIE, DAIRY PRODUCE-FREE AND DIABETIC DIETS.

NOTE: If using cooked prawns instead of raw, add with the lime juice and heat for 1 minute at step 3.

3 tbsp olive oil

4 shallots or 1 small onion, peeled and finely chopped

3 garlic cloves, peeled and crushed or chopped

1 tbsp tomato paste

150 ml (¼ pint) white wine

700 g (1½ lb) tomatoes, preferably plum tomatoes, skinned, deseeded and roughly chopped

1 bouquet garni (see Note)

salt and freshly ground black pepper

700 g (1½ lb) raw scampi, peeled tiger prawns or langoustines

finely sliced spring onions, chopped chives and prawns, to garnish

SCAMPI PROVENÇAL

SERVES 4 • PREPARATION: 25 MINUTES • COOKING TIME: 20 MINUTES

1 Heat the olive oil in a large frying pan, add the shallots and cook for 1–2 minutes. Add the garlic and cook for 30 seconds, then add the tomato paste and cook for 1 minute. Pour in the white wine, bring to the boil and bubble for about 10 minutes until very well reduced and syrupy.

2 Add the chopped tomatoes and bouquet garni, then season to taste. Bring to the boil and simmer gently for 5 minutes or until pulpy.

3 Add the raw scampi to the hot sauce, then return to the boil and simmer gently, stirring, for 1–2 minutes or until the scampi are pink and just cooked through to the centre.

4 Garnish with finely sliced spring onions, chopped chives and prawns and serve immediately.

NUTRITIONAL ANALYSIS (per portion)	
Energy	270 cals
Protein	32.0 g
Carbohydrate	7.0 g
(of which sugars)	7.0 g
Fat	10.0 g
(of which saturates)	1.5 g
Fibre	2.0 g

SUITABLE FOR:
GLUTEN-FREE, NUT-FREE, LOW-CALORIE, DAIRY PRODUCE-FREE AND DIABETIC DIETS.

NOTE: To make a home-made bouquet garni, simply tie together a few sprigs of fresh thyme, a bay leaf, some parsley stalks and a 5 cm (2 inch) piece of celery.

1.8 kg (4 lb) live mussels

125 g (4 oz) red onion, peeled and finely chopped

2 garlic cloves, peeled and chopped

1 cm (½ inch) piece fresh root ginger, peeled and sliced

3 sticks lemon grass, very finely chopped

75 ml (3 fl oz) rice wine vinegar

75 ml (3 fl oz) dry white wine

a squeeze of lemon juice

1 tbsp chopped fresh parsley

STEAMED MUSSELS WITH LEMON GRASS

SERVES 4 • PREPARATION: 30 MINUTES • COOKING TIME: 10 MINUTES

1 Scrub the mussels and pull any 'beards' from the shells. Tap any open mussels, discarding those that do not close when you do so. Wash the mussels in two or three changes of clean water. Place in a bowl, cover with a damp cloth and refrigerate until required.

2 Put the onion, garlic, ginger and lemon grass in a large saucepan. Pour over the vinegar, wine and 175 ml (6 fl oz) water. Bring to the boil and simmer for 5 minutes. Add the mussels, cover the pan with a lid and cook over a low heat for 3 minutes or until the mussels are open. Discard any mussels that remain shut.

3 Using a slotted spoon, transfer the mussels to a serving dish and keep warm. Strain the cooking liquid into a clean saucepan and bubble vigorously for 1–2 minutes. Add the lemon juice and parsley, then pour over the mussels and serve immediately.

NUTRITIONAL ANALYSIS (per portion)	
Energy	140 cals
Protein	24.0 g
Carbohydrate	2.5 g
(of which sugars)	2.0 g
Fat	3.0 g
(of which saturates)	0.5 g
Fibre	0.5 g

SUITABLE FOR:
GLUTEN-FREE, LOW-FAT, NUT-FREE, LOW-CALORIE, DAIRY PRODUCE-FREE AND DIABETIC DIETS.

225 g (8 oz) sushi rice

4 tbsp rice wine vinegar or white wine vinegar

1 tsp caster sugar

1 tsp salt

4 sheets of Nori seaweed

125 g (4 oz) cooked white crab meat

2 tsp sesame seeds, toasted

dark soy sauce, wasabi (Japanese Horseradish) and pickled ginger, to serve

NOTE: Japanese ingredients are now available from large supermarkets.

CRAB SUSHI ROLLS

SERVES 4 • PREPARATION: 30 MINUTES, PLUS STANDING • COOKING TIME: 10 MINUTES

1 Soak the rice in cold water for 15 minutes. Drain and rinse under cold water for 10 seconds.

2 Put the rice in a saucepan with 450 ml (¾ pint) water; stand for 10 minutes. Cover and bring to the boil. Reduce the heat to low and cook for 10 minutes. Remove from heat; stand for 5 minutes.

3 Heat the vinegar, sugar and salt in a saucepan. Turn the rice on to a plate and pour over the hot vinegar. Stir with a fork for 5 minutes to cool and coat with vinegar, then leave to cool completely.

4 To toast the seaweed, quickly pass it through a gas flame, or run a lit match across the surface.

5 Place 4 sheets of cling film on a work surface and put a piece of seaweed on each. Divide the cold rice between the seaweed and spread it evenly over the surface. Place a line of crab meat across the middle of the rice and scatter the sesame seeds across the top. Roll up the sushi, then wrap in the cling film. Chill for 30 minutes.

6 Cut the sushi into 2.5 cm (1 inch) pieces and serve with soy sauce, wasabi and pickled ginger.

NUTRITIONAL ANALYSIS (per portion)	
Energy	264 cals
Protein	12.0 g
Carbohydrate	46.0 g
(of which sugars)	1.0 g
Fat	3.5 g
(of which saturates)	0.5 g
Fibre	1.0 g

SUITABLE FOR:

GLUTEN-FREE, LOW-FAT, NUT-FREE, LOW-CALORIE, DAIRY PRODUCE-FREE AND DIABETIC DIETS.

700 g (1½ lb) prepared squid pouches and tentacles

2 tsp chilli oil

grated rind and juice of 1 lime

salt and very finely ground black pepper

SALSA

1 ripe mango, peeled and cut into small chunks

1 red chilli, deseeded and finely chopped

25 g (1 oz) red onion, peeled and finely chopped

1 tbsp chopped fresh coriander

1 tbsp rice wine vinegar

a pinch of ground coriander

coriander sprigs and lime wedges, to serve

GRILLED SQUID WITH CHILLI AND MANGO SALSA

SERVES 4 • PREPARATION: 15 MINUTES, PLUS MARINATING • COOKING TIME: 5 MINUTES

1 Cut the squid pouches open and lay flat on a chopping board. Using a sharp knife, mark one side of the flesh in a lattice pattern; do not cut all the way through the squid. Mix the oil with the lime rind and juice, then brush over the squid. Season with ground pepper and marinate for 30 minutes.

2 To make the salsa, mix the mango with the remaining ingredients and season to taste with salt and pepper. Chill for 30 minutes.

3 Season the squid with a little salt and char-grill or barbecue the tentacles and squid on the patterned side for only 30–60 seconds.

4 Divide the salsa between 4 plates and arrange the squid on top. Garnish with coriander and lime.

NUTRITIONAL ANALYSIS (per portion)	
Energy	175 cals
Protein	26.0 g
Carbohydrate	8.0 g
(of which sugars)	5.5 g
Fat	4.5 g
(of which saturates)	1.0 g
Fibre	1.0 g

SUITABLE FOR:
GLUTEN-FREE, LOW-FAT, NUT-FREE, LOW-CALORIE, DAIRY PRODUCE-FREE AND DIABETIC DIETS.

meat

1 corn-fed or free-range
chicken, about 1.5 kg
(3¼ lb)

salt and freshly ground
black pepper

15 g (½ oz) butter

1 tbsp olive oil

3 dessert apples, peeled,
quartered and cored

350 g (12 oz) shallots or
baby onions, peeled and
left whole

150 ml (¼ pint) chicken
stock

300 ml (½ pint) dry cider

2 bay leaves

8 large sprigs tarragon

150 ml (¼ pint) half-fat
crème fraîche

POT ROASTED CHICKEN WITH APPLES AND CIDER

SERVES 4 • PREPARATION: 15 MINUTES •
COOKING TIME: ABOUT 1½ HOURS

1 Season the chicken. Melt the butter with the oil in a flameproof casserole and fry the chicken on all sides until golden, then remove from the pan.

2 Add the apples and shallots to the pan and fry for 3–4 minutes until pale golden. Remove with a slotted spoon and set aside. Wipe out the casserole. Return the chicken to the casserole, with the stock, cider, bay leaves and 4 tarragon sprigs. Bring to a simmer, then cover and cook in the oven at 180°C (350°F) Mark 4 for 45 minutes.

3 Add the apples and shallots to the casserole and return to the oven for a further 35–45 minutes or until the chicken is cooked through. Transfer the chicken to a warmed serving dish and keep warm.

4 Remove the tarragon from the cooking juices, then stir in the crème fraîche. Strip the leaves from the remaining tarragon sprigs and add to the sauce. Bring to the boil and cook until the sauce has reduced by about a third and the apples start to break up. Using a fork, mash the apples into the sauce. Adjust the seasoning and serve.

NUTRITIONAL ANALYSIS (per portion)	
Energy	470 cals
Protein	35.0 g
Carbohydrate	16.0 g
(of which sugars)	14.0 g
Fat	28.0 g
(of which saturates)	14.0 g
Fibre	2.0 g

SUITABLE FOR:
GLUTEN-FREE, NUT-FREE, LOW-
CALORIE AND DIABETIC DIETS.

---

75 g (3 oz) cheese, such
as Red Leicester, white
Stilton or creamy
Gorgonzola

50 ml (2 fl oz) dry white
wine

150 ml (¼ pint) chicken
stock

4 skinless chicken breast
fillets

4 tbsp half-fat crème
fraîche

wilted spinach, to serve

chopped fresh chives, to
garnish

POACHED CHICKEN WITH CHEESE

SERVES 4 • PREPARATION: 5 MINUTES •
COOKING TIME: 25 MINUTES

1 Roughly grate or chop the cheese. Place the wine and stock in a large saucepan and bring to the boil. Add the chicken breasts, reduce the heat, cover with a lid and simmer for about 10 minutes or until the chicken is cooked through. Using a slotted spoon, remove the chicken and set aside in a warm place.

2 Bring the liquor back to the boil and bubble for 10–15 minutes or until it starts to become syrupy.

3 Remove from the heat and add the cheese, stirring until melted. Add the crème fraîche. Slice the chicken breasts on the diagonal and pour the sauce over. Serve immediately on a bed of spinach and garnish with chopped fresh chives.

NUTRITIONAL ANALYSIS (per portion)	
Energy	282 cals
Protein	32.0 g
Carbohydrate	0.6 g
(of which sugars)	0.4 g
Fat	15.5 g
(of which saturates)	8.0 g
Fibre	0.0 g

SUITABLE FOR:
GLUTEN-FREE, NUT-FREE, LOW-
CALORIE AND DIABETIC DIETS.

1 tbsp fennel seeds, lightly crushed

1 tbsp chopped oregano or marjoram

small handful of chopped parsley

2 garlic cloves, peeled and crushed

salt and freshly ground black pepper

4 free-range chicken legs, halved through joints, or 8 thighs

2 fennel bulbs, trimmed and each cut into 4 wedges (reserve any trimmed fronds)

1 lemon, thickly sliced

2 tbsp olive oil

4 large plum tomatoes, quartered

75 g (3 oz) black olives

150 ml (¼ pint) dry white wine

2 tsp light brown (muscovado) sugar

flat-leaf parsley, to decorate

CHICKEN WITH FENNEL

SERVES 4 • PREPARATION: 20 MINUTES • COOKING TIME: 1 HOUR

1 Mix the fennel seeds with the oregano, parsley, garlic and salt and pepper.

2 Remove any excess skin and fat from the chicken. Push your fingers between the skin and flesh of each chicken piece and tuck 1 tsp of the garlic mixture into each, spreading it over the flesh but keeping the skin intact.

3 Place the chicken pieces in a large roasting tin, skin sides uppermost. Add the fennel quarters and tuck the lemon slices around the chicken pieces. Drizzle with 1 tbsp oil and roast at 200°C (400°F) Mark 6 for 40 minutes.

4 Add the tomatoes to the roasting tin and drizzle with the remaining oil. Roast for a further 15 minutes, or until the chicken pieces are cooked through, basting half way through. Add the olives and cook for 5 minutes. Drain and keep warm.

5 Stir the wine, sugar and any chopped fennel fronds into the roasting tin and cook over a gentle heat, stirring. Season, spoon the gravy over the chicken and serve scattered with parsley.

NUTRITIONAL ANALYSIS (per portion)	
Energy	315 cals
Protein	30.0 g
Carbohydrate	6.0 g
(of which sugars)	6.0 g
Fat	16.0 g
(of which saturates)	4.0 g
Fibre	3.0 g

SUITABLE FOR:

GLUTEN-FREE, NUT-FREE, LOW-CALORIE, DAIRY PRODUCE-FREE AND DIABETIC DIETS.

3 skinless chicken breasts, about 350 g (12 oz)

150 ml (¼ pint) dry white wine

225 g (8 oz) reduced-fat soft cheese with garlic and herbs

400 g (14 oz) can artichoke hearts in water, drained and quartered

salt and freshly ground black pepper

4 sheets filo pastry, about 40 g (1½ oz)

olive oil, for brushing

1 tsp sesame seeds

thyme sprigs, to garnish

CHICKEN AND ARTICHOKE FILO PIE

SERVES 4 • PREPARATION: 20 MINUTES • COOKING TIME: 45 MINUTES

1 In a large saucepan, bring the chicken and wine to the boil, cover and simmer for 10 minutes. Remove the chicken with a slotted spoon and set aside. Add the cheese to the wine and mix until smooth. Bring to the boil, lower the heat and simmer until thickened.

2 Cut the chicken into bite-sized pieces. Add the artichokes to the sauce with the chicken. Season with salt and pepper, and mix well.

3 Place the mixture in a shallow ovenproof dish. Brush the pastry lightly with oil, then scrunch slightly and place on top of the chicken. Sprinkle with the sesame seeds.

4 Cook at 200°C (400°F) Mark 6 for 30–35 minutes or until the filo is crisp. Serve garnished with thyme.

NUTRITIONAL ANALYSIS (per portion)	
Energy	320 cals
Protein	37.0 g
Carbohydrate	12.0 g
(of which sugars)	2.5 g
Fat	15.0 g
(of which saturates)	6.0 g
Fibre	3.5 g

SUITABLE FOR:
NUT-FREE, LOW-CALORIE AND DIABETIC DIETS.

VARIATION:
Replace the artichoke hearts with 225 g (8 oz) brown cap mushrooms, cooked in a little water and lemon juice.

2 eating apples, such as Granny Smith, Braeburn or Cox's

pared rind and juice of 2 large oranges

4 cinnamon sticks, split in half lengthways

1 tsp cardamom pods

6-8 cloves

4 vanilla pods, split in half lengthways

salt and freshly ground black pepper

8 skinless chicken breast fillets, total weight 1.2 kg (2¾ lb)

1 tbsp oil

350 g (12 oz) small shallots, peeled

1 garlic bulb, cloves peeled

450 g (1 lb) celery, trimmed and sliced

450 g 86

(1 lb) carrots, peeled and sliced

1 tbsp tomato paste

300 ml (½ pint) unsweetened apple juice

2 x 400 g (14 oz) cans chopped tomatoes

1 tsp harissa

extra oil, for brushing

NOTE: Grinding the spices will release their aromatic flavours. However, if you don't have time to do this, omit the cardamom pods and cloves. In step 2, simply dry-fry the cinnamon sticks and orange rind then go straight to step 3 and dust the chicken breasts with 1 tsp each dried cloves and mixed spice instead.

AROMATIC CHICKEN PARCELS

SERVES 8 • PREPARATION: 1 HOUR, PLUS COOLING • COOKING TIME: 1 HOUR

1 Peel, core and roughly chop the apples, then stir them into the orange juice.

2 Place the cinnamon sticks in a heavy-based frying pan with the orange rind, cardamom pods and cloves. Heat, stirring, until the cardamom pods darken and the spices start to smell aromatic. Cool, lift out the cinnamon sticks and orange rind and set aside with the vanilla pods. Remove the seeds from the cardamom pods and crush to a fine powder, with the cloves, in a pestle and mortar, or in a heavy bowl using a rolling pin.

3 Season the chicken breasts and dust with the ground spices. Place a piece of orange rind, cinnamon stick and vanilla pod in the centre of each breast. Fold the chicken around the spices and cover with cling film; chill for 30 minutes.

4 Meanwhile, make the sauce. Heat the oil in a large frying pan, add the shallots and fry for 5–10 minutes or until beginning to brown and soften. Add the garlic, celery, carrots and the drained apples to the pan, reserving the orange juice. Cook over a high heat, stirring, for 10 minutes or until they brown and caramelise.

5 Add the tomato paste and cook for 1 minute, then pour in the apple juice and the reserved orange juice. Bring to the boil and bubble until the sauce is reduced by half. Stir in the chopped tomatoes and harissa, bring back to the boil and bubble, stirring occasionally, for 10 minutes. Allow to cool.

6 Cut out eight 35.5 cm (14 inch) squares of greaseproof paper, then brush very lightly with oil. Place 2 tbsp of the cooled tomato mixture in the middle of each square, then place a chicken breast on top. Spoon 1 tbsp of the tomato sauce over each. Bring the edges of the paper together to make a 'money bag' parcel then tie securely with fine string. Repeat with the remaining chicken breasts and the tomato mixture.

7 Place the prepared chicken parcels in a large roasting tin and cook at 200°C (400°F) Mark 6 for 30 minutes or until cooked to the centre.

NUTRITIONAL ANALYSIS (per portion)	
Energy	290 cals
Protein	34.5 g
Carbohydrate	16.0 g
(of which sugars)	15.0 g
Fat	10.5 g
(of which saturates)	2.5 g
Fibre	3.5 g

SUITABLE FOR:
GLUTEN-FREE, NUT-FREE, LOW-CHOLESTEROL, LOW-CALORIE, DAIRY PRODUCE-FREE AND DIABETIC DIETS.

3 garlic cloves, peeled and crushed

1 tbsp caster sugar

3 tbsp balsamic vinegar

125 g (4 oz) cherry tomatoes, halved

salt and freshly ground black pepper

125 g (4 oz) spring onions, trimmed and finely sliced

50 g (2 oz) butter

150 ml (¼ pint) semi-skimmed milk

900 g (2 lb) large potatoes, peeled and cut into even-sized pieces

4 chicken legs or breasts, skin on

2 tbsp olive oil

NOTE: If the tomato juices reduce too much, add a little water to the pan.

CHICKEN AND CHAMP WITH CHERRY TOMATO DRESSING

SERVES 4 • PREPARATION: 10 MINUTES, PLUS INFUSING • COOKING TIME: 40 MINUTES

1 In a bowl, whisk together the garlic, sugar and balsamic vinegar. Stir in the tomatoes and seasoning; set aside.

2 Place the spring onions, butter and milk in a small pan, bring to the boil, then set aside for 15 minutes to infuse. Cook the potatoes in boiling salted water until tender. Drain, dry and mash over a low heat. Beat in the flavoured hot milk mixture and season.

3 Season the chicken. Heat the oil in a large heavy-based frying pan, add the chicken and cook skin-side down over a high heat for 6–7 minutes. Turn over and cook for a further 6–7 minutes or until cooked to the centre. Add the tomato mixture and bubble for 2–3 minutes (see Note).

4 To serve, arrange the chicken breasts on top of the champ, then spoon the tomatoes and juices over.

NUTRITIONAL ANALYSIS (per portion)	
Energy	564 cals
Protein	31.0 g
Carbohydrate	46.0 g
(of which sugars)	8.0 g
Fat	30.0 g
(of which saturates)	10.0 g
Fibre	4.0 g

SUITABLE FOR:
GLUTEN-FREE, NUT-FREE AND DIABETIC DIETS.

---

2 tbsp oil

4 chicken breast quarters

450 g (1 lb) baby carrots, pared and trimmed

225 g (8 oz) baby parsnips, pared and trimmed

225 g (8 oz) thin leeks, trimmed and thickly sliced

350 g (12 oz) button onions, peeled and trimmed

pinch of chopped fresh sage (optional)

125 g (4 oz) Puy lentils

200 ml (7 fl oz) pure unsweetened apple juice

300 ml (½ pint) good chicken stock

2 small Granny Smith apples, cored and thickly sliced

salt and freshly ground black pepper

2 tbsp chopped parsley

SIMMERED CHICKEN WITH APPLE AND LENTILS

SERVES 4 • PREPARATION: 15 MINUTES • COOKING TIME: ABOUT 1¼ HOURS

1 Heat the oil in a large flameproof casserole and brown the chicken well, a few pieces at a time. Remove from the casserole with a slotted spoon and drain on kitchen paper.

2 Add all the vegetables to the casserole and fry for 4–5 minutes or until golden brown. Add the sage, if using, lentils, apple juice and chicken stock and bring to the boil. Season well with salt and pepper, then return all of the chicken to the casserole.

3 Cover and simmer in the oven at 190°C (375°F) Mark 5 for 30 minutes. Stir in the apple and cook for a further 30 minutes or until the chicken is very tender. Adjust the seasoning and stir in the parsley just before serving.

NUTRITIONAL ANALYSIS (per portion)	
Energy	490 cals
Protein	44.0 g
Carbohydrate	47.0 g
(of which sugars)	25.0 g
Fat	15.0 g
(of which saturates)	3.0 g
Fibre	11.0 g

SUITABLE FOR:
HIGH-FIBRE, GLUTEN-FREE, NUT-FREE, LOW-CHOLESTEROL, LOW-CALORIE, DAIRY PRODUCE-FREE AND DIABETIC DIETS.

1 tbsp balsamic vinegar

6 tbsp olive oil

grated rind of 1 lime and juice of 2

2 garlic cloves, peeled and crushed

4 large skinless chicken breasts, approximately 700 g (1½ lb), cut into 2.5 cm (1 inch) cubes

soured cream, to serve

lime wedges and mint sprigs, to garnish

TABBOULEH
75 g (3 oz) bulghar wheat

½ cucumber, deseeded and diced

4 plum tomatoes, deseeded and diced

1 small red onion, peeled and finely chopped

4 tbsp chopped fresh mint

4 tbsp chopped fresh flat-leaf parsley

freshly ground black pepper

CHICKEN KEBABS WITH TABBOULEH

SERVES 4 • PREPARATION: 35 MINUTES, PLUS MARINATING AND SOAKING • COOKING TIME: 5 MINUTES

1 In a large bowl, whisk together the vinegar, 3 tbsp olive oil, the rind and juice of 1 lime, and 1 garlic clove. Add the cubed chicken, mix well, then cover and chill for 2 hours, preferably overnight.

2 To make the tabbouleh, place the bulghar wheat in a bowl, cover with double its volume of boiling water and leave to soak for 15 minutes.

3 Drain the bulghar wheat, squeeze out the liquid and place in a bowl. Stir in the cucumber, tomatoes, onion and herbs. Season with ground black pepper. In a small bowl, whisk together the remaining olive oil, lime juice and garlic. Add to the bulghar wheat and mix gently but thoroughly.

4 Remove the chicken from the marinade, thread on to 8 wooden skewers (see Note) and place under a hot grill or on a hot griddle. Cook for 5 minutes or until the chicken is cooked through.

5 Serve the kebabs with the tabbouleh and soured cream. Garnish with lime wedges and mint.

NUTRITIONAL ANALYSIS (per portion)	
Energy	445 cals
Protein	40.0 g
Carbohydrate	18.0 g
(of which sugars)	4.0 g
Fat	23.0 g
(of which saturates)	5.0 g
Fibre	1.5 g

SUITABLE FOR:
NUT-FREE, LOW-CALORIE AND DIABETIC DIETS.

NOTE: Wooden skewers need to be soaked in water for 30 minutes before use to prevent them from burning.

coarsely grated rind of 2 lemons
2 tbsp balsamic vinegar
3 tbsp olive oil
1 tbsp chopped fresh rosemary
salt and freshly ground black pepper
6 chicken breast fillets
1 tbsp chopped flat-leaf parsley
2 tbsp chopped fresh chives

GRILLED LEMON AND HERB CHICKEN

SERVES 6 • PREPARATION: 10 MINUTES, PLUS MARINATING • COOKING TIME: 20 MINUTES

1 Mix the lemon rind with the vinegar, oil, rosemary, salt and pepper.

2 Season the chicken, lay in a shallow, non-metallic dish just big enough to hold the chicken in a single layer. Pour the marinade over, then cover and leave in a cool place for at least 1 hour, preferably overnight.

3 Lift the chicken from the marinade, reserving the marinade. Cook the chicken under the grill for 8–10 minutes on each side or until cooked through.

4 Bring the reserved marinade to the boil, then remove from the heat and add the parsley and chives. Spoon the marinade over the chicken.

NUTRITIONAL ANALYSIS (per portion)	
Energy	243 cals
Protein	32.0 g
Carbohydrate	0.0 g
(of which sugars)	0.0 g
Fat	13.0 g
(of which saturates)	3.0 g
Fibre	0.0 g

SUITABLE FOR:
GLUTEN-FREE, NUT-FREE, LOW-CHOLESTEROL, LOW-CALORIE, DAIRY PRODUCE-FREE AND DIABETIC DIETS.

300 ml (½ pint) low-fat natural yogurt
4 tbsp olive oil
3 garlic cloves, peeled and crushed
1½ tsp each ground cumin, curry powder and cayenne pepper
½ tsp each dry English mustard, ground ginger and ground cinnamon
salt and freshly ground black pepper
900 g (2 lb) skinless chicken thighs
225 g (8 oz) red onions, peeled and finely chopped
225 g (8 oz) cucumber, peeled and sliced
2 x 400 g (14 oz) cans chopped tomatoes
1 lemon, cut into wedges
75 g (3 oz) prepared fresh spinach

ASIAN SPICED CHICKEN

SERVES 6 • PREPARATION: 15 MINUTES, PLUS MARINATING • COOKING TIME: ABOUT 1 HOUR 20 MINUTES

1 Place the yogurt in a wide bowl with 2 tbsp olive oil, 1 crushed garlic clove, ½ tsp each ground cumin, curry powder, cayenne pepper, all the dry English mustard, ground ginger, ground cinnamon and 1 tsp salt. Stir to blend well. Add the chicken to the marinade, cover and chill overnight.

2 Heat the remaining oil in a large pan, add the onions, cucumber and remaining garlic and cook for 4–5 minutes or until softened. Stir in the remaining cumin, curry powder and cayenne pepper. Add the tomatoes and simmer for 15–20 minutes. Season and add the lemon pieces. Spoon the tomato sauce mixture into a large, shallow ovenproof dish.

3 Place the chicken thighs, skin-side up, with the marinade, on a baking sheet. Place the dish of sauce on the shelf beneath the chicken and cook at 200°C (400°F) Mark 6 for 50–55 minutes.

4 About 5 minutes before the end of the cooking time, stir the spinach into the tomato sauce mixture then return to the oven to finish cooking.

5 Serve the chicken with the tomato mixture.

NUTRITIONAL ANALYSIS (per portion)	
Energy	300 cals
Protein	37.0 g
Carbohydrate	12.0 g
(of which sugars)	10.0 g
Fat	15.0 g
(of which saturates)	3.0 g
Fibre	2.5 g

SUITABLE FOR:
GLUTEN-FREE, NUT-FREE, LOW-CHOLESTEROL, LOW-CALORIE AND DIABETIC DIETS.

NOTE: The flavour of the chicken is enhanced if it is allowed to marinate overnight in the yogurt and spices, making it succulent and tender.

2 tbsp sunflower oil

1 large onion, about 225 g (8 oz), peeled and thickly sliced

2 tsp ground turmeric

12 chicken thighs, skin on

4 tbsp runny honey

salt and freshly ground black pepper

2 tbsp chopped fresh mint

2 tbsp slivered almonds

juice of ½ lemon

fresh mint, to garnish

NOTE: If your dish isn't suitable for placing under the grill, transfer everything to the grill pan (remove the wire rack and line the pan with foil).

STICKY CHICKEN

SERVES 6 • PREPARATION: 5 MINUTES • COOKING TIME: 50 MINUTES

1 Heat the oil in a shallow flameproof casserole or gratin dish (see Note). Add the onion and cook slowly for 10–15 minutes until soft but not coloured. Add the turmeric and cook for 1 minute. Remove from the heat, then add the chicken, honey, seasoning and half the chopped mint, making sure the chicken is skin-side up in a single layer.

2 Place the dish about 5 cm (2 inches) away from the heat of a hot grill. Cook for about 30 minutes, basting the chicken from time to time. As the chicken begins to brown, reduce the grill to a low to medium heat.

3 Stir in the almonds and continue to cook for 5 minutes until the nuts are golden and the chicken is charred and tender. (To tell whether the chicken thighs are cooked, cut into one to make sure there's no trace of pink flesh.) Just before serving, add the lemon juice to taste and stir in the remaining chopped mint. Garnish and serve.

NUTRITIONAL ANALYSIS (per portion)	
Energy	380 cals
Protein	32.0 g
Carbohydrate	15.5 g
(of which sugars)	14.5 g
Fat	22.0 g
(of which saturates)	5.0 g
Fibre	1.0 g

SUITABLE FOR:

GLUTEN-FREE, LOW-CALORIE AND DAIRY PRODUCE-FREE DIETS.

CHICKEN AND MUSHROOM ENCHILADAS

SERVES 6 • PREPARATION: 30 MINUTES • COOKING TIME: 45 MINUTES

450 g (1 lb) skinless chicken breast fillets, cut into strips

1 tsp each dried oregano and cumin seeds

salt and freshly ground black pepper

4 tbsp olive oil

225 g (8 oz) onions, peeled and finely sliced

125 g (4 oz) celery, trimmed and cut into matchsticks

2 garlic cloves, peeled and crushed

50 g (2 oz) sun-dried tomatoes, chopped

225 g (8 oz) brown-cap or shiitake mushrooms, roughly chopped

250 g (9 oz) reduced-fat Cheddar cheese, grated

2 tbsp chopped fresh coriander

2 tbsp lemon juice

6-8 flour tortillas

oil, for greasing

basil leaves, to garnish

salsa verde, to serve (see Note)

1 Place the chicken in a bowl with the oregano, cumin seeds and seasoning. Toss to coat.

2 Heat half the oil in a large frying pan. Add the onions, celery and crushed garlic and cook for 3–4 minutes. Add the sun-dried tomatoes and mushrooms and cook for a further 2–3 minutes. Remove and set aside.

3 Add the remaining oil to the pan and stir-fry the chicken in batches for 2–3 minutes. Mix together the chicken, mushroom mixture, 175 g (6 oz) grated Cheddar cheese, chopped fresh coriander and the lemon juice. Season well.

4 Divide the chicken mixture among the tortillas and roll them up. Place, seam-side down, in a greased baking dish, then sprinkle with the remaining cheese.

5 Cook the tortillas at 180°C (350°F) Mark 4 for 25–30 minutes or until golden and bubbling. Garnish with basil and serve with salsa verde.

NUTRITIONAL ANALYSIS (per portion)	
Energy	474 cals
Protein	35.0 g
Carbohydrate	36.0 g
(of which sugars)	3.0 g
Fat	22.0 g
(of which saturates)	7.0 g
Fibre	2.5 g

SUITABLE FOR:
NUT-FREE AND DIABETIC DIETS.

NOTE: To make salsa verde, put 25 g (1 oz) breadcrumbs, 75 g (3 oz) mixed basil and flat-leaf parsley, 2 chopped garlic cloves, 3 anchovy fillets and 2 tbsp lemon juice in a food processor. Season. Blend for 1–2 minutes. With the motor running, gradually add 100 ml (3½ fl oz) olive oil. This will add 65 cals per 1 tbsp.

1.4 kg (3 lb) oven-ready chicken

225 g (8 oz) onions, peeled and roughly chopped

1 medium carrot, peeled and roughly chopped

50 g (2 oz) celery, trimmed and roughly chopped

1 bay leaf

salt and freshly ground black pepper

1 tbsp olive oil

900 g (2 lb) leeks, trimmed and sliced

125 g (4 oz) self-raising flour

½ tsp baking powder

50 g (2 oz) butter

1 tsp each chopped flat-leaf parsley and fresh thyme

125 g (4 oz) ready-to-eat stoned prunes

chopped fresh chives, to garnish

CHICKEN CASSEROLE

SERVES 6 • PREPARATION: 50 MINUTES • COOKING TIME: 1 HOUR 25 MINUTES

1 Place the chicken in a large pan. Add the onions, carrot, celery, bay leaf and 1 tsp salt. Add 1.7 litres (3 pints) cold water, bring to the boil, then cover and simmer for 45–60 minutes until cooked.
2 Meanwhile, heat the oil and cook the leeks for 5-6 minutes or until lightly golden. Add to the casserole for the last 20 minutes of cooking time.
3 Remove and discard the skin and bones from the chicken, roughly shred the meat and return to the saucepan with the stock.
4 Sift the flour, baking powder and a pinch of salt into a bowl. Rub in the butter, herbs and 4 tbsp water, then shape into twelve 2.5 cm (1 inch) balls. Place on a baking sheet lined with greaseproof paper and cook at 200°C (400°F) Mark 6 for 15–20 minutes or until golden.
5 Bring the casserole to the boil, season, then add the prunes and simmer gently for 5 minutes. Garnish with chives and serve hot.

NUTRITIONAL ANALYSIS (per portion)	
Energy	295 cals
Protein	18.0 g
Carbohydrate	32.0 g
(of which sugars)	14.0 g
Fat	13.0 g
(of which saturates)	6.0 g
Fibre	6.0 g

SUITABLE FOR:
HIGH-FIBRE, NUT-FREE, LOW-CALORIE AND DIABETIC DIETS.

Chicken... lower the fat

For low-fat cooking, always use skinless chicken: 150 g (5 oz) chicken breast with skin contains 345 cals/26.6 g fat, while a 150 g (5 oz) skinless chicken breast contains a mere 181 cals/6.4 g fat.

---

6 garlic cloves, peeled and crushed

1 tsp each salt and ground black peppercorns

1 tsp ground ginger

½ tsp ground cumin

½ tsp paprika

4 skinless chicken breast fillets, surface slashed with a sharp knife

150 ml (¼ pint) fresh orange juice

pared rind of 1 orange

150 g (5 oz) ready-to-eat apricots

¼ tsp saffron strands

150 ml (¼ pint) sherry

3 tbsp sherry vinegar

2 tbsp vegetable oil

1 onion, peeled and sliced

3 tbsp plain flour

300 ml (½ pint) chicken stock

parsley sprigs, to garnish

MOROCCAN CHICKEN

SERVES 4 • PREPARATION: 25 MINUTES, PLUS MARINATING • COOKING TIME: 30 MINUTES

1 Place the garlic in a large bowl with the salt, peppercorns, ginger, cumin and paprika. Stir well.
2 Place the chicken in the bowl with the spices. Add the orange juice and rind and stir well. Cover and chill for at least 4 hours, preferably overnight.
3 Place the apricots, saffron, sherry and vinegar in another bowl. Cover and leave to marinate at room temperature for at least 4 hours, or overnight.
4 Heat the oil in a large, flameproof casserole. Transfer the chicken to the casserole (reserve the marinade) and brown over a high heat; set aside. Add the onion, cook for 5 minutes until softened.
5 Add the flour, stir well and cook for a further minute. Add the marinade, stock and the apricots with their soaking liquid. Stir and bring to the boil. Return the chicken to the pan, then simmer (see Note). Cover and cook for 25 minutes or until the chicken is tender. Serve garnished with parsley.

NUTRITIONAL ANALYSIS (per portion)	
Energy	360 cals
Protein	29.0 g
Carbohydrate	28.0 g
(of which sugars)	19.0 g
Fat	11.0 g
(of which saturates)	2.5 g
Fibre	3.0 g

SUITABLE FOR:
NUT-FREE, LOW-CHOLESTEROL, LOW-CALORIE, DAIRY PRODUCE-FREE AND DIABETIC DIETS.

NOTE: Instead of cooking the chicken in a casserole on the hob, you can cook it in the oven at 180°C (350°F) Mark 4 for about 30–35 minutes.

350 g (12 oz) cooked chicken breast, skinned and cut into long strips

2 oranges

2 large heads of chicory, roughly sliced

50 g (2 oz) pecan nuts or walnuts, toasted and roughly chopped

tarragon sprigs, to garnish

DRESSING

rind and juice of 2 oranges

2 tbsp white wine vinegar

1 tsp caster sugar

4-5 tbsp olive oil

3 tbsp fresh tarragon

1 large egg yolk

salt and freshly ground black pepper

ZESTY ORANGE, CHICKEN AND TARRAGON SALAD

SERVES 4 • PREPARATION: 15 MINUTES, PLUS CHILLING

1 To make the dressing, place the orange rind and juice in a small bowl. Add the vinegar, sugar, oil, tarragon, egg yolk and salt and pepper to taste. Mix to combine well.

2 To make the salad, place the chicken strips in a bowl, spoon over the dressing, cover and chill for at least 1 hour. Using a sharp knife, remove and discard the peel and pith from the oranges, then cut the flesh into thick slices.

3 Place a layer of chicory in a large flat salad bowl, spoon over the chicken and the dressing. Scatter over the orange slices and pecan nuts and garnish with tarragon sprigs.

NUTRITIONAL ANALYSIS (per portion)	
Energy	360 cals
Protein	31.5 g
Carbohydrate	8.0 g
(of which sugars)	7.0 g
Fat	23.0 g
(of which saturates)	3.5 g
Fibre	2.0 g

SUITABLE FOR:
LOW-CALORIE, DAIRY PRODUCE-FREE AND DIABETIC DIETS.

---

125 g (4 oz) Puy lentils

225 g (8 oz) broccoli, cut into small florets

salt and freshly ground black pepper

1 large garlic clove, peeled

1 tsp sea salt

1 tsp English mustard powder

2 tbsp balsamic vinegar

4 tbsp olive oil

1 red onion, peeled and thinly sliced

175 g (6 oz) back bacon, roughly chopped

350 g (12 oz) smoked chicken breast, roughly chopped

WARM LENTIL, CHICKEN AND BROCCOLI SALAD

SERVES 4 • PREPARATION: 20 MINUTES • COOKING TIME: 45 MINUTES

1 Cook the lentils in plenty of unsalted water for about 35 minutes or until soft.

2 Blanch the broccoli in a saucepan of boiling salted water for 2 minutes, drain and plunge into a bowl of ice-cold water. When cold, drain well and set aside.

3 Using a pestle and mortar, or a heavy bowl and the end of a rolling pin, pound the garlic and sea salt together until creamy, add the mustard and continue mixing. Whisk in the vinegar, then 3 tbsp olive oil and set the dressing aside.

4 Heat the remaining oil in a frying pan, add the onion and bacon and cook over a medium heat for 5 minutes or until the onion is beginning to soften and the bacon is crisp. Add the chicken and broccoli and stir-fry for 1–2 minutes.

5 Drain the lentils, add the chicken and broccoli mixture, then toss with the dressing. Season to taste and serve warm.

NUTRITIONAL ANALYSIS (per portion)	
Energy	450 cals
Protein	48.0 g
Carbohydrate	19.0 g
(of which sugars)	3.5 g
Fat	20.0 g
(of which saturates)	5.0 g
Fibre	5.0 g

SUITABLE FOR:
GLUTEN-FREE, NUT-FREE, LOW-CHOLESTEROL, LOW-CALORIE, DAIRY PRODUCE-FREE AND DIABETIC DIETS.

Right: Zesty Orange, Chicken and Tarragon Salad

500 g (1 lb 2 oz) chicken
livers, thawed if frozen

2 tbsp olive oil

1 small red onion, peeled
and chopped

2 garlic cloves, peeled
and crushed

3 sprigs rosemary

2 bay leaves

8 juniper berries, lightly
crushed

250 g (9 oz) baby button
mushrooms

225 g (8 oz) cherry
tomatoes, halved

5 tbsp Marsala or sherry

salt and freshly ground
black pepper

CHICKEN LIVERS WITH MUSHROOMS AND TOMATOES

*SERVES 4 • PREPARATION: 15 MINUTES •
COOKING TIME: ABOUT 20 MINUTES*

1 Wash the chicken livers, pat dry on kitchen
paper, then cut into chunky pieces discarding the
white cores.

2 Heat 1 tbsp oil in a frying pan. Add the onion
and cook gently for 5 minutes until golden. Add
the garlic, chicken livers, herbs and juniper berries
and cook for 5 minutes, stirring, until the livers are
lightly browned. Drain the contents of the pan and
reserve.

3 Heat the remaining oil in the frying pan. Add the
mushrooms and fry quickly until browned. Return
the chicken liver mixture to the pan. Stir in the
tomatoes, Marsala and a little seasoning. Cook
gently for 4–5 minutes, until the tomatoes are soft
and the sauce is syrupy. Serve immediately.

NUTRITIONAL ANALYSIS (per portion)	
Energy	270 cals
Protein	26.0 g
Carbohydrate	6.0 g
(of which sugars)	4.0 g
Fat	14.0 g
(of which saturates)	3.5 g
Fibre	2.0 g

SUITABLE FOR:
GLUTEN-FREE, NUT-FREE, LOW-
CALORIE, DAIRY PRODUCE-FREE
AND DIABETIC DIETS.

---

15 g (½ oz) mixed dried
mushrooms, rinsed

2 garlic cloves, peeled
and crushed

2 oven-ready young
pheasants

25 g (1 oz) butter

10 juniper berries, lightly
crushed

1 small onion, peeled and
finely chopped

125 g (4 oz) piece smoked
bacon, diced

2 tsp plain white flour

300 ml (½ pint) red wine

150 ml (¼ pint) chicken or
pheasant stock

175 g (6 oz) brown cap
mushrooms, halved

2 tbsp redcurrant jelly

salt and freshly ground
black pepper

parsley sprigs, to garnish

*NOTE: The wonderful rich
flavours of this dish
develop even more if it's
made the day before.*

PHEASANT WITH BACON AND MUSHROOMS

*SERVES 4 • PREPARATION: 35 MINUTES •
COOKING TIME: 1 HOUR 10 MINUTES*

1 Soak the dried mushrooms in 300 ml (½ pint)
warm water for 20 minutes, then drain.

2 Spread the garlic over the pheasants. Melt the
butter in a frying pan and brown the pheasants on
all sides. Drain and place in a casserole dish, then
add the juniper berries.

3 Add the onion and bacon to the frying pan and
fry gently for 10 minutes. Stir in the flour, then the
wine and stock. Bring to the boil and pour over the
pheasants. Cover and cook at 200°C (400°F)
Mark 6 for 25 minutes.

4 Tuck the fresh and dried mushrooms around
the pheasant. Return to the oven and cook,
uncovered, for 20–25 minutes or until tender.

5 Using a slotted spoon, transfer the pheasant
and mushrooms to a platter and keep warm. Add
the redcurrant jelly to the cooking juices and heat
until melted; adjust the seasoning if necessary.
Garnish with parsley and serve with the sauce.

NUTRITIONAL ANALYSIS (per portion)	
Energy	650 cals
Protein	78.0 g
Carbohydrate	11.5 g
(of which sugars)	6.5 g
Fat	28 0 g
(of which saturates)	11.0 g
Fibre	1.0 g

SUITABLE FOR:
NUT-FREE AND DIABETIC DIETS.

4 lemons

8 garlic cloves, peeled and crushed

4 tbsp runny honey

4 poussins

4 sprigs rosemary

salt and freshly ground black pepper

4 red chillies (optional)

TUNISIAN LEMON-MARINATED POUSSINS

SERVES 4 • PREPARATION: 15 MINUTES, PLUS MARINATING • COOKING TIME: 50 MINUTES

1 Wash the lemons, then cut in half and squeeze the juice into a bowl, reserving the squeezed lemon skins. Stir the garlic and honey into the lemon juice.

2 Place the poussins in a large dish, pour the lemon marinade over and sprinkle with the rosemary sprigs. Season with salt and pepper to taste and add the reserved lemon skins to the dish. Marinate overnight or for at least 1 hour.

3 Meanwhile, line a large roasting tin with foil.

4 Transfer the poussins to the foil-lined tin and spoon over the marinade, adding the lemon skins, and cook in the oven at 200°C (400°F) Mark 6 for 40–50 minutes, or until the birds are golden brown and the lemon skins are nicely charred. If using the chillies, after 30 minutes cooking remove the poussins from the oven and place one chilli diagonally over the breast of each poussin, then return to the oven for the remaining cooking time.

5 Serve garnished with the roasted lemon skins.

NUTRITIONAL ANALYSIS (per portion)	
Energy	524 cals
Protein	43.0 g
Carbohydrate	18.0 g
(of which sugars)	18.0 g
Fat	31.0 g
(of which saturates)	9.0 g
Fibre	0.0 g

SUITABLE FOR:
GLUTEN-FREE, NUT-FREE, LOW-CHOLESTEROL, DAIRY PRODUCE-FREE AND DIABETIC DIETS.

450 g (1 lb) lean turkey pieces

salt and freshly ground black pepper

¼ tsp ground cloves

1 tbsp olive oil

75 g (3 oz) smoked bacon lardons

2 onions, peeled and chopped

400 g (14 oz) can chopped tomatoes

2 tbsp tomato paste

2 garlic cloves, peeled and crushed

2 bay leaves

several sprigs thyme

300 ml (½ pint) chicken or vegetable stock

3 x 400 g (14 oz) cans mixed beans, drained and rinsed

100 g (3½ oz) white or granary breadcrumbs

TURKEY AND MIXED BEAN CASSOULET

SERVES 6 • PREPARATION: 15 MINUTES • COOKING TIME: 40 MINUTES

1 Pat the turkey dry between sheets of kitchen paper. Season with the salt, pepper and ground cloves. Heat the oil in a large flameproof casserole. Add the turkey and cook quickly until lightly browned; remove from the pan with a slotted spoon and set aside. Add the bacon and onions to the pan and fry gently for a further 5 minutes, until lightly browned. Return the turkey to the pan.

2 Add the chopped tomatoes, tomato paste, garlic, herbs and stock and bring to the boil. Stir in the beans, cover and bake in the oven at 200°C (400°F) Mark 6 for 15 minutes.

3 Remove from the oven and season to taste. Scatter the top with the breadcrumbs and return to the oven for a further 20–25 minutes until the breadcrumbs have formed a lightly browned crust.

NUTRITIONAL ANALYSIS	
(per portion)	
Energy	433 cals
Protein	37.0 g
Carbohydrate	54.0 g
(of which sugars)	12.0 g
Fat	9.0 g
(of which saturates)	2.5 g
Fibre	14.0 g

SUITABLE FOR:

HIGH-FIBRE, NUT-FREE, LOW-CHOLESTEROL, LOW-CALORIE, DAIRY PRODUCE-FREE AND DIABETIC DIETS.

DUCK BREASTS WITH CARAMELISED ORANGES

SERVES 4 • PREPARATION: 20 MINUTES, PLUS MARINATING • COOKING TIME: 30 MINUTES

2 garlic cloves, crushed

¼ tsp ground allspice

salt and freshly ground black pepper

2 tbsp balsamic vinegar

2 tbsp fresh orange juice

4 duck breasts, trimmed of excess fat and skin scored

1 tbsp light brown sugar

1 medium orange, cut into 8 wedges

150 ml (¼ pint) chicken stock

PISTACHIO RICE

225 g (8 oz) long grain rice

4 spring onions, trimmed, halved lengthways and finely chopped

65 g (2½ oz) pistachio nuts, roughly chopped

3 tbsp roughly chopped coriander

1 Mix together the garlic, allspice, seasoning, vinegar and orange juice and pour over the duck in a shallow bowl. Marinate for at least 1 hour.

2 Drain the duck breasts, reserving the marinade, and pat dry on kitchen paper. Heat a large non-stick frying pan. Add the duck breasts, skin-side down. When the fat starts to run, add the sugar and orange wedges. Cook very gently for 8–10 minutes until the duck skin is crisp and golden. Turn the duck and orange wedges and fry for 8 more minutes (see Note). Remove the caramelised oranges when lightly charred; keep warm.

3 Meanwhile, cook the rice in plenty of boiling, salted water until just tender. Drain the rice and return to the saucepan. Stir in the spring onions, pistachio nuts, coriander and a little seasoning.

4 Remove the cooked duck from the pan with a slotted spoon and keep warm. Put the reserved marinade juices into the pan, add the stock and bring to the boil, stirring. Reduce the heat and simmer gently for 2 minutes. Strain into a jug.

5 Spoon the rice on to plates, top with the duck and orange wedges, then pour over the sauce.

NOTE: The meat will be slightly pink in the centre with this cooking time; increase the cooking time to 12 minutes for medium cooked.

NUTRITIONAL ANALYSIS (per portion)	
Energy	680 cals
Protein	40.0 g
Carbohydrate	54.0 g
(of which sugars)	8.0 g
Fat	34.0 g
(of which saturates)	8.0 g
Fibre	2.0 g

SUITABLE FOR:

GLUTEN-FREE, DAIRY PRODUCE-FREE AND DIABETIC DIETS.

CRISP CHILLI DUCK

SERVES 6 • PREPARATION: 10 MINUTES • COOKING TIME: 20 MINUTES

3 duck breasts, about 550 g (1¼ lb) total weight, trimmed of excess fat

6 tbsp plum sauce

4 tbsp chilli sauce

2 garlic cloves, peeled and crushed

6 tbsp fresh orange juice

225 g (8 oz) green beans, trimmed

salt and freshly ground black pepper

350 g (12 oz) canteloupe or charentais melon flesh, cut into rough chunks

1 Place the duck breasts skin-side down in a hot, heavy-based frying pan. Fry for 10 minutes without turning, spooning off any fat.

2 Mix together the plum and chilli sauces, then stir in the garlic and orange juice. Place the duck in a roasting tin, skin-side up. Brush with 2 tbsp sauce and cook at 200°C (400°F) Mark 6 for 8–10 minutes for medium-rare. Rest for 5 minutes.

3 Cook the beans in boiling salted water for 3–4 minutes, drain and refresh in cold water.

4 Slice the duck and arrange on top of the beans and melon, then spoon over the remaining sauce.

NUTRITIONAL ANALYSIS (per portion)	
Energy	175 cals
Protein	20.0 g
Carbohydrate	13.0 g
(of which sugars)	11.0 g
Fat	5.0 g
(of which saturates)	1.0 g
Fibre	2.0 g

SUITABLE FOR:

GLUTEN-FREE, LOW-FAT, NUT-FREE, LOW-CALORIE, DAIRY PRODUCE-FREE AND DIABETIC DIETS.

125 g (4 oz) couscous

salt and freshly ground black pepper

900 ml (1½ pints) chicken stock

1.1 kg (2½ lb) pork tenderloin fillets, trimmed

3 tbsp oil

175 g (6 oz) onion, peeled and finely chopped

3 garlic cloves, peeled and crushed

25 g (1 oz) pine nuts, toasted

1 tsp ground cinnamon

125 g (4 oz) spinach, washed and roughly chopped

50 g (2 oz) raisins

3 tbsp each chopped fresh chives and flat-leaf parsley

finely grated rind of 2 oranges and juice of 3 large oranges

finely grated rind of 1 lemon

8 tbsp port

finely grated orange rind and parsley sprigs, to garnish

AROMATIC PORK FILLETS WITH COUSCOUS

SERVES 6 • PREPARATION: 30 MINUTES, PLUS SOAKING • COOKING TIME: 55 MINUTES

1 Place the couscous in a bowl, season, add 300 ml (½ pint) boiling stock and leave for 20 minutes. In each pork fillet, make a 2–2.5 cm (¾-1 inch) cut lengthways to form a deep pocket.

2 Heat the oil in a saucepan, add the onion and cook for 7–10 minutes or until soft. Stir in the garlic, pine nuts and cinnamon; cook for 1 minute. Remove the pan from the heat, add the spinach, raisins, herbs, orange and lemon rinds. Mix with the couscous and season well. Divide the filling among the fillets, pressing the mixture in well.

3 Place the pork in a roasting tin with the orange juice and port. Cook at 200°C (400°F) Mark 6 for 20–30 minutes or until the pork is cooked. Lift out the pork, set aside and keep warm.

4 For the sauce, add the remaining stock to the pan juices and bubble for 10 minutes until syrupy.

5 Thickly slice the pork, then serve with the sauce, garnished with orange rind and parsley.

NUTRITIONAL ANALYSIS (per portion)	
Energy	435 cals
Protein	43.0 g
Carbohydrate	24.0 g
(of which sugars)	13.0 g
Fat	16.0 g
(of which saturates)	3.5 g
Fibre	1.0 g

SUITABLE FOR:

LOW-CHOLESTEROL, LOW-CALORIE, DAIRY PRODUCE-FREE AND DIABETIC DIETS.

2 tbsp oil

225 g (8 oz) crisp eating apples, cored and cut into wedges

1 kg (2¼ lb) shoulder pork, cut into 2.5 cm (1 inch) cubes

200 g (7 oz) onions, peeled and chopped

1 tbsp plain flour

275 ml can dry cider

300 ml (½ pint) chicken stock

salt and freshly ground black pepper

2 tsp cider vinegar (see Note)

125 g (4 oz) French beans

125 g (4 oz) asparagus tips

125 g (4 oz) mangetout

2 bunches spring onions

NOTE: The amount of vinegar required will depend on the sharpness of the apples.

CIDER PORK WITH SPRING VEGETABLES

SERVES 6 • PREPARATION: 1 HOUR • COOKING TIME: 1¼ HOURS

1 Heat the oil in a large flameproof casserole. Fry the apples until a light golden brown, then drain and set aside. Add the pork to the pan in batches and fry over a high heat until browned; reserve. Lower the heat, add the onions and cook gently for 5–6 minutes.

2 Stir in the flour, pour in the cider and blend until smooth. Bring to the boil and bubble until reduced by two-thirds. Return the pork to the casserole with the stock, then season with salt and pepper.

3 Bring to the boil, then cook in the oven at 180°C (350°F) Mark 4 for 1¼ hours or until tender. Add the apples to the casserole 5 minutes before the end of the cooking time. Adjust the seasoning and add the vinegar.

4 Meanwhile, cut the vegetables diagonally into short lengths. Cook individually in boiling, salted water until just tender; French beans for 5 minutes, asparagus for 3 minutes, mangetout and spring onions for 2 minutes. Drain and season. Spoon the vegetables over the pork to serve.

NUTRITIONAL ANALYSIS (per portion)	
Energy	300 cals
Protein	39.0 g
Carbohydrate	9.0 g
(of which sugars)	5.5 g
Fat	11.0 g
(of which saturates)	3.0 g
Fibre	2.0 g

SUITABLE FOR:
NUT-FREE, LOW-CHOLESTEROL, LOW-CALORIE, DAIRY PRODUCE-FREE AND DIABETIC DIETS.

---

fresh sage leaves

2 tbsp Dijon mustard

2 tbsp wholegrain mustard

50 ml (2 fl oz) apple juice

2 tbsp cider vinegar

salt and freshly ground black pepper

350 g (12 oz) pork tenderloin, cut into small cubes

2 crisp red apples

coarse sea salt, to garnish

rocket or watercress salad, to serve

PORK KEBABS WITH MUSTARD MARINADE

SERVES 4 • PREPARATION: 20 MINUTES, PLUS MARINATING • COOKING TIME: 15 MINUTES

1 To make the marinade, finely chop 1 tbsp sage. Place in a bowl, with the mustards, apple juice and cider vinegar. Season with salt and pepper.

2 Place the pork in the marinade, cover and leave in a cool place for at least 1 hour.

3 Cut the apples into quarters, remove the cores and cut into thick slices. Reserving the marinade, thread the pork cubes and apple slices alternately on to skewers, interspersing them with one or two fresh sage leaves.

4 Place the skewers under a hot grill for 10–15 minutes or until cooked, basting occasionally with the marinade. Serve on a bed of rocket or water-cress salad, garnished with sea salt.

NUTRITIONAL ANALYSIS (per portion)	
Energy	143 cals
Protein	20.0 g
Carbohydrate	6.0 g
(of which sugars)	6.0 g
Fat	4.5 g
(of which saturates)	1.5 g
Fibre	1.0 g

SUITABLE FOR:
GLUTEN-FREE, LOW-FAT, NUT-FREE, LOW-CHOLESTEROL, LOW-CALORIE, DAIRY PRODUCE-FREE AND DIABETIC DIETS.

1.1 kg (2½ lb) boneless loin of pork, rind removed

2 garlic cloves, peeled and thinly sliced

1 large red chilli, deseeded and finely chopped

2.5 cm (1 inch) piece fresh root ginger, peeled and finely chopped

150 ml (¼ pint) plum sauce

1 tbsp dark soy sauce

1 tsp Chinese five-spice powder

2 tbsp oil

CHINESE GARNISH
½ cucumber, deseeded and cut into thin matchsticks

5 spring onions, trimmed and cut into thin matchsticks

1 red chilli, deseeded and cut into thin matchsticks

NOTE: Cover the pork with a sheet of greaseproof paper and flatten with a rolling pin to a thickness of about 6.5 cm (2½ inches) – any more and the pork will take longer to cook.

SWEET AND SOUR SPICED PORK

SERVES 4 • PREPARATION: 30 MINUTES • COOKING TIME: 50 MINUTES

1 Trim the fat side of the loin of pork and lightly bat out (see Note). Turn the loin over and, using a small sharp knife, make deep slits in the meat then insert the slices of garlic.

2 Place the chilli and ginger in a bowl with 1 tbsp water, the plum sauce, soy sauce and Chinese five-spice powder.

3 Heat the oil in a small roasting tin on the hob and brown the meat, fat-side down, for 5 minutes. Turn over and brown the other side for 2–3 minutes. Brush the surface of the pork with a little of the plum sauce mixture and transfer to the oven. Cook at 200°C (400°F) Mark 6 for about 40 minutes. Baste the pork occasionally, brushing with some of the plum sauce mixture until the fat has caramelised and the pork is cooked.

4 For the garnish, place the cucumber and spring onions in a large bowl of ice-cold water for about 15 minutes until the onions curl. Drain and dry well.

5 Lift the pork from the roasting tin, cover loosely with foil; keep warm. Tilt the roasting tin and skim off the fat. Add the remaining plum sauce mixture to the juices in the roasting tin, bring to the boil and simmer for 1–2 minutes.

6 To serve, thickly slice the pork, spoon the sauce around it and garnish with the vegetables.

NUTRITIONAL ANALYSIS (per portion)	
Energy	420 cals
Protein	54.0 g
Carbohydrate	16.0 g
(of which sugars)	15.5 g
Fat	15.5 g
(of which saturates)	4.5 g
Fibre	0.5 g

SUITABLE FOR:
GLUTEN-FREE, NUT-FREE, LOW-CHOLESTEROL, LOW-CALORIE AND DAIRY PRODUCE-FREE.

Pork... a good buy

Pork is an ideal meat for busy cooks – quick to prepare and cook, it absorbs flavours well. And it's a healthy choice because pigs are now reared to have much less fat (less than chicken and other lean meat). A 100 g (3½ oz) portion of trimmed lean pork provides around 125 cals and only 4 g fat. Pork is a major source of zinc and of B vitamins, particularly niacin and B12.

50 g (2 oz) fresh breadcrumbs

50 ml (2 fl oz) coconut milk

450 g (1 lb) minced pork

2 tbsp Thai red curry paste

1 tbsp Thai fish sauce

2 tbsp chopped fresh basil

1 tbsp chopped fresh coriander

pinch of sugar

grated rind of 1 lime

1 tbsp squeezed lime juice

1 tbsp oil

HOT COCONUT PORK PATTIES

SERVES 4 • PREPARATION: 30 MINUTES, PLUS SOAKING • COOKING TIME: ABOUT 20 MINUTES

1 In a bowl, combine the breadcrumbs with the coconut milk. Allow to soak for 10 minutes.

2 In a bowl or food processor (with the plastic blade attached), mix the pork with breadcrumbs and the remaining ingredients, except the oil. Shape the mixture into 20 small patties.

3 Heat the oil in a large, non-stick frying pan and fry the patties in batches for 5 minutes on each side or until golden brown and cooked through.

NUTRITIONAL ANALYSIS (per portion)	
Energy	255 cals
Protein	26.0 g
Carbohydrate	11.5 g
(of which sugars)	1.0 g
Fat	11.5 g
(of which saturates)	5.5 g
Fibre	0.5 g

SUITABLE FOR:
NUT-FREE, LOW-CALORIE, DAIRY PRODUCE-FREE AND DIABETIC DIETS.

Right: Sweet and Sour Spiced Pork

4 pork shoulder steaks, about 150 g (5 oz) each

4 thin slices Parma ham, about 50 g (2 oz)

6 fresh sage leaves

ground black pepper

150 ml (¼ pint) pure, unsweetened apple juice (see Note)

25 g (1 oz) chilled butter, diced

squeeze of lemon juice

NOTE: Pure unsweetened apple juice makes a great substitute for white wine in many recipes if you don't want to use alcohol. There are plenty to choose from in all the supermarkets – look out for a clear juice with a sharp, clean flavour.

PORK STEAKS WITH SAGE AND APPLE

SERVES 4 • PREPARATION: 5 MINUTES • COOKING TIME: 10 MINUTES

1 Halve any large steaks. Lay a slice of Parma ham on top with a sage leaf, then secure to the meat with a wooden cocktail stick. Season the steaks with pepper.

2 In a non-stick, shallow frying pan, fry the pork for about 3–4 minutes on each side until golden brown.

3 Pour in the apple juice – it will sizzle and start to evaporate immediately. Scrape the bottom of the pan to loosen any crusty bits and let the liquid bubble until reduced by half. Lift the pork out on to a warm plate.

4 Return the pan to the heat, add the butter and swirl it around. When it has melted into the pan juices, add some lemon juice and pour over the pork before serving.

NUTRITIONAL ANALYSIS (per portion)	
Energy	258 cals
Protein	34.0 g
Carbohydrate	4.0 g
(of which sugars)	4.0 g
Fat	12.0 g
(of which saturates)	6.0 g
Fibre	0.0 g

SUITABLE FOR:
GLUTEN-FREE, NUT-FREE, LOW-CALORIE AND DIABETIC DIETS.

1.4 kg (3 lb) pork spare ribs

7.5 cm (3 inch) piece fresh root ginger, peeled and grated

6 garlic cloves, peeled and crushed

6 tbsp runny honey

6 tbsp light soy sauce

6 tbsp dry sherry

2 tsp hot chilli sauce

lime halves and coriander sprigs, to garnish

NOTE: Alternatively, the spare ribs may be cooked in a roasting tin at 240°C (475°F) Mark 9 for 35–40 minutes.

STICKY RIBS

SERVES 4 • PREPARATION: 5 MINUTES, PLUS MARINATING • COOKING TIME: 10 MINUTES

1 Cut the spare ribs into individual ribs, if necessary. Mix the ginger in a medium-sized bowl with the garlic, honey, soy sauce, sherry and chilli sauce. Add the spare ribs and stir to coat in the marinade. Cover and leave in the refrigerator for at least 4 hours, preferably overnight.

2 Reserving the marinade, cook the ribs under a hot grill for 4–5 minutes on each side or until the meat is well browned and comes off the bone easily (see Note). Transfer to a serving dish and keep warm.

3 Pour the grill pan juices into a small saucepan and add the reserved marinade. Bring to the boil and bubble to reduce until sticky. Brush over the ribs. Garnish with lime halves and coriander sprigs.

NUTRITIONAL ANALYSIS (per portion)	
Energy	270 cals
Protein	25.0 g
Carbohydrate	28.0 g
(of which sugars)	28.0 g
Fat	6.0 g
(of which saturates)	2.0 g
Fibre	0.0 g

SUITABLE FOR:

GLUTEN-FREE, NUT-FREE, LOW-CHOLESTEROL, LOW-CALORIE AND DAIRY PRODUCE-FREE DIETS.

---

6 large pork chops

3 tbsp plain flour

1 tbsp ground cumin

¾ tsp ground coriander

salt and freshly ground black pepper

2-3 tbsp olive oil

3 onions, peeled and thinly sliced

450 ml (¾ pint) white wine

¾ tsp caster sugar

1½ lemons, thinly sliced

350 g (12 oz) brown cap or chestnut mushrooms, quartered

LEMON-BRAISED PORK CHOPS WITH CUMIN AND MUSHROOMS

SERVES 6 • PREPARATION: 20 MINUTES • COOKING TIME: 45 MINUTES

1 Trim the pork chops of any excess fat. Sift the flour with the cumin, coriander, salt and pepper. Turn the chops in the spiced flour to coat.

2 Heat the oil in a frying pan, add the pork chops and brown on both sides. Using a slotted spoon, transfer the chops to a plate.

3 Stir the onions into the fat remaining in the pan and cook gently for 10 minutes or until soft and golden. Add the wine and caster sugar. Bring to the boil and boil briskly for about 5 minutes until reduced and slightly syrupy.

4 Arrange the lemon slices over the base of an ovenproof dish. Cover with the onions and wine, then place the chops on top. Cover with foil and bake at 190°C (375°F) Mark 5 for 20 minutes.

5 Remove the foil and add the quartered mushrooms, pushing them into the gaps between the pork chops. Bake, uncovered, for a further 15 minutes. Serve at once.

NUTRITIONAL ANALYSIS (per portion)	
Energy	470 cals
Protein	51.0 g
Carbohydrate	10.5 g
(of which sugars)	3.5 g
Fat	20.0 g
(of which saturates)	6.0 g
Fibre	1.5 g

SUITABLE FOR:

NUT-FREE, LOW-CHOLESTEROL, DAIRY PRODUCE-FREE AND DIABETIC DIETS.

4 lean pork escalopes, each weighing about 100 g (3½ oz)

2 tbsp olive oil

1 small onion, peeled and finely chopped

40 g (1½oz) pine nuts

25 g (1 oz) granary breadcrumbs

250 g (9 oz) baby spinach

40 g (1½ oz) freshly grated Parmesan cheese

¼ tsp freshly grated nutmeg

salt and freshly ground black pepper

150 ml (¼ pint) chicken stock

flat-leaf parsley, to garnish

PORK WITH SPINACH AND PINE NUTS

SERVES 4 • PREPARATION: 25 MINUTES • COOKING TIME: ABOUT 40 MINUTES

1 Lay the pork escalopes between two sheets of cling film and beat with a rolling pin to flatten.

2 Heat 1 tbsp oil in a frying pan. Add the onion and cook for 4 minutes. Add the pine nuts and breadcrumbs and cook for 2 minutes until lightly roasted. Stir in the spinach and cook briefly, stirring, until the spinach has wilted. Transfer the mixture to a bowl and stir in the cheese, nutmeg and salt and pepper. Leave to cool slightly.

3 Spoon the filling on to the pork escalopes and spread to within 1 cm (½ inch) of the edges. Roll up the escalopes and secure with cocktail sticks, or tie at several intervals with string.

4 Heat the remaining oil in the pan and fry the escalopes on all sides to brown. Transfer to an ovenproof dish. Stir the stock into the pan and bring to the boil. Pour into the dish, cover and bake at 180°C (350°F) Mark 4 for 25–30 minutes or until the pork is tender.

5 Lift out the pork and keep warm. Bring the juices to the boil and cook until slightly reduced. Season to taste. Slice the pork and serve with the sauce spooned over and garnished with parsley.

NUTRITIONAL ANALYSIS (per portion)	
Energy	340 cals
Protein	31.0 g
Carbohydrate	6.5 g
(of which sugars)	3.0 g
Fat	21.0 g
(of which saturates)	5.0 g
Fibre	2.0 g

SUITABLE FOR:

LOW-CHOLESTEROL, LOW-CALORIE AND DAIRY PRODUCE-FREE DIETS.

350 g (12 oz) stir-fry pork (see Note)

4 tbsp rice wine or dry sherry

2 tbsp soy sauce

3 tbsp stir-fry oil

450 g (1 lb) Chinese greens, such as pak choi and ung choi

2 x 300 g (10 oz) bags fresh stir-fry vegetables

about 1 tbsp Chinese five-spice paste

NOTE: Most super-markets sell stir-fry pork strips – neat lengths of pork with no waste and little fat.

STIR-FRIED PORK WITH CHINESE GREENS

SERVES 6 • PREPARATION: 5 MINUTES • COOKING TIME: 10 MINUTES

1 Toss together the pork, rice wine and soy sauce with 1 tbsp oil (if you have time, leave the pork to marinate for 1 hour at this stage). Shred the Chinese greens and, together with the stir-fry vegetables, rinse in cold water.

2 Use a slotted spoon to lift the pork from the marinade; reserve marinade. Heat a wok or large deep frying pan until very hot. Add 1 tbsp oil to the wok, with half the pork (cook it in batches to ensure it fries and seals quickly) and stir-fry for about 1 minute or until beginning to brown at the edges. Set aside and stir-fry the remaining pork.

3 Wipe out the wok, add the remaining oil and heat. Add the Chinese five-spice paste and all the vegetables and fry for a further 3–4 minutes. Return the pork and reserved marinade to the wok, bring to the boil and bubble for 1–2 minutes. Serve immediately.

NUTRITIONAL ANALYSIS (per portion)	
Energy	200 cals
Protein	18.0 g
Carbohydrate	5.0 g
(of which sugars)	4.5 g
Fat	10.0 g
(of which saturates)	5.0 g
Fibre	4.0 g

SUITABLE FOR:
GLUTEN-FREE, LOW-CHOLESTEROL, LOW-CALORIE, DAIRY PRODUCE-FREE AND DIABETIC DIETS.

400 g (14 oz) smoked or unsmoked gammon steaks, about 8 mm (⅜ inch) thick

2 tbsp olive oil

150 g (5 oz) baby onions, peeled and left whole

2 large carrots, peeled and thickly sliced

3 sticks celery, trimmed and sliced

4 garlic cloves, peeled and left whole

2 bay leaves

several sprigs thyme

2 tsp ground paprika

250 g (9 oz) Puy lentils, rinsed

600 ml (1 pint) light chicken or vegetable stock

black pepper

200 g (7 oz) spring greens, trimmed and shredded

150 ml (¼ pint) white wine

GAMMON WITH LENTILS

SERVES 4 • PREPARATION: 15 MINUTES • COOKING TIME: ABOUT 50 MINUTES

1 Cut the rind and excess fat from the gammon steaks. Cut each steak into large pieces, measuring about 7.5 x 5 cm (3 x 2 inches). Heat the oil in a large frying pan, add the steaks and fry briefly on both sides. Remove with a slotted spoon.

2 Add the onions, carrots and celery to the pan and fry for about 5 minutes until golden. Transfer to a casserole dish with the garlic, herbs, paprika, lentils and gammon.

3 Add the stock to the frying pan and bring to the boil. Season with pepper and pour into the casserole. Cover and bake at 160°C (325°F) Mark 3 for 35 minutes until the lentils are tender.

4 Stir in the spring greens and wine and return to the oven for a further 10 minutes until the greens are tender.

NUTRITIONAL ANALYSIS (per portion)	
Energy	450 cals
Protein	37.5 g
Carbohydrate	39.0 g
(of which sugars)	8.0 g
Fat	14.0 g
(of which saturates)	3.5 g
Fibre	8.0 g

SUITABLE FOR:
HIGH-FIBRE, GLUTEN-FREE, NUT-FREE, LOW-CHOLESTEROL, LOW-CALORIE, DAIRY PRODUCE-FREE AND DIABETIC DIETS.

1 lemon

350 g (12 oz) onions, peeled and thickly sliced

½ tsp ground cumin

¾ tsp salt

4 tbsp olive oil

450 g (1 lb) boned leg of lamb, cut into 2.5 cm (1 inch) cubes

cooked basmati rice, to serve

coriander sprigs, to garnish

NOTE: Grilling is one of the best methods of cooking lamb. Not only is it quick, it also produces delicious crispy lamb outside with a tender pink middle. Leg meat is the best cut for grilling and most supermarkets now sell it ready-diced.

SPICED LAMB WITH MELTING ONIONS

SERVES 4 • PREPARATION: 5 MINUTES • COOKING TIME: 15 MINUTES

1 Squeeze the lemon, then cut into quarters. Mix the lemon quarters, 3 tbsp lemon juice, the onions, ground cumin, salt and oil with the lamb until the meat and onions are thoroughly coated in the seasoning and oil. Place in an even layer in the bottom of a grill pan and sprinkle 3 tbsp water over the mixture.

2 Heat the grill to high and place the lamb, in the pan, about 5 cm (2 inches) away from the heat. Cook for 15 minutes until the lamb is well charred but pink in the middle, and the onions are soft and golden, stirring the mixture with a wooden spoon as it browns. (Some liquid will come out of the lamb and onions and this needs to evaporate before the lamb browns.)

3 Serve each portion with the grilled lemon (the flesh will be soft and mellow now) on a bed of basmati rice. Garnish with coriander.

NUTRITIONAL ANALYSIS (per portion)	
Energy	315 cals
Protein	23.0 g
Carbohydrate	7.5 g
(of which sugars)	7.0 g
Fat	21.0 g
(of which saturates)	7.0 g
Fibre	1.0 g

SUITABLE FOR:
GLUTEN-FREE, NUT-FREE, LOW-CHOLESTEROL, LOW-CALORIE, DAIRY PRODUCE-FREE AND DIABETIC DIETS.

GUARD OF HONOUR WITH HAZELNUT HERB CRUST

SERVES 6 • PREPARATION: 30 MINUTES • COOKING TIME: 35 MINUTES, PLUS COOLING

2 trimmed racks of lamb, about 800 g – 1 kg (1¾-2 ¼ lb) total weight
salt and freshly ground black pepper

HAZELNUT HERB CRUST
75 g (3 oz) fresh breadcrumbs, made from Italian bread, such as ciabatta
2 tbsp chopped fresh parsley
2 tbsp chopped fresh thyme
1 tbsp chopped fresh rosemary
2 garlic cloves, peeled and crushed
2 tbsp olive oil
50 g (2 oz) hazelnuts, toasted and roughly chopped
4 tbsp Dijon mustard

1 Trim the lamb racks and remove the fat and sinew from the ends of the rib bones. If the meat is very fatty, remove as much of the fat as possible and reserve. Season the racks with pepper.

2 Melt the reserved fat in a heavy-based frying pan, add the racks of lamb and sear on both sides. Remove the lamb from the pan and set aside until cool enough to handle. Join the racks together so the ribs interlock. Place in a roasting tin (clean rib bones uppermost) with the lamb juices, and roast at 200°C (400°F) Mark 6 for 10 minutes.

3 Meanwhile, make the crust. Combine the breadcrumbs, herbs, garlic, olive oil and seasoning for 30 seconds in a food processor, then add the hazelnuts and pulse for a further 30 seconds.

4 Remove the racks from the oven and spread the fatty side with the mustard; press the crust on.

5 Baste the lamb with the juices and return to the oven for 15–20 minutes. Remove from oven, cover with foil and leave for 10 minutes before carving.

NUTRITIONAL ANALYSIS
(per portion)

Energy	340 cals
Protein	25.5 g
Carbohydrate	10.0 g
(of which sugars)	0.5 g
Fat	22.0 g
(of which saturates)	7.0 g
Fibre	0.5 g

SUITABLE FOR:
LOW-CHOLESTEROL, LOW-CALORIE, DAIRY PRODUCE-FREE AND DIABETIC DIETS.

NOTE: Cooking the lamb for 15–20 minutes will produce medium rare meat. If preferred, cook for 20–25 minutes for medium and 25–30 minutes for well done.

SPICED AFRICAN LAMB

SERVES 6 • PREPARATION: 30 MINUTES, PLUS MARINATING • COOKING TIME: 2 HOURS

6 garlic cloves, sliced
3 tbsp chopped coriander
2 tsp each ground cumin, paprika and sea salt
½ tsp saffron strands
2 tsp Dijon mustard
1 tbsp runny honey
2 tbsp sun-dried tomato paste
4 tbsp olive oil
1.6 kg (3½ lb) shoulder of lamb, cut into large pieces (see Note)
225 g (8 oz) potatoes, peeled and cut into chunks
225 g (8 oz) carrots, peeled and cut into chunks
225 g (8 oz) shallots, peeled, leaving roots intact
300 ml (½ pint) white wine
2 sticks cinnamon
225 g (8 oz) can chick peas
225 g (8 oz) sultanas
salt and freshly ground black pepper

1 Mix the first 10 ingredients together. Place in a bowl with the lamb, stir to coat well, then cover and marinate overnight.

2 Place the potatoes, carrots and shallots in a roasting tin with the meat, marinade, wine, 150 ml (¼ pint) water and cinnamon sticks. Cover with foil and cook at 200°C (400°F) Mark 6 for 1 hour.

3 Drain the chick peas and add to the roasting tin with the sultanas. Cook for 30 minutes, then uncover and cook for a further 30 minutes to brown the ingredients. Season with salt and pepper to taste and serve.

NUTRITIONAL ANALYSIS
(per portion)

Energy	750 cals
Protein	57.0 g
Carbohydrate	54.0 g
(of which sugars)	41.0 g
Fat	38.0 g
(of which saturates)	15.0 g
Fibre	4.0 g

SUITABLE FOR:
GLUTEN-FREE, NUT-FREE, LOW-CHOLESTEROL, DAIRY PRODUCE-FREE AND DIABETIC DIETS.

NOTE: Ask your butcher to cut the lamb shoulder into large pieces, leaving the bone in.

1.8 kg (4 lb) leg of lamb, boned, or 2.7 kg (6 lb) shoulder of lamb, boned

2 tbsp olive oil

300 ml (½ pint) robust red wine

6 sprigs each rosemary and thyme

4 bay leaves

1 tsp redcurrant jelly

450 ml (¾ pint) lamb stock

TAPENADE

50 g (2 oz) can anchovy fillets, drained and chopped

125 g (4 oz) stoned black olives

2 garlic cloves, peeled

1 tbsp each chopped fresh rosemary, thyme and flat-leaf parsley

2 tbsp olive oil

salt and freshly ground black pepper

MARINATED LAMB WITH TAPENADE STUFFING

SERVES 6 • PREPARATION: 30 MINUTES, PLUS MARINATING • COOKING TIME: 1 HOUR 40 MINUTES

1 To make the tapenade, process the anchovies in a food processor with the olives, garlic and herbs until smooth. Gradually add the oil; season with pepper.

2 Stuff the bone cavity of the lamb with the mixture and sew up with thread or secure with cocktail sticks. Season again with pepper.

3 Make incisions all over the lamb and place in a large non-metallic bowl with the olive oil, wine, rosemary, thyme and bay leaves. Marinate for at least 6 hours or overnight.

4 Drain the lamb, reserving the marinade, then pat dry. Heat a large frying pan and quickly brown the lamb on all sides over a high heat. Place in a roasting tin, cook at 220°C (425°F) Mark 7 for 30 minutes, then turn the oven down to 200°C (400°F) Mark 6 for a further 45–60 minutes, basting from time to time.

5 Remove the lamb and keep warm. Skim the fat from the tin and discard. Add the reserved marinating liquor, redcurrant jelly and stock. Bring to the boil and bubble for 5–10 minutes. Adjust the seasoning and strain.

6 Thickly carve the lamb and serve with the juices.

NUTRITIONAL ANALYSIS (per portion)	
Energy	444 cals
Protein	35.0 g
Carbohydrate	2.0 g
(of which sugars)	1.5 g
Fat	30.0 g
(of which saturates)	10.0 g
Fibre	0.5 g

SUITABLE FOR:
GLUTEN-FREE, NUT-FREE, LOW-CHOLESTEROL, LOW-CALORIE, DAIRY PRODUCE-FREE AND DIABETIC DIETS.

NOTE: If you prefer lamb well done, cook for 1–1¾ hours.

Lamb... natural and flavoursome

Unlike some meats, lamb is naturally reared and produces good, flavoursome meat. It is particularly rich in niacin, one of the B vitamins required for the release of energy from food. It also provides useful amounts of zinc, needed especially by teenage boys. A 100 g (3½ oz) lean portion provides about 155 cals/8 g fat.

4 lean lamb leg steaks, each about 150 g (5 oz), trimmed of excess fat

salt and freshly ground black pepper

2 garlic cloves, peeled and roughly chopped

3 tbsp capers, drained

handful of parsley sprigs

75 g (3 oz) celeriac, peeled

50 g (2 oz) fresh white breadcrumbs

1 tbsp olive oil

150 ml (¼ pint) lamb or chicken stock

flat-leaf parsley, to garnish

grilled cherry tomatoes, to serve

NOTE: Cook and purée the leftover celeriac with a little thyme or rosemary and a spoonful of half-fat crème fraîche and use as an accompaniment.

LAMB STEAKS WITH A HERB AND CAPER CRUST

SERVES 4 • PREPARATION: 10 MINUTES • COOKING TIME: ABOUT 20 MINUTES

1 Pat the lamb dry on kitchen paper and season.

2 Put the garlic, capers and parsley sprigs in a blender or food processor and blend briefly until chopped. Add the celeriac and blend until finely chopped. Briefly blend in the breadcrumbs until evenly combined. Season.

3 Heat the oil in a frying pan, add the lamb steaks and fry quickly on both sides until browned. Transfer to a roasting tin with any cooking juices. Spoon the breadcrumb mixture on top of the steaks, packing down gently.

4 Roast in the oven at 190°C (375°F) Mark 5 for 15–18 minutes until the topping is crisp and golden. Transfer the lamb to serving plates and keep warm while making the gravy. Add the stock to the roasting tin and bring slowly to the boil, scraping up any residue. Pour around the lamb, garnish with parsley and serve with tomatoes.

NUTRITIONAL ANALYSIS (per portion)	
Energy	345 cals
Protein	32.0 g
Carbohydrate	10.0 g
(of which sugars)	1.0 g
Fat	20.0 g
(of which saturates)	8.0 g
Fibre	1.0 g

SUITABLE FOR:
NUT-FREE, LOW-CHOLESTEROL, LOW-CALORIE, DAIRY PRODUCE-FREE AND DIABETIC DIETS.

1 small onion, peeled and roughly chopped

2 garlic cloves, peeled and roughly chopped

500 g (1 lb 2oz) lean minced lamb

2 tsp coriander seeds

4 tsp mustard seeds

2 tsp ground cumin

salt and freshly ground black pepper

TO FINISH

2 tbsp olive oil

1 small onion, peeled and finely chopped

150 ml (¼ pint) lamb or chicken stock

3 tbsp chopped dill

4 tbsp half-fat crème fraîche

juice of 1 lemon

dill sprigs, to garnish

LAMB AND MUSTARD MEATBALLS WITH DILL

SERVES 6 • PREPARATION: 20 MINUTES • COOKING TIME: ABOUT 40 MINUTES

1 Put the onion and garlic in a food processor and blend briefly until chopped into small pieces. Add the lamb mince, seeds, cumin and a little seasoning and blend until the ingredients are evenly combined.

2 Take teaspoonfuls of the mixture and, using wet hands, shape into small balls, about 3 cm (1¼ inches) in diameter.

3 Heat the oil in a large frying pan and fry the meatballs for about 5 minutes until browned on all sides, shaking the pan frequently. Transfer to a small roasting tin and stir in the chopped onion. Roast at 180°C (350°F) Mark 4 for 30 minutes, shaking the pan occasionally until the meatballs are cooked through. Drain and keep warm.

4 Stir the stock, dill, crème fraîche and lemon juice into the tin and bring slowly to the boil, scraping up any residue in the pan. Cook, stirring for about 3 minutes until the sauce is slightly thickened. Return the meatballs to the sauce; heat through for 1 minute, then serve garnished with dill.

NUTRITIONAL ANALYSIS (per portion)	
Energy	211 cals
Protein	17.0 g
Carbohydrate	20.0 g
(of which sugars)	1.5 g
Fat	15.0 g
(of which saturates)	6.0 g
Fibre	0.4 g

SUITABLE FOR:

GLUTEN-FREE, NUT-FREE, LOW-CHOLESTEROL, LOW-CALORIE AND DIABETIC DIETS.

---

700 g (1½ lb) boned leg of lamb

75 g (3 oz) ready-to-eat dried apricots

150 g (5 oz) ready-to-eat dried figs

1 garlic clove, peeled and crushed

juice of 2 lemons

50 g (2 oz) spring onions, finely chopped

6 tbsp Greek yogurt

5 tbsp smooth peanut butter

2 tsp each ground coriander and cumin seeds

1 tsp ground fenugreek

½ tsp chilli powder

3 tbsp olive oil

salt and freshly ground black pepper

225 g (8 oz) onions

2 large oranges

MARINATED LAMB KEBABS

SERVES 8 • PREPARATION: 45 MINUTES, PLUS MARINATING • COOKING TIME: 30 MINUTES

1 Trim the lamb and cut into large cubes, allowing about three pieces per skewer. Place the apricots and figs in a bowl; add water to cover completely.

2 Mix the garlic with 8 tbsp lemon juice, the spring onions and all the remaining ingredients apart from the whole onions and oranges. Add the lamb to the marinade and stir to coat well. Cover and refrigerate, along with the soaking apricots and figs, for at least 6 hours or overnight.

3 Peel and quarter the onions, then separate the quarters into leaves. Thickly slice the oranges. Thread the meat on to metal skewers, alternating with onions and fruit.

4 Barbecue for 25–30 minutes or until the lamb is pink to the centre.

NUTRITIONAL ANALYSIS (per portion)	
Energy	345 cals
Protein	22.0 g
Carbohydrate	20 0g
(of which sugars)	18.5 g
Fat	20.0 g
(of which saturates)	7.0 g
Fibre	3.5 g

SUITABLE FOR:

GLUTEN-FREE, NUT-FREE, LOW-CHOLESTEROL, LOW-CALORIE AND DIABETIC DIETS.

450 g (1 lb) minced lamb

225 g (8 oz) large onion, peeled and finely chopped

1 sprig fresh rosemary or large pinch dried

200 ml (7 fl oz) red wine

350 g (12 oz) well-flavoured fresh tomato sauce (see Note)

salt and freshly ground black pepper

350 g (12 oz) dried tagliatelle

feta cheese shavings, to serve

sprigs of fresh rosemary, to garnish

VARIATION:

This tasty ragu sauce can also be made with minced beef.

LAMB AND ROSEMARY RAGU

SERVES 6 • PREPARATION: 5 MINUTES • COOKING TIME: 40 MINUTES

1 In a non-stick pan, brown the minced lamb for 5–7 minutes, stirring to break down any lumps. Remove the mince and set aside.

2 Add the onion to the pan with the rosemary (you don't need to add any extra oil – there should be enough fat left over from the mince) and fry together for about 10 minutes until the onion is soft and golden.

3 Return the mince to the pan, keep over a high heat and stir in the wine; it should bubble immediately. Scrape the bottom of the pan to loosen any crusty bits, then bubble for 1–2 minutes until reduced by half. Stir in the tomato sauce. Cover and simmer gently for 20 minutes. Season with salt and pepper to taste.

4 Meanwhile, cook the tagliatelle in boiling salted water for about 10 minutes; drain. Stir in the lamb ragu, sprinkle the cheese over, garnish with rosemary and serve.

NUTRITIONAL ANALYSIS (per portion)	
Energy	390 cals
Protein	23.0 g
Carbohydrate	49.0 g
(of which sugars)	5.0 g
Fat	9.0 g
(of which saturates)	4.0 g
Fibre	3.0 g

SUITABLE FOR:

NUT-FREE, LOW-CHOLESTEROL, LOW-CALORIE AND DIABETIC DIETS.

NOTE: It's a good idea to have a stock of home-made tomato sauce in the freezer, ready to use for creating quick dishes like this one.

2 large red chillies, halved and deseeded

3 large garlic cloves, peeled and thinly sliced

1 stick lemon grass, thinly sliced

2.5 cm (1 inch) piece galangal or fresh root ginger, peeled and thinly sliced

8 shallots, peeled and thinly sliced

2 tbsp palm sugar or dark soft brown (muscovado) sugar, plus extra to taste

1 tbsp tamarind paste (see Note)

1 tbsp Thai fish sauce

juice of 1 lime

450 g (1 lb) beef fillet

1 tbsp oil

1 small head Chinese leaves, roughly chopped

3 ripe tomatoes, roughly sliced

1 cucumber, roughly sliced

handful fresh mint sprigs

handful fresh coriander sprigs

GRILLED BEEF WITH JAEW

SERVES 4 • PREPARATION: 20 MINUTES • COOKING TIME: 25 MINUTES

1 Put the chillies, garlic, lemon grass and galangal in a dry wok or frying pan with 2 tbsp shallots. Fry over a high heat until the mixture begins to char, but not burn.

2 Transfer the contents of the pan to a food processor, add 2 tbsp sugar, the tamarind paste and fish sauce. Blend to a paste. Add 200 ml (7 fl oz) water; blend again for 2–3 minutes. Strain, pressing mixture firmly to extract the flavoured liquid; reserve the mixture left in the sieve. Taste the extracted liquid and add lime juice a little at a time. Add sugar to taste, for a good balance of sweet and sour. Set aside.

3 Rub the beef with a little of the reserved mixture from the sieve. Moisten a griddle or a shallow, non-stick frying pan with oil and brown the fillet well on all sides. Continue to cook for 15 minutes for medium-rare or 20 minutes for just pink. Cool.

4 Fry the remaining shallots in the rest of the oil until well browned and crisp. Drain well and cool.

5 Toss the Chinese leaves, tomatoes and cucumber with the mint, coriander, crisp shallots and reserved dressing. Thinly slice the beef, cut into bite-sized pieces, toss into the salad; serve.

NUTRITIONAL ANALYSIS (per portion)	
Energy	209 cals
Protein	27.0 g
Carbohydrate	5.5 g
(of which sugars)	5.0 g
Fat	9.0 g
(of which saturates)	3.0 g
Fibre	2.0 g

SUITABLE FOR:
GLUTEN-FREE, NUT-FREE, LOW-CHOLESTEROL, LOW-CALORIE, DAIRY PRODUCE-FREE AND DIABETIC DIETS.

NOTE: Tamarind is a spice pod usually sold in a sticky block, which you thin with water; tamarind paste is also available and is easier to use.

---

225 g (8 oz) broad beans, cooked and shelled

1 garlic clove, peeled and crushed

50 g (2 oz) freshly grated Pecorino or Parmesan cheese

1-2 tbsp lemon juice

2 tsp creamed horseradish sauce

1 tbsp fresh mint

120 ml (4 fl oz) extra-virgin olive oil

4 rump steaks, each about 175 g (6 oz)

salt and freshly ground black pepper

225 g (8 oz) cherry tomatoes

STEAK WITH BEAN PESTO

SERVES 4 • PREPARATION: 20 MINUTES • COOKING TIME: 10 MINUTES

1 Place the broad beans and the next 5 ingredients in a food processor. Pulse for about 30 seconds or until well blended. With the machine running, gradually add the olive oil. Set aside.

2 Season the steaks well with black pepper. Brush a frying pan or heavy-based, ridged, cast iron pan with oil. Heat until very hot and cook the steaks quickly, for about 1 minute on each side for rare, 2 minutes for medium and 3–4 minutes for well done, depending on thickness. Keep warm. Cook the tomatoes for 1–2 minutes in the hot pan.

3 To serve, spoon the pesto over the steaks and serve with the cherry tomatoes.

NUTRITIONAL ANALYSIS (per portion)	
Energy	540 cals
Protein	48.0 g
Carbohydrate	6.0 g
(of which sugars)	3.0 g
Fat	36.0 g
(of which saturates)	10.0 g
Fibre	4.0 g

SUITABLE FOR:
GLUTEN-FREE, NUT-FREE, AND DIABETIC DIETS.

Right: Grilled Beef with Jaew

125 g (4 oz) dried egg thread noodles

3 tbsp sunflower oil

1 tbsp dark soy sauce

1 small onion, peeled and finely chopped

2 garlic cloves, peeled and finely chopped

2.5 cm (1 inch) piece fresh root ginger, peeled and grated

4 kaffir lime leaves, shredded

225 g (8 oz) lean minced beef (see Note)

2 tbsp Indian medium curry paste

1 tsp turmeric

½ tsp paprika

¼ tsp chilli powder

1 red pepper, deseeded and sliced

125 g (4 oz) French beans

coriander, to garnish

SAUCE

2 tbsp tamarind paste

1 tbsp Thai fish sauce

2 tsp sugar

90 ml (3 fl oz) beef stock

STIR-FRIED BEEF WITH NOODLES

SERVES 4 • PREPARATION: 20 MINUTES • COOKING TIME: 15 MINUTES

1 Soak the noodles according to the packet instructions; drain well and pat dry.

2 Meanwhile, prepare the sauce. Place the tamarind paste in a bowl and whisk in the remaining ingredients until smooth.

3 Heat 1 tbsp oil in a wok or large frying pan, add the noodles and soy sauce and stir-fry for 30 seconds. Remove from the pan and set aside.

4 Add the remaining oil to the pan. Add the onion, garlic, ginger and lime leaves and fry, stirring, for 5 minutes. Add the beef, curry paste and spices and stir-fry for 3 minutes.

5 Add the red pepper and halved French beans and stir-fry for 3 minutes. Blend in the sauce and simmer for a further 3 minutes. Carefully stir in the noodles and heat through for 2 minutes. Transfer to a serving dish. Garnish with coriander and serve at once.

NUTRITIONAL ANALYSIS (per portion)	
Energy	340 cals
Protein	18.0 g
Carbohydrate	31.0 g
(of which sugars)	7.5 g
Fat	16.5 g
(of which saturates)	4.0 g
Fibre	2.5 g

SUITABLE FOR:
NUT-FREE, LOW-CHOLESTEROL, LOW-CALORIE, DAIRY PRODUCE-FREE AND DIABETIC DIETS.

NOTE: When buying minced beef, look at the colour – the darker it is, the leaner the mince will be. Nowadays the percentage of fat is usually declared on the packaging – 85% lean minced beef is common. The leaner the better!

300 g (10 oz) fillet steak, cut into thin strips

4 tsp mild chilli powder

salt and freshly ground black pepper

3 tbsp oil

140 g (4½ oz) pack chorizo sausage, sliced and cut into strips

2 sticks celery, trimmed and cut into thin 5 cm (2 inch) strips

2 red peppers, deseeded and cut into thin 5 cm (2 inch) strips

150 g (5 oz) onions, peeled and chopped

2 garlic cloves, peeled and crushed

300 g (10 oz) long-grain white rice

1 tbsp tomato paste

1 tbsp ground ginger

2 tsp Cajun seasoning (see Note)

900 ml (1½ pints) beef stock

8 large cooked prawns

BEEF JAMBALAYA

SERVES 4 • PREPARATION: 10 MINUTES • COOKING TIME: 30 MINUTES

1 Mix the sliced steak with 1 tsp each mild chilli powder and ground black pepper.

2 Heat 1 tbsp oil in a large frying pan and cook the chorizo until golden. Add the celery and peppers to the pan and cook for 3–4 minutes or until just beginning to soften and brown. Remove from the pan and set aside. Add 2 tbsp oil to the pan and fry the steak; lift out and keep warm.

3 Add the onions and cook until softened. Add the garlic, rice, tomato paste, remaining chilli powder, ground ginger and Cajun seasoning, then cook for 2 minutes until the rice turns translucent.

4 Stir in the stock, season with salt and bring to the boil. Cover and simmer for about 20 minutes, stirring occasionally, until the rice is tender and most of the liquid absorbed.

5 Add the reserved steak, chorizo, peppers, celery and prawns. Heat gently, stirring, until hot.

NUTRITIONAL ANALYSIS (per portion)	
Energy	664 cals
Protein	36.0 g
Carbohydrate	64.0 g
(of which sugars)	8.0 g
Fat	28.0 g
(of which saturates)	2.6 g
Fibre	2.2 g

SUITABLE FOR:
NUT-FREE, DAIRY PRODUCE-FREE AND DIABETIC DIETS.

NOTE: Cajun seasoning can be found in the spice section of most supermarkets.

3 tbsp olive oil

700 g (1½ lb) piece braising steak cut into small 'steaks'

350 g (12 oz) onion, peeled and thickly sliced

25 g (1 oz) can anchovy fillets in oil, drained and chopped

2 tbsp capers, chopped (see Note)

2 tbsp chopped fresh parsley

1 tbsp chopped fresh thyme, plus extra sprigs to garnish

1 tsp ready-made English mustard

SLOW-BRAISED BEEF

SERVES 4 • PREPARATION: 15 MINUTES •
COOKING TIME: 2 HOURS 10 MINUTES

1 Heat the oil in a deep flameproof casserole and brown the meat well, a few pieces at a time. When the last of the meat has been browned, stir in 4 tbsp cold water to loosen any sediment from the bottom of the pan. Return all the meat to the casserole.

2 Add the onions, anchovies, capers, herbs and mustard. Mix together until thoroughly combined.

3 Crumple a sheet of greaseproof paper, then wet it. Open out and press down over the surface of the meat. Cover the casserole tightly and cook at 170°C (325°F) Mark 3 for 2 hours or until the beef is meltingly tender. Check the pot after an hour to make sure the mixture is still moist. Add water if it looks dry.

4 Garnish with thyme and serve at once.

NUTRITIONAL ANALYSIS (per portion)	
Energy	335 cals
Protein	42.0 g
Carbohydrate	6.0 g
(of which sugars)	5.0 g
Fat	18.0 g
(of which saturates)	5.0 g
Fibre	1.5 g

SUITABLE FOR:
GLUTEN-FREE, NUT-FREE, LOW-CHOLESTEROL, LOW-CALORIE, DAIRY PRODUCE-FREE AND DIABETIC DIETS.

NOTE: Capers now come in more than one form. Don't use the salted variety for this recipe but opt for capers in vinegar – the tiny ones will not need to be chopped.

2 tbsp wine vinegar

6-7 tbsp olive oil

1 tbsp each chopped fresh chives and parsley

1 tsp caster sugar

50 g (2 oz) black olives, finely chopped

sea salt flakes and freshly ground black pepper

350 g (12 oz) plum tomatoes, finely sliced

50 g (2 oz) shallots, peeled and finely chopped

4 fillet steaks, each about 125 g (4 oz)

250 g (9 oz) tub ricotta cheese

flat-leaf parsley sprigs, to garnish

rocket and toasted ciabatta, to accompany

WARM STEAK ESCALOPES AND TOMATO SALAD

SERVES 4 • PREPARATION: 20 MINUTES • COOKING TIME: 5 MINUTES

1 Combine the vinegar, 5 tbsp oil, herbs, sugar and olives in a small bowl and season well. Place the tomatoes in a shallow dish with the shallots and spoon the dressing over. Set aside while you prepare the steaks.

2 Place the steaks between 2 sheets of greaseproof paper or cling film and gently flatten with a rolling pin to form very thin escalopes; season with ground black pepper. Heat the remaining oil in a large heavy-based frying pan. Add the steaks in batches and cook over a high heat for 30 seconds on each side.

3 Arrange the tomato salad on 4 individual serving plates and top each serving with a large spoonful of ricotta cheese. Arrange the steak on top of the tomatoes, garnish with parsley sprigs and serve immediately, accompanied by rocket leaves and toasted ciabatta slices.

NUTRITIONAL ANALYSIS (per portion)	
Energy	450 cals
Protein	35.0 g
Carbohydrate	6.0 g
(of which sugars)	6.0 g
Fat	31.0 g
(of which saturates)	10.0 g
Fibre	1.5 g

SUITABLE FOR:
GLUTEN-FREE, NUT-FREE, LOW-CALORIE AND DIABETIC DIETS.

2 tbsp olive oil

225 g (8 oz) red onions, roughly chopped

1 garlic clove, peeled and crushed

1 large red chilli, deseeded and finely chopped

1 tsp ground cumin

450 g (1 lb) lean minced beef

400 g (14 oz) can chopped tomatoes

1 tbsp tomato paste

450 ml (¾ pint) beef stock

400 g (14 oz) can pinto beans, drained

salt and freshly ground black pepper

tortilla chips (optional) and grated reduced-fat Cheddar cheese, to serve

tomato and avocado salsa, to serve (see Note)

CHILLI BEEF

SERVES 4 • PREPARATION: 25 MINUTES • COOKING TIME: 40 MINUTES

1 Heat 1 tbsp oil in a frying pan, add the onions and cook, stirring, for 10 minutes or until soft but not coloured. Add the garlic, chilli and cumin, cook for 1 minute, then set aside.

2 Wipe out the pan, add the remaining oil and mince, then cook for 10 minutes. Add the onion mixture, tomatoes, tomato paste and stock. Bring to the boil and simmer for 15 minutes. Add the pinto beans and cook for a further 15 minutes; season with salt and pepper.

3 Pile the chilli into a heatproof serving dish with a handful of tortilla chips, if using, and sprinkle some cheese over the top. Place under a hot grill for few minutes or until bubbling. Serve with a tomato and avocado salsa spooned over the top.

NUTRITIONAL ANALYSIS
(per portion)

Energy	360 cals
Protein	27.0 g
Carbohydrate	26.0 g
(of which sugars)	9.0 g
Fat	17.0 g
(of which saturates)	6.0 g
Fibre	8.0 g

SUITABLE FOR:
HIGH-FIBRE, GLUTEN-FREE, NUT-FREE, LOW-CHOLESTEROL, LOW-CALORIE AND DIABETIC DIETS.

---

4 small lean venison steaks, about 2-2.5 cm (¾-1 inch) thick

150 ml (¼ pint) chicken stock

1 tbsp olive oil

15 g (½ oz) butter

2 small firm pears, cut into wedges

150 g (5 oz) fresh or frozen blackberries

2 tbsp redcurrant jelly

MARINADE
1 onion, peeled and chopped

2 carrots, peeled and chopped

2 sticks celery, trimmed and chopped

4 garlic cloves, peeled and chopped

6 juniper berries, crushed

2 bay leaves

several sprigs rosemary

300 ml (½ pint) red wine

salt and freshly ground black pepper

VENISON WITH FRUIT

SERVES 4 • PREPARATION: 20 MINUTES, PLUS MARINATING • COOKING TIME: 40 MINUTES

1 To make the marinade, mix all the ingredients in a shallow dish. Add the venison steaks and turn lightly to coat. Cover and marinate for 24 hours.

2 Drain the venison from the marinade, reserving the marinade. Pat the venison dry thoroughly on kitchen paper. Put the marinade ingredients into a saucepan, add the stock and bring to the boil. Reduce the heat, cover and simmer gently for about 25 minutes until the vegetables are tender.

3 Heat the oil and butter in a frying pan. Add the pear wedges and fry quickly until golden. Remove with a slotted spoon and reserve. Add the venison steaks and fry for 3 minutes. Turn the steaks over and cook for a further 3 minutes (see Note).

4 Remove the meat with a slotted spoon and keep warm. Strain the stock into the frying pan. Add the blackberries and pears and cook for 1–2 minutes until heated through. Remove the fruit from the pan and keep warm.

5 Add the redcurrant jelly to the pan, season and bring to the boil. Cook for about 1 minute until slightly thickened. Serve with the venison and fruit.

NUTRITIONAL ANALYSIS
(per portion)

Energy	325 cals
Protein	35.0 g
Carbohydrate	15.0 g
(of which sugars)	14.0 g
Fat	8.5 g
(of which saturates)	3.5 g
Fibre	2.6 g

SUITABLE FOR:
GLUTEN-FREE, NUT-FREE, LOW-CHOLESTEROL, LOW-CALORIE, DAIRY PRODUCE-FREE AND DIABETIC DIETS.

NOTE: Cooking the venison for this time leaves the venison pink in the centre. If you prefer the meat cooked through, allow about 6 minutes each side.

900 g (2 lb) sweet
potatoes

125 g (4 oz) Swiss red
chard, shredded

120 ml (4 fl oz) skimmed
milk

3 spring onions, trimmed
and finely sliced

salt and freshly ground
black pepper

500 g (1 lb) calves' liver,
cut into strips

2 tbsp olive oil

3 tbsp balsamic vinegar

1 tbsp finely chopped
fresh sage leaves

1 tbsp finely chopped
fresh basil leaves

fresh basil and sage
leaves, to garnish

GLAZED CALVES' LIVER WITH SWEET POTATO AND SWISS CHARD MASH

SERVES 4 • PREPARATION: 20 MINUTES • COOKING TIME: 30 MINUTES

1 Peel the sweet potatoes and cut into chunks, then cook in boiling water for 15–20 minutes until tender. Add the chard and cook for 1 minute. Drain and return to the pan.

2 Place the milk in a small pan with the spring onions and bring to the boil. Remove from the heat and add to the sweet potatoes. Mash lightly and season with salt and pepper. Cover and keep warm in a very low oven.

3 Season the liver with black pepper. Heat a non-stick frying pan over moderate heat. When hot add the oil and stir-fry the strips of calves liver for 3 minutes. Add the balsamic vinegar and continue cooking until most of the liquid has evaporated. Stir in the sage and basil, then add a little salt to taste.

4 Arrange mounds of the sweet potato mash on individual plates and spoon the liver on top. Garnish with basil and sage leaves and serve.

NUTRITIONAL ANALYSIS (per portion)	
Energy	455 cals
Protein	30.0 g
Carbohydrate	53.0 g
(of which sugars)	15.0 g
Fat	15.0 g
(of which saturates)	4.0 g
Fibre	5.5 g

SUITABLE FOR:

GLUTEN-FREE, NUT-FREE, LOW-CALORIE AND DIABETIC DIETS.

vegetarian

CARIBBEAN RATATOUILLE

175 g (6 oz) sweet potato, peeled

175 g (6 oz) pumpkin, peeled

1 aubergine

1 red pepper, deseeded

2 tbsp olive oil

1 large onion, peeled and finely sliced

2 garlic cloves, peeled and crushed

1 fresh chilli, deseeded and finely chopped

2 sticks celery, trimmed and chopped

125 g (4 oz) okra, trimmed and chopped

1 tsp dried thyme

2 tsp finely chopped fresh basil

400 g (14 oz) can tomatoes, drained and chopped

salt and freshly ground black pepper

basil leaves, to garnish

SERVES 6 • PREPARATION: 20 MINUTES • COOKING TIME: 50 MINUTES

1 Cut the sweet potato, pumpkin, aubergine and red pepper into 2.5 cm (1 inch) cubes.

2 Place the olive oil in a roasting tin. Add the onion, garlic, sweet potato, pumpkin, aubergine and red pepper. Cook in the oven at 220°C (425°F) Mark 7 for 20 minutes.

3 Add the chilli, celery, okra and dried thyme to the pan and continue to cook for a further 10–15 minutes or until all the vegetables are just tender.

4 Add the basil and canned tomatoes and mix well. Season with salt and pepper, then return to the oven for 15 minutes. Adjust the seasoning and serve garnished with basil.

NUTRITIONAL ANALYSIS (per portion)	
Energy	111 cals
Protein	3.0 g
Carbohydrate	16.0 g
(of which sugars)	10.0 g
Fat	4.5 g
(of which saturates)	1.0 g
Fibre	4.5 g

SUITABLE FOR:
GLUTEN-FREE, LOW-FAT, NUT-FREE, LOW-CHOLESTEROL, LOW-CALORIE, DAIRY PRODUCE-FREE AND DIABETIC DIETS.

Vegetables... a vital role

Together with fruit, vegetables play a key role in the diet, as they contain a host of important vitamins and minerals which work together to protect us from disease.

MIXED VEGETABLE CURRY

450 g (1 lb) small potatoes or sweet potatoes

2 tbsp oil

1 onion, peeled and sliced

6 garlic cloves, peeled and finely chopped

50 g (2 oz) creamed coconut, coarsely grated

4 tbsp mild curry paste

225 g (8 oz) tomatoes, finely chopped

225 g (8 oz) carrots, peeled and sliced

225 g (8 oz) cauliflower, divided into bite-sized florets

1 tsp salt

225 g (8 oz) French beans, trimmed

225 g (8 oz) spinach, washed, drained and roughly chopped

1 tbsp black mustard seeds

fresh coriander, to garnish

SERVES 4 • PREPARATION: 25 MINUTES • COOKING TIME: 45 MINUTES

1 Boil the potatoes in salted water for 10 minutes (peel and chop the sweet potatoes into bite-sized pieces). Drain and set aside.

2 Heat the oil in a large sauté pan, add the onion and garlic and cook for about 5 minutes, stirring occasionally. Add the coconut and curry paste and cook, stirring, for 1 minute. Add the tomatoes and cook for 3–4 minutes until the mixture resembles a thick paste.

3 Add the carrots, potatoes, cauliflower, salt and 150 ml (¼ pint) water (no more than this as the thick sauce will thin out).

4 Bring to the boil, cover and simmer for about 15 minutes, then add the beans, spinach and mustard seeds. Cook for 10 minutes or until the vegetables are cooked.

5 Adjust the seasoning if necessary, then garnish with coriander and serve.

NUTRITIONAL ANALYSIS (per portion)	
Energy	300 cals
Protein	9.0 g
Carbohydrate	33.0 g
(of which sugars)	12.0 g
Fat	16.0 g
(of which saturates)	8.5 g
Fibre	7.0 g

SUITABLE FOR:
HIGH-FIBRE, GLUTEN-FREE, LOW-CALORIE, DAIRY PRODUCE-FREE AND DIABETIC DIETS.

Right: Caribbean Ratatouille

3 tbsp olive oil

2 large onions, peeled and thinly sliced

2 garlic cloves, peeled and crushed

1 tbsp chopped fresh thyme

2 tsp paprika

2 large carrots, peeled and chopped

2 large potatoes, peeled and chopped

600 ml (1 pint) tomato juice

450 ml (¾ pint) vegetable stock

2 tbsp tomato paste

2 tsp chilli sauce

2 bay leaves

2 red peppers

soured cream (optional)

VEGETABLE GOULASH

SERVES 6 • PREPARATION: 20 MINUTES •
COOKING TIME: 1¼ HOURS

1 Heat 3 tbsp oil in a flameproof casserole, add the onions, garlic, thyme and paprika and cook gently for 5 minutes. Add the carrots and potatoes and cook for 10 minutes, stirring occasionally.

2 Add the tomato juice, stock, tomato paste, chilli sauce and bay leaves. Bring to the boil, cover and simmer for 30 minutes.

3 Meanwhile, grill the peppers for 15–20 minutes, turning frequently, until the skin is charred. Cover with a damp cloth and leave to cool slightly, then peel off the skins, deseed and slice thickly.

4 Add the peppers to the goulash. Cover and simmer gently for a further 25 minutes until the vegetables are cooked. Adjust the seasoning.

5 Serve topped with soured cream, if wished.

NUTRITIONAL ANALYSIS (per portion)	
Energy	160 cals
Protein	4.0 g
Carbohydrate	24.0 g
(of which sugars)	10.0 g
Fat	6.0 g
(of which saturates)	0.8 g
Fibre	3.5 g

SUITABLE FOR:

GLUTEN-FREE, NUT-FREE, LOW-CHOLESTEROL, LOW-CALORIE AND DIABETIC DIETS.

---

50 g (2 oz) dried porcini mushrooms

450 g (1 lb) small button onions

1 tbsp sunflower oil

2 garlic cloves, peeled and crushed

2 tsp flour

75 ml (3 fl oz) red wine

450 ml (¾ pint) well-flavoured vegetable stock

1 tbsp dark soy sauce or mushroom ketchup

1 tbsp cider vinegar

1 bay leaf

1 sprig thyme

1 sprig sage

225 g (8 oz) small button mushrooms

125 g (4 oz) shiitake mushrooms, sliced

225 g (8 oz) oyster mushrooms, sliced

4 slices French bread, toasted

1 tbsp fresh chopped parsley, to garnish

MIXED MUSHROOM STEW

SERVES 4 • PREPARATION: 10 MINUTES, PLUS
SOAKING • COOKING TIME: 30 MINUTES

1 Soak the dried porcini mushrooms in boiling water for 15 minutes. Drain and rinse well.

2 Cook the onions in boiling water for 2 minutes. Drain, then peel away the skins and trim the ends.

3 Heat the oil in a large flameproof casserole, add the onions and cook, stirring, for 5–6 minutes or until beginning to brown. Stir in the garlic and flour and cook for a further minute. Blend in the wine, stock, soy sauce and cider vinegar, then bring to the boil and simmer for 2 minutes.

4 Tie the bay leaf, thyme and sage together and add to the casserole. Simmer over a very low heat for 12–15 minutes or until the onions are tender.

5 Stir the button, shiitake and soaked porcini mushrooms into the casserole and bring to the boil. Simmer for 3 minutes. Add the oyster mushrooms and cook for 2–3 minutes until tender.

6 Lift the mushrooms and onions on to a warmed serving dish; keep warm. Discard the herbs, then bubble the cooking liquid for 5 minutes, until syrupy. Season and pour over the mushrooms. Serve with toasted bread, sprinkled with parsley.

NUTRITIONAL ANALYSIS (per portion)	
Energy	248 cals
Protein	10.0 g
Carbohydrate	41.0 g
(of which sugars)	7.0 g
Fat	5.0 g
(of which saturates)	0.5 g
Fibre	3.0 g

SUITABLE FOR:

LOW-FAT, NUT-FREE, LOW-CHOLESTEROL, LOW-CALORIE, DAIRY PRODUCE-FREE AND DIABETIC DIETS.

2 tbsp olive oil

175 g (6 oz) red onions, peeled and finely chopped

4 garlic cloves, peeled and crushed

2 tbsp sun-dried tomato paste

½ tsp chilli powder (optional)

125 g (4 oz) carrots, peeled and sliced

75 g (3 oz) celery, trimmed and sliced

4 tomatoes, preferably plum, skinned, deseeded and roughly chopped

2 sprigs thyme or a large pinch dried

2 bay leaves

salt and freshly ground black pepper

450 ml (¾ pint) vegetable stock

2 x 400 g (14 oz) cans beans, such as butter, flageolet, kidney or chick peas, drained and rinsed

50 g (2 oz) French beans, trimmed and cut into short lengths

thyme sprigs, to garnish

TUSCAN BEAN STEW

SERVES 4 • PREPARATION: 30 MINUTES • COOKING TIME: 50 MINUTES

1 In a non-stick pan, heat the oil, add the onions and cook for 10 minutes or until soft. Add the garlic, tomato paste and chilli powder (if using) and cook for 1–2 minutes.

2 Add the next 5 ingredients and season with salt and pepper. Pour in the stock, bring to the boil and simmer, stirring occasionally, for 20–30 minutes or until soft.

3 Add the canned beans and French beans, then simmer for 5-10 minutes or until the beans have heated through and the French beans are just tender. Serve hot, garnished with thyme and accompanied by pesto croûtes (see Note).

NUTRITIONAL ANALYSIS (per portion)	
Energy	295 cals
Protein	15.5 g
Carbohydrate	44.0 g
(of which sugars)	15.0 g
Fat	7.0 g
(of which saturates)	1.0 g
Fibre	15.0 g

SUITABLE FOR:
HIGH-FIBRE, GLUTEN-FREE, LOW-CHOLESTEROL, LOW-CALORIE, DAIRY PRODUCE-FREE AND DIABETIC DIETS.

Beans... mean more

Beans are an excellent source of soluble dietary fibre, which helps reduce high blood cholesterol levels. Their other advantage, particularly if you have a hearty appetite or are trying to slim, is that they are incredibly filling but low in fat.

2 tbsp vegetable oil

1 large onion, peeled and finely chopped

4 tsp Thai green curry paste

600 ml (1 pint) vegetable stock

200 g (7 oz) washed new potatoes, cut in half

225 g (8 oz) easy-cook long grain rice

200 g (7 oz) courgettes, sliced

200 g (7 oz) carrots, peeled and sliced

150 g (5 oz) broccoli, divided into florets

125 g (4 oz) tomatoes, cut into quarters

150 g (5 oz) frozen spinach, thawed

300 ml (½ pint) coconut milk

THAI VEGETABLE CURRY

SERVES 6 • PREPARATION: 15 MINUTES • COOKING TIME: 35 MINUTES

1 Heat the oil in a large frying pan. Add the onion and green curry paste, then cook for 4–5 minutes. Add the stock and potatoes, bring to the boil, then cover and cook for 20 minutes or until the potatoes are just tender.

2 Meanwhile, cook the rice according to the packet instructions.

3 Add the courgettes, carrots and broccoli to the curry. Cook for 3–4 minutes or until the vegetables are tender. At the last minute, add the tomatoes, spinach and coconut milk and heat through thoroughly. Serve the curry on a bed of rice.

NUTRITIONAL ANALYSIS (per portion)	
Energy	490 cals
Protein	8.0 g
Carbohydrate	44.0 g
(of which sugars)	7.0 g
Fat	13.0 g
(of which saturates)	8.0 g
Fibre	3.5 g

SUITABLE FOR:
GLUTEN-FREE, NUT-FREE, DAIRY PRODUCE-FREE AND DIABETIC DIETS.

---

2 large potatoes, peeled

2 medium-sized turnips, peeled

2 parsnips, peeled

2 carrots, peeled

1 leek, trimmed

2 courgettes, trimmed

1 aubergine, trimmed

3 tbsp olive oil

2 onions, peeled and chopped

2 garlic cloves, peeled and chopped

1 fresh red chilli, deseeded and sliced

1 tsp ground allspice

1 stick cinnamon

1 litre (1¾ pints) vegetable stock

400 g (14 oz) can chopped tomatoes

400 g (14 oz) can chick peas, drained

½ tsp salt and freshly ground black pepper

500 g (1 lb) couscous

125 g (4 oz) seedless raisins

4 tomatoes, skinned, deseeded and chopped

75 g (3 oz) dried apricots, stoned

75 g (3 oz) prunes, stoned

chopped flat-leaf parsley and coriander, to garnish

MOROCCAN TAGINE

SERVES 8 • PREPARATION: 30 MINUTES • COOKING TIME: 55 MINUTES

1 Cut the larger prepared vegetables into chunks.

2 Heat the oil in a large saucepan (over which a steamer or colander fits). Add the onion and garlic and cook over a low heat for 5 minutes, stirring frequently, until softened. Add the chilli, allspice and cinnamon, then pour in the stock and canned tomatoes and cook for a further 5 minutes.

3 Add the potatoes, turnips, parsnips, carrots and chick peas, then season with the salt and pepper and bring to the boil. Reduce the heat to low and simmer for 30 minutes, stirring from time to time.

4 Meanwhile, place the couscous in a large bowl and stir in the raisins together with 1 litre (1¾ pints) boiling water. Cover and stand for 10 minutes until the water is absorbed. Line a steamer or metal colander with muslin; spoon in the couscous.

5 Add the fresh tomatoes, leek, courgettes, aubergine and dried fruit to the pan and bring back to a simmer. Place the steamer or colander over the pan of vegetables, cover with a lid and steam the couscous while the vegetables continue to cook for 15 minutes; remove cinnamon stick.

6 Spoon the couscous on to a warmed platter, top with the vegetables and sprinkle with herbs.

NUTRITIONAL ANALYSIS (per portion)	
Energy	430 cals
Protein	13.0 g
Carbohydrate	82.0 g
(of which sugars)	30.0 g
Fat	8.0 g
(of which saturates)	1.0 g
Fibre	11.0 g

SUITABLE FOR:
HIGH-FIBRE, NUT-FREE, LOW-CALORIE, DAIRY PRODUCE-FREE AND DIABETIC DIETS.

NOTE: Packed with vitamins, minerals and fibre, this tagine should be served with harissa sauce to complete the Middle Eastern flavours.

Right: Moroccan Tagine

350 g (12 oz) sweet potatoes, peeled and roughly chopped

salt and freshly ground black pepper

225 g (8 oz) plum tomatoes, chopped

225 g (8 oz) aubergines, roughly chopped

225 g (8 oz) courgettes, trimmed and halved

225 g (8 oz) red peppers, halved and deseeded

225 g (8 oz) onions, peeled and chopped

2 garlic cloves, peeled

1 tsp chopped fresh thyme

50 ml (2 fl oz) olive oil

50 ml (2 fl oz) white wine

225 g (8 oz) passata or 400 g (14 oz) can chopped plum tomatoes (see Note)

1 tsp caster sugar

175 g (6 oz) firm goat's cheese, thickly sliced

thyme sprigs and roasted garlic slivers, to garnish

ROASTED VEGETABLE RATATOUILLE

SERVES 6 • PREPARATION: 30 MINUTES • COOKING TIME: 1½ HOURS

1 Cook the sweet potatoes in a pan of boiling salted water for 10 minutes or until tender, then drain. Place in a large roasting tin with the remaining vegetables, garlic, thyme and oil; season. Cook at 220°C (425°F) Mark 7 for 45–60 minutes, turning occasionally, until golden brown.

2 Meanwhile, place the wine, passata and sugar in a pan. Bring to the boil and bubble for 10 minutes or until thick, then season well.

3 Place the roasted vegetables in an ovenproof dish. Mash the roasted garlic and mix into the tomato sauce. Spoon over the vegetables and arrange the cheese on top.

4 Return to the oven for 20 minutes or until golden. Leave for 5 minutes, then garnish with thyme and roasted garlic and serve.

NUTRITIONAL ANALYSIS (per portion)	
Energy	225 cals
Protein	7.0 g
Carbohydrate	23.0 g
(of which sugars)	13.0 g
Fat	11.5 g
(of which saturates)	4.0 g
Fibre	4.5 g

SUITABLE FOR:
GLUTEN-FREE, NUT-FREE, LOW-CALORIE AND DIABETIC DIETS.

NOTE: Passata is made from puréed tomatoes – great for tomato sauces. It's available from most supermarkets.

---

2 tbsp olive oil

1 small onion, peeled and chopped

¼ tsp chilli flakes

2 garlic cloves, peeled and finely chopped

200 ml (7 fl oz) dry white wine

400 g (14 oz) can green lentils, drained and rinsed

450 g (1 lb) broccoli, cut into small florets

225 g (8 oz) baby spinach

LOW-FAT HOLLANDAISE
150 ml (¼ pint) low-fat natural yogurt

1 tsp lemon juice

2 egg yolks

1 tsp Dijon mustard

salt and freshly ground black pepper

SAUTÉED BROCCOLI AND GREEN LENTILS WITH LOW-FAT HOLLANDAISE

SERVES 4 • PREPARATION: 10 MINUTES: • COOKING TIME: 30 MINUTES

1 To make the hollandaise, beat together the yogurt, lemon juice and egg yolks in a heatproof bowl (or the top of a double boiler). Place over simmering water and cook, stirring, for 15 minutes or until thick. (The sauce will become thinner after 10 minutes, but will thicken again). Keep warm.

2 Heat the olive oil in a wok or large frying pan (with a lid). Add the onion, chilli flakes and garlic and fry for 5 minutes.

3 Pour the wine into the pan and bubble for 2–3 minutes until reduced slightly. Add the lentils and heat through for 2 minutes.

4 Stir in the broccoli, cover and simmer for 2 minutes. Add the spinach, cover and cook for a further 1–2 minutes until the spinach has wilted. Season and serve with the hollandaise on top.

NUTRITIONAL ANALYSIS (per portion)	
Energy	295 cals
Protein	19.0 g
Carbohydrate	24.0 g
(of which sugars)	7.0 g
Fat	11.0 g
(of which saturates)	2.0 g
Fibre	8.0 g

SUITABLE FOR:
HIGH-FIBRE, GLUTEN-FREE, LOW-CALORIE AND DIABETIC DIETS.

WATCHPOINT:
The young, the elderly, pregnant women and those with immune-deficiency diseases should not eat raw or lightly cooked eggs, to avoid the possible risk of salmonella.

300 g (10 oz) packet tofu, drained and cut into 2.5 cm (1 inch) cubes

2 tbsp sunflower oil

2 carrots, peeled and thinly sliced

175 g (6 oz) broccoli, cut into small florets

125 g (4 oz) shiitake mushrooms, halved

1 leek, trimmed and sliced

4 spring onions, trimmed and sliced

125 g (4 oz) mangetout, trimmed

toasted sesame seeds, to garnish

GLAZE

2 tbsp hoisin sauce

2 tbsp dark soy sauce

2 tbsp sherry vinegar

1 tbsp chilli sauce

1 tbsp runny honey

2 tsp sesame oil

STIR-FRIED VEGETABLES WITH HOISIN AND TOFU

SERVES 4 • PREPARATION: 20 MINUTES • COOKING TIME: 30 MINUTES

1 To make the glaze, combine the hoisin sauce, soy sauce, sherry vinegar, chilli sauce, honey and sesame oil in a bowl.

2 Place the tofu in a shallow roasting tin, pour two-thirds of the glaze over the tofu and toss to coat. Bake on the top shelf of the oven at 230°C (445°F) Mark 8 for 20 minutes, stirring halfway through cooking.

3 Heat the sunflower oil in a wok or large, non-stick frying pan. When hot, add the carrots, broccoli and mushrooms and stir-fry for 3 minutes. Add the leek, spring onions and mangetout and stir-fry for a further 2 minutes.

4 Stir 3 tbsp water into the remaining glaze and add to the wok. Cook for 3–4 minutes until all the vegetables are tender. Stir in the roasted tofu and serve at once, sprinkled with the sesame seeds.

NUTRITIONAL ANALYSIS	
(per portion)	
Energy	190 cals
Protein	11.0 g
Carbohydrate	13.0 g
(of which sugars)	10.0 g
Fat	11.0 g
(of which saturates)	1.5 g
Fibre	3.5 g

SUITABLE FOR:

GLUTEN-FREE, NUT-FREE, LOW-CHOLESTEROL, LOW-CALORIE, DAIRY PRODUCE-FREE AND DIABETIC DIETS.

5 cm (2 inch) piece fresh root ginger, peeled and chopped

3 garlic cloves, peeled and roughly chopped

2 tbsp olive oil

1 large onion, peeled and finely sliced

1 red chilli, deseeded and chopped

¼ tsp cayenne pepper

2 tsp ground cumin

1 tsp ground coriander

1 tsp ground turmeric

juice of 1 lime

150 ml (¼ pint) vegetable stock

500 g (1¼ lb) peeled pumpkin or squash

salt and freshly ground black pepper

420 g (15 oz) can mixed beans, drained and rinsed

225 g (8 oz) young spinach

3 tbsp chopped fresh coriander

LIME RAITA
1 cucumber

225 ml (8 fl oz) Greek yogurt

grated rind of 1 lime

SPICY BEANS WITH PUMPKIN AND SPINACH

SERVES 6 • PREPARATION: 20 MINUTES • COOKING TIME: 40 MINUTES

1 Put the ginger, garlic and 4 tbsp water in a spice blender and blend to form a smooth paste.

2 Heat the oil in large saucepan, add the onion and chilli and cook gently for 5–7 minutes or until softened. Add the cayenne, cumin, coriander and turmeric and cook for 1 minute.

3 Stir in the ginger and garlic paste and cook for a further minute. Add the lime juice, vegetable stock and pumpkin. Season with salt and pepper, bring to the boil, then reduce the heat slightly and simmer for 15–20 minutes or until the pumpkin is tender.

4 Meanwhile, make the lime raita: grate the cucumber and squeeze out the excess liquid. Place in a bowl and stir in the yogurt and lime rind, then season with salt and pepper. Cover and chill until required.

5 Add the beans to the pan and cook for 2 minutes until heated. Finally stir in the spinach, cover with a lid and cook until just wilted, stirring once. Stir in the coriander; adjust the seasoning.

6 Serve in individual bowls, topped with the raita.

NUTRITIONAL ANALYSIS (per portion)	
Energy	200 cals
Protein	10.0 g
Carbohydrate	19.0 g
(of which sugars)	3.0 g
Fat	10.0 g
(of which saturates)	3.0 g
Fibre	6.5 g

SUITABLE FOR:
HIGH-FIBRE, GLUTEN-FREE, NUT-FREE, LOW-CHOLESTEROL, LOW-CALORIE AND DIABETIC DIETS.

---

2 tbsp olive oil

225 g (8 oz) onion, peeled and finely chopped

2 garlic cloves, peeled and crushed

400 g (14 oz) arborio (risotto) rice

120 ml (4 fl oz) dry white wine

1.7 litres (3 pints) well-flavoured vegetable stock

350 g (12 oz) cooked petit pois or very young peas

2 tbsp chopped fresh mint

salt and freshly ground black pepper

PEA AND MINT RISOTTO

SERVES 4 • PREPARATION: 5 MINUTES • COOKING TIME: 45 MINUTES

1 Heat the oil in a large flameproof casserole, add the onion and cook over a very low heat for 10 minutes or until the onion is soft, but not coloured. Add the garlic and cook for a further 2 minutes.

2 Stir the rice into the onion mixture and cook for 3 minutes, stirring. Add the wine and simmer for 2 minutes.

3 Heat the vegetable stock in a separate pan and very gradually add to the rice, stirring continuously, until all the stock has been absorbed. (This will take about 30 minutes.)

4 Stir in the peas and mint, season and serve.

NUTRITIONAL ANALYSIS (per portion)	
Energy	510 cals
Protein	14.0 g
Carbohydrate	92.0 g
(of which sugars)	5.5 g
Fat	7.0 g
(of which saturates)	1.0 g
Fibre	5.0 g

SUITABLE FOR:
GLUTEN-FREE, NUT-FREE, LOW-CHOLESTEROL, LOW-CALORIE, DAIRY PRODUCE-FREE AND DIABETIC DIETS.

VARIATION:

Try sprinkling this fresh-tasting risotto with a little crumbled feta cheese just before serving.

4 large yellow peppers

2 tbsp extra-virgin olive oil

2 garlic cloves, peeled and crushed

2 shallots, peeled and finely chopped

½ red chilli, deseeded and finely chopped

50 g (2 oz) basmati rice

1 tsp ground cumin

4 large tomatoes, skinned, deseeded and diced

1 small red onion, peeled and finely chopped

2 tbsp chopped fresh coriander

½ tsp dried oregano

juice of 1 lime

2 tbsp sunflower oil

salt and freshly ground black pepper

finely chopped tomato and coriander sprigs, to garnish

STUFFED YELLOW PEPPERS

SERVES 4 • PREPARATION: 15 MINUTES • COOKING TIME: 1¼ HOURS

1 Cut the tops off the peppers and scoop out the seeds and membranes. Trim the tops; reserve.

2 Heat the oil in a saucepan, add the garlic, shallots and chilli and cook for 1 minute. Stir in the rice and pour over 450 ml (¾ pint) boiling water. Bring back to the boil, cover the pan and reduce the heat to low. Cook for 12 minutes or until all the water has been absorbed and the rice is cooked.

3 Stir the cumin, tomatoes, red onion, coriander, oregano, lime and sunflower oil into the cooked rice. Season with salt and pepper.

4 Spoon the rice mixture into the peppers, and replace the tops. Place in a greased roasting tin, cover with foil and bake at 190°C (375°F) Mark 5 for 1 hour.

5 Remove the peppers from the oven and serve garnished with the tomatoes and coriander sprigs.

NUTRITIONAL ANALYSIS (per portion)	
Energy	220 cals
Protein	4.0 g
Carbohydrate	25.0 g
(of which sugars)	14.0 g
Fat	12.0 g
(of which saturates)	1.5 g
Fibre	4.5 g

SUITABLE FOR:

GLUTEN-FREE, NUT-FREE, LOW-CHOLESTEROL, LOW-CALORIE, DAIRY PRODUCE-FREE AND DIABETIC DIETS.

8 large flat mushrooms, wiped

4½ tbsp olive oil

salt and freshly ground black pepper

2 tbsp balsamic vinegar

2 tsp soft brown (muscovado) sugar

1-2 tbsp chopped flat-leaf parsley, to garnish

BEAN MASH
400 g (14 oz) can cannellini beans, drained

400 g (14 oz) can flageolet beans, drained

squeeze of lemon juice

2 garlic cloves, peeled and crushed

2 tbsp olive oil

3 tbsp chopped flat-leaf parsley

GRILLED MUSHROOMS WITH BEAN MASH

SERVES 4 • PREPARATION: 15 MINUTES • COOKING TIME: 15 MINUTES

1 Brush the mushrooms with 1 tbsp olive oil and season with salt and pepper. Grill for 5–6 minutes, then turn over, brush with ½ tbsp oil and cook for another 5–6 minutes until softened and golden.

2 In a small bowl, whisk 3 tbsp olive oil with the balsamic vinegar and sugar.

3 To make the bean mash, put the beans in a large saucepan and roughly mash. Stir in the remaining ingredients and season with salt and pepper. Gently heat through until the mash is piping hot.

4 Divide the mash between 4 warmed serving plates, arrange the mushrooms on top and spoon over the dressing. Sprinkle with parsley and serve.

NUTRITIONAL ANALYSIS (per portion)	
Energy	335 cals
Protein	15.0 g
Carbohydrate	29.0 g
(of which sugars)	5.0 g
Fat	18.0 g
(of which saturates)	3.0 g
Fibre	11.0 g

SUITABLE FOR:
HIGH-FIBRE, GLUTEN-FREE, NUT-FREE, LOW-CHOLESTEROL, LOW-CALORIE, DAIRY PRODUCE-FREE AND DIABETIC DIETS.

2 aubergines

salt and cayenne pepper

1 tbsp extra-virgin olive oil

1 tbsp balsamic vinegar

225 g (8 oz) cooked chick peas

½ tsp ground coriander

2 garlic cloves, peeled and crushed

125 g (4 oz) red onion, peeled and finely chopped

grated rind and juice of 1 lemon

1 tbsp chopped fresh parsley

50 g (2 oz) black olives, stoned and chopped

purple basil sprigs, to garnish

PISTOU
2 garlic cloves, peeled and crushed

3 tbsp chopped fresh purple basil

2 tbsp extra-virgin olive oil

freshly ground black pepper

AUBERGINE AND CHICK PEA STACKS WITH PISTOU

SERVES 4 • PREPARATION: 30 MINUTES, PLUS STANDING • COOKING TIME: 20 MINUTES

1 Slice the aubergines into thick rounds. Place in a colander and lightly sprinkle with salt. Leave to stand for 15 minutes. Rinse the aubergines and pat dry and sprinkle with cayenne pepper.

2 Brush a large griddle with oil, and cook the aubergine slices on the hot griddle for 3 minutes on each side.

3 Transfer the cooked aubergines to a platter and drizzle with balsamic vinegar. Leave to marinate.

4 Chop the chick peas, then place in a bowl and add the ground coriander, garlic, onion, lemon rind and juice, parsley and olives. Stir well; set aside.

5 To make the pistou, mix the garlic and basil together, stir in the olive oil and season to taste.

6 Layer up the 'stacks' – put a slice of aubergine on 4 individual plates. Spread half of the chick pea mixture over the aubergine slices. Arrange a second slice of aubergine on top of each stack and spread with the remaining chick pea mixture. Finish with a layer of aubergine.

7 Drizzle over the pistou, garnish and serve.

NUTRITIONAL ANALYSIS (per portion)	
Energy	246 cals
Protein	10.0 g
Carbohydrate	23.0 g
(of which sugars)	5.0 g
Fat	13.0 g
(of which saturates)	2.0 g
Fibre	8.0 g

SUITABLE FOR:
HIGH-FIBRE, GLUTEN-FREE, NUT-FREE, LOW-CHOLESTEROL, LOW-CALORIE, DAIRY PRODUCE-FREE AND DIABETIC DIETS.

Right: Aubergine and Chick Pea Stacks with Pistou

350 g (12 oz) waxy potatoes, peeled

225 g (8 oz) parsnips, peeled

1 onion, peeled and sliced

1 garlic clove, peeled and crushed

1 tbsp chopped fresh sage

salt and freshly ground black pepper

1 egg, lightly beaten

2 tbsp sunflower oil

175 g (6 oz) reduced-fat Cheddar cheese, grated

salad leaves, to serve

PARSNIP, POTATO AND CHEESE RÖSTI

SERVES 4 • PREPARATION: 10 MINUTES• COOKING TIME: 20 MINUTES

1 Grate the potatoes and parsnips using the medium grater attachment of a food processor; squeeze out the excess liquid.

2 Place the grated vegetables, onion, garlic and sage in a large bowl. Season with salt and pepper, then stir in the egg.

3 Heat the oil in a large, non-stick frying pan. When hot, spread half of the vegetable mixture over the base of the pan. Scatter over the cheese, then top with the remaining vegetable mixture, spreading it flat.

4 Cook over a low heat for about 10 minutes until golden underneath. Slide the rösti out on to a large plate and flip back into the pan. Cook for a further 10 minutes until the underside is browned and the vegetables are cooked through.

5 Cut into wedges and serve with salad leaves.

NUTRITIONAL ANALYSIS (per portion)	
Energy	295 cals
Protein	19.0 g
Carbohydrate	23.0 g
(of which sugars)	4.5 g
Fat	14.5 g
(of which saturates)	5.5 g
Fibre	4.0 g

SUITABLE FOR:
GLUTEN-FREE, NUT-FREE, LOW-CALORIE AND DIABETIC DIETS.

300 ml (½ pint) vegetable stock

25 g (1 oz) dried mushrooms

450 g (1 lb) fresh spinach, washed and prepared, or 350 g (12 oz) frozen leaf spinach, thawed

225 g (8 oz) reduced-fat soft cheese

1 tbsp vegetable oil

450 g (1 lb) brown-cap mushrooms, roughly chopped

1 bunch spring onions, trimmed and roughly chopped

flat-leaf parsley, to garnish

PANCAKES
50 g (2 oz) plain white flour

50 g (2 oz) plain wholemeal flour

1 egg

350 ml (12 fl oz) skimmed milk

salt and freshly ground black pepper

vegetable oil, for greasing

NOTE: Interleave leftover pancakes with greaseproof paper, wrap and freeze for future use.

MUSHROOM AND SPINACH PANCAKES

SERVES 4 • PREPARATION: 1 HOUR, PLUS STANDING AND SOAKING • COOKING TIME: 1 ½ HOURS

1 To make the pancake batter, blend together the flours, egg, milk and a pinch of salt in a blender or food processor. Cover and set aside for 30 minutes.

2 Pour the stock over the dried mushrooms and leave to soak for 30 minutes.

3 Lightly oil a small non-stick crêpe pan. When hot, add enough batter to coat the base of the pan thinly. Cook the pancake for 1–2 minutes until golden brown, then turn and cook for a further 30 seconds. Transfer to a plate. Continue with the remaining batter to make 10–12 pancakes.

4 Cook the spinach in a pan for 2–3 minutes until just wilted. Cool, squeeze out the excess moisture and chop. Mix with the soft cheese and season with salt and pepper to taste.

5 Heat 1 tbsp oil in a pan, add the chopped brown-cap mushrooms and spring onions and cook for about 10 minutes or until lightly browned. Add the soaked dried mushrooms and stock and bring to the boil, then reduce the heat and simmer for 15–20 minutes or until syrupy. Season. Blend half the mushroom mixture in a food processor until smooth. Return to the pan and combine with the remaining mushrooms.

6 Place half the spinach mixture in a lightly oiled, 1.1 litre (2 pint) shallow, ovenproof dish. Using about 6 pancakes (see Note), layer them with the mushroom mixture and the remaining spinach mixture, finishing with a mushroom layer.

7 Cook at 200°C (400°F) Mark 6 for 30 minutes or until well browned and hot. Serve garnished with flat-leafed parsley.

NUTRITIONAL ANALYSIS (per portion)	
Energy	375 cals
Protein	16.5 g
Carbohydrate	28.0 g
(of which sugars)	7.0 g
Fat	22.0 g
(of which saturates)	11.6 g
Fibre	4.0 g

SUITABLE FOR:
NUT-FREE, LOW-CALORIE AND DIABETIC DIETS.

Mushrooms... high on flavour

Mushrooms are valuable in a vegetarian diet as they provide robust flavour and texture. They also contain more protein, riboflavin and niacin than most vegetables. Raw mushrooms are virtually fat-free, but they are often cooked in fat which of course increases the calorie count. It's best to use a non-stick pan and a minimum of fat.

Left: Mushroom and Spinach Pancakes

2 red peppers

4 tbsp olive oil

3 tbsp lemon juice

1 red onion, peeled and finely chopped

75 g (3 oz) sun-dried tomatoes, drained and sliced

1 tbsp chopped fresh red or green basil

salt and freshly ground black pepper

700 g (1½ lb) asparagus

crusty bread, to serve

ROASTED ASPARAGUS AND RED PEPPER SALAD

SERVES 4 • PREPARATION: 15 MINUTES • COOKING TIME: 50 MINUTES

1 Place the peppers, skin-side up, in a roasting tin and cook at 220°C (425°F) Mark 7 for 30 minutes or until the skin is charred. Place in a bowl and cover with cling film until cool enough to handle. Remove the skin from the peppers and slice.

2 In a large bowl, whisk together 2 tbsp oil and the lemon juice, then mix in the onion, tomatoes, basil and sliced red peppers. Season to taste.

3 Remove the tough ends of the asparagus and pare a little of the tough outer skin from the base of each stalk. Arrange the asparagus in a roasting tin.

4 Spoon the remaining oil over the asparagus and shake lightly to mix. Roast in the oven at 200°C (400°F) Mark 6 for about 20 minutes until just tender, turning once during cooking.

5 Serve the asparagus with the red pepper salad and chunks of crusty bread.

NUTRITIONAL ANALYSIS (per portion)	
Energy	270 cals
Protein	7.0 g
Carbohydrate	12.0 g
(of which sugars)	10.5 g
Fat	22.0 g
(of which saturates)	3.0 g
Fibre	5.0 g

SUITABLE FOR:
GLUTEN-FREE, NUT-FREE, LOW-CHOLESTEROL, LOW-CALORIE, DAIRY PRODUCE-FREE AND DIABETIC DIETS.

---

225 g (8 oz) polenta

salt and freshly ground black pepper

4 tbsp chopped fresh herbs, such as oregano, chives and flat-leaf parsley

100 g (3½ oz) freshly grated Parmesan cheese

vegetable oil, for brushing

basil leaves, to garnish

TOMATO AND BASIL SAUCE
1 tbsp olive oil

3 garlic cloves, peeled and crushed

500 g (1 lb) carton creamed tomatoes or passata

1 bay leaf

sprig of fresh thyme

caster sugar

3 tbsp chopped fresh basil

CHEESY POLENTA WITH TOMATO AND BASIL SAUCE

SERVES 6 • PREPARATION: 15 MINUTES, PLUS COOLING • COOKING TIME: 35 MINUTES

1 Lightly oil a 25 x 16.5 cm (10 x 6½ inch) dish. In a large pan, bring 1.1 litres (2 pints) water and ¼ tsp salt to the boil. Sprinkle in the polenta, whisking constantly. Reduce the heat and simmer, stirring frequently, for 10–15 minutes or until the mixture leaves the side of the pan.

2 Stir in the herbs and Parmesan and season to taste. Turn into the prepared dish and cool.

3 Meanwhile, make the sauce. Heat the olive oil in a pan and fry the garlic for 30 seconds (do not brown). Add the tomatoes, bay leaf, thyme and a large pinch of sugar. Season, bring to the boil and simmer, uncovered, for 5–10 minutes. Remove the bay leaf and thyme; add the chopped basil.

4 To serve, cut the polenta into pieces and lightly brush with oil. Cook on a hot griddle for 3–4 minutes on each side, or grill for 7–8 minutes on each side. Serve with the sauce and basil leaves.

NUTRITIONAL ANALYSIS (per portion)	
Energy	275 cals
Protein	11.0 g
Carbohydrate	30.0 g
(of which sugars)	2.5 g
Fat	11.0 g
(of which saturates)	4.0 g
Fibre	1.5 g

SUITABLE FOR:
GLUTEN-FREE, NUT-FREE, LOW-CALORIE AND DIABETIC DIETS.

NOTE: A popular staple in northern Italy, polenta is now widely available in supermarkets. It's bland by itself, but add plenty of fresh herbs and a little Parmesan, serve with a rich tomato sauce and the result is delicious!

2 small red onions, peeled and each cut into 4 petals, roots left on

1 fennel bulb, trimmed and cut into 8 pieces

4 baby courgettes, about 175 g (6 oz), trimmed and cut in half on the diagonal

175 g (6 oz) baby corn, cut on the diagonal

50 g (2 oz) baby asparagus or tips

1 tbsp olive oil

125 g (4 oz) feta cheese, to serve

basil sprigs, to garnish

BASIL DRESSING
2 garlic cloves, peeled and crushed

juice of 1 lemon

3 tbsp olive oil

3 tbsp chopped fresh basil

salt and freshly ground black pepper

CHAR-GRILLED SUMMER VEGETABLE KEBABS

SERVES 4 • PREPARATION: 15 MINUTES • COOKING TIME: 35 MINUTES

1 Soak 8 bamboo skewers in cold water for 30 minutes.

2 Assemble the dressing: put all the ingredients into a small saucepan.

3 Blanch the onion for 8–10 minutes or until tender. Blanch the fennel for 5–7 minutes or until tender. Blanch the courgettes for 4–5 minutes or until tender. Blanch the baby corn for 3–4 minutes or until tender. Blanch the asparagus for 2–3 minutes or until tender.

4 Thread a variety of blanched vegetables on to each skewer. Lightly oil a griddle pan and when hot, brown a batch of kebabs for 2–3 minutes on each side until evenly browned. Repeat with the remaining kebabs.

5 Meanwhile, gently heat the dressing in the pan.

6 To serve, crumble the feta over the kebabs, drizzle with the basil dressing and garnish with basil sprigs.

NUTRITIONAL ANALYSIS (per portion)	
Energy	245 cals
Protein	8.0 g
Carbohydrate	13.0 g
(of which sugars)	5.0 g
Fat	18.5 g
(of which saturates)	6.0 g
Fibre	3.0 g

SUITABLE FOR:
GLUTEN-FREE, NUT-FREE, LOW-CALORIE AND DIABETIC DIETS.

4 baby cauliflowers

salt and freshly ground black pepper

CHEESE SAUCE

25 g (1 oz) plain white flour

450 ml (¾ pint) skimmed or semi-skimmed milk

75 g (3 oz) mature Cheddar, grated

25 g (1 oz) freshly grated Parmesan cheese

LOW-FAT CHEESE SAUCE WITH BABY CAULIFLOWER

SERVES 4 • PREPARATION: 5 MINUTES • COOKING TIME: 15 MINUTES

1 Cook the cauliflowers in a large saucepan of boiling, salted water for 15 minutes or until tender.

2 Meanwhile, make the sauce. Place the flour in a saucepan, slowly whisk in the milk and bring to the boil, stirring continuously. Reduce the heat and simmer gently for 1 minute. Remove from the heat. Stir in the grated Cheddar and Parmesan cheese and season to taste.

3 Drain the cauliflowers, transfer to a warmed serving dish, pour the sauce over and serve.

NUTRITIONAL ANALYSIS (per portion)	
Energy	200 cals
Protein	15.0 g
Carbohydrate	13.5 g
(of which sugars)	8.0 g
Fat	10.0 g
(of which saturates)	6.0 g
Fibre	2.0 g

SUITABLE FOR:
LOW-CALORIE AND DIABETIC DIETS.

---

4 tomatoes, preferably large plum, halved and deseeded

3 red peppers, deseeded and roughly chopped

225 g (8 oz) onions, preferably red, peeled and roughly chopped

1 red chilli, deseeded and finely chopped

6 garlic cloves, unpeeled

1 tsp sugar

salt and freshly ground black pepper

4 tbsp olive oil

2 tbsp sun-dried tomato paste

6 small eggs

chopped or dried parsley, to garnish

EGG AND ROASTED PEPPER STEW

SERVES 3 • PREPARATION: 10 MINUTES • COOKING TIME: 55 MINUTES

1 Roughly chop two tomato halves; reserve the remaining halves. Place the chopped tomatoes and peppers in a roasting tin, to form a layer. Add the onions to the tin with the chilli and unpeeled garlic. Sprinkle with the sugar and season well with salt and pepper.

2 Drizzle with the oil. Cook at 230°C (450°F) Mark 8 for 25 minutes, stirring occasionally. Stir in the tomato paste. Sit the reserved tomato halves on top and continue to cook for 20 minutes or until the peppers are charred.

3 Crack an egg into each tomato half. Season well and spoon the pan juices over. Reduce the oven temperature to 180°C (350°F) Mark 4. Return to the oven for 7 minutes or until the eggs are just set. Serve, garnished with parsley.

NUTRITIONAL ANALYSIS (per portion)	
Energy	380 cals
Protein	16.0 g
Carbohydrate	21.0 g
(of which sugars)	19.0 g
Fat	26.5 g
(of which saturates)	5.5 g
Fibre	4.5 g

SUITABLE FOR:
GLUTEN-FREE, NUT-FREE, LOW-CALORIE, DAIRY PRODUCE-FREE AND DIABETIC DIETS.

WATCHPOINT:
The young, the elderly, pregnant women and those with immune-deficiency diseases should not eat raw or lightly cooked eggs, to avoid the possible risk of salmonella.

CRUNCHY CHICK PEA EGGS

SERVES 6 • PREPARATION: 30 MINUTES, PLUS CHILLING • COOKING TIME: 15 MINUTES

2 x 400 g (14 oz) cans chick peas, drained

2 garlic cloves, peeled and crushed

1-2 red chillies, deseeded and finely chopped

2 tomatoes, preferably plum, skinned, deseeded and finely chopped

4 spring onions, roughly chopped

125 g (4 oz) stoned black olives, roughly chopped

4 tbsp chopped, fresh flat-leaf parsley

salt and freshly ground black pepper

6 hard-boiled eggs

1 egg, beaten

75 g (3 oz) fine fresh white breadcrumbs

oil, for deep-frying

1 Place the drained chick peas in a food processor with the garlic and process for 1 minute or until roughly chopped.

2 Turn the mixture into a bowl and add the chopped chillies, tomatoes, spring onions, olives and parsley. Season with salt and pepper and mix together well.

3 Divide the mixture into 6 equal portions. Form each into a flat cake and shape it round the shelled, hard-boiled eggs, making it as even as possible (see Note). Brush with beaten egg and roll in breadcrumbs. Chill, uncovered, for up to 4 hours or overnight.

4 Heat the oil in a deep-fat fryer or large saucepan to 160°C (325°F) or until a cube of bread begins to sizzle, then gently lower each egg into the oil and fry for 7–8 minutes or until golden brown. Remove and drain thoroughly on kitchen paper. Serve hot.

NUTRITIONAL ANALYSIS
(per portion)

Energy	415 cals
Protein	19.0 g
Carbohydrate	32.0 g
(of which sugars)	2.0 g
Fat	24.0 g
(of which saturates)	4.0 g
Fibre	7.0 g

SUITABLE FOR:

HIGH-FIBRE, NUT-FREE, LOW-CALORIE, DAIRY PRODUCE-FREE AND DIABETIC DIETS.

NOTE: Make sure the shelled eggs are dry as this will allow the chick pea mixture to stick more easily. The chick pea mixture may seem too crumbly, but keep squeezing and pressing the mixture well around the egg and it will stick.

1 tbsp porcini pieces or snipped dried mushrooms

450 g (1 lb) floury old potatoes, such as Desirée or King Edward's

salt and freshly ground black pepper

40 g (1½ oz) plain flour

350 ml (12 fl oz) low-fat cheese sauce (see page 236), using Gruyère cheese instead of the Cheddar

grated Parmesan and Gruyère cheese, for sprinkling

rocket, to garnish

MUSHROOM GNOCCHI WITH CHEESE SAUCE

SERVES 4 • PREPARATION: 30 MINUTES, PLUS SOAKING • COOKING TIME: 30 MINUTES

1 Soak the porcini in 1 tbsp boiling water for 15 minutes.

2 To make the gnocchi, cook the potatoes in boiling, salted water until very tender. Drain. When cool enough to handle, remove the skins and press the potatoes through a sieve or potato ricer.

3 While the potatoes are still warm, add 1 tsp salt, the soaked mushrooms with their liquid and the flour. Mix together, then turn out on to a lightly floured board. If the dough is too soft, add a little more flour (it should be soft but manageable).

4 Roll the dough into a sausage 2 cm (¾ inch) in diameter. Cut it into 2.5 cm (1 inch) pieces. Roll each one on a lightly floured work surface with the back of a fork to make ridges all over.

5 Bring a pan of salted water to the boil; reduce the heat to a fast simmer. Drop a dozen gnocchi into the boiling water. Cook for 2–3 minutes, until they float to the surface. Remove with a slotted spoon; drain well. Place in a warm oiled dish and keep warm in a low oven while you cook the rest.

6 Gently reheat the sauce, pour over the gnocchi, sprinkle with a little cheese and cook under a hot grill until browned. Garnish with rocket.

NUTRITIONAL ANALYSIS (per portion)	
Energy	240 cals
Protein	12.0 g
Carbohydrate	36.0 g
(of which sugars)	5.0 g
Fat	8.0 g
(of which saturates)	5.0 g
Fibre	2.0 g

SUITABLE FOR:

NUT-FREE, LOW-CALORIE AND DIABETIC DIETS.

VARIATION:

The gnocchi are also delicious flavoured with 1 tbsp chopped basil.

light meals

1 large onion, peeled and thinly sliced

2 tbsp light oil

550 g (1¼ lb) waxy potatoes, such as Desirée, peeled

salt and freshly ground black pepper

1 garlic clove, peeled and crushed

1 tbsp chopped fresh chives

1 large egg, beaten

50 g (2 oz) Gouda cheese, coarsely grated

TOPPING
1 red pepper

50 g (2 oz) chorizo sausage, finely chopped

125 g (4 oz) feta cheese or fresh goat's cheese, crumbled

2 tsp roughly chopped fresh rosemary or thyme

freshly ground black pepper

1 tbsp olive oil

POTATO 'PIZZA'

SERVES 4 • PREPARATION: 15 MINUTES • COOKING TIME: 35 MINUTES

1 To make the 'pizza', fry the onion in 1 tbsp oil for about 12 minutes, until golden. Cook the potatoes in boiling salted water for 10 minutes. Drain and coarsely grate; squeeze out any excess liquid.

2 Mix the potatoes with the onion, garlic and chives. Season well, then stir in the egg.

3 Heat the remaining oil in a large non-stick frying pan, about 23 cm (9 inches). Spread half the potato mixture over the pan and press down firmly. Sprinkle over the grated cheese and top with the remaining potato.

4 Cook the potato over a low heat for a good 10 minutes or until well-browned underneath. Ease the edges of the potato away from the pan, place a plate on top and flip over. Slide the potato back into the pan and cook for a further 10 minutes until browned on the underside and tender.

5 To make the topping, grill the whole pepper for 10–12 minutes, turning occasionally, until the skin is black and the flesh very soft. Halve and deseed the pepper while still warm. Slice the flesh and scatter over the potato base. Sprinkle over the chorizo, followed by the feta cheese and rosemary. Season and drizzle over the oil.

6 Place under a hot grill for 7–10 minutes, then serve cut into wedges.

NUTRITIONAL ANALYSIS	
(per portion)	
Energy	410 cals
Protein	15.5 g
Carbohydrate	32.0 g
(of which sugars)	7.5 g
Fat	25.0 g
(of which saturates)	7.0 g
Fibre	3.5 g

SUITABLE FOR:
GLUTEN-FREE, NUT-FREE, LOW-CALORIE AND DIABETIC DIETS.

VARIATION:

For a tomato topping, toss together 50 g (2 oz) chopped anchovy fillets, 1 crushed garlic clove, 350 g (12 oz) cherry tomatoes, halved, 2 tbsp rinsed capers, 1 tbsp olive oil, 2 tbsp balsamic vinegar and black pepper. Spoon over the hot potato base and place under a hot grill for 7–10 minutes. Garnish with chopped parsley and serve at once.

squeeze of lemon juice

25 g (1 oz) low-fat soft cheese

2 small smoked mackerel fillets, skinned and flaked

1 tsp creamed horseradish

freshly ground black pepper

4 thick slices brown bread

watercress salad, to serve

SMOKED MACKEREL TOASTY

SERVES 2 • PREPARATION: 10 MINUTES • COOKING TIME: 5 MINUTES

1 Beat enough lemon juice into the cheese to give the consistency of soft butter (taste as you go to avoid the cheese becoming too lemony). Stir the mackerel and creamed horseradish into the cheese and season with pepper.

2 Toast the bread, spoon the mackerel on to 2 slices and grill for 2–3 minutes. Top with the remaining 2 toast slices, press together firmly and cut each sandwich in half. Serve with watercress salad.

NUTRITIONAL ANALYSIS	
(per portion)	
Energy	275 cals
Protein	15.0 g
Carbohydrate	16.0 g
(of which sugars)	0.7 g
Fat	17.0 g
(of which saturates)	4.0 g
Fibre	2.0 g

SUITABLE FOR:
NUT-FREE, LOW-CHOLESTEROL, LOW-CALORIE AND DIABETIC DIETS.

50 g (2 oz) block of fresh
Parmesan cheese
8 garlic cloves
550 g (1¼ lb) cherry
tomatoes, preferably still
on the vine
50 g (2 oz) can anchovy
fillets, drained, rinsed and
halved lengthways
2 tbsp salted capers,
rinsed
2 tbsp olive oil
freshly ground black
pepper
2 tbsp balsamic vinegar
1 ciabatta loaf

NOTE: Use vine tomatoes
if you can find them, as
they look particularly
pretty.

ROASTED TOMATO BRUSCHETTA

SERVES 4 • PREPARATION: 10 MINUTES •
COOKING TIME: 20 MINUTES

1 Using a vegetable peeler, pare the Parmesan cheese into shavings.

2 Put the garlic cloves in a pan of cold water, bring to the boil and bubble for 3–4 minutes; drain and peel.

3 Place the tomatoes in a roasting tin with the anchovies, capers, garlic and oil. Season with pepper. Cook at 220°C (425°F) Mark 7 for 15 minutes. Drizzle with vinegar.

4 Meanwhile, halve the ciabatta lengthways and then cut it into four portions. Toast on the cut side.

5 Serve the hot tomato mixture on the ciabatta, spooning the roasting juices over the top. Top with the Parmesan.

NUTRITIONAL ANALYSIS (per portion)	
Energy	285 cals
Protein	12.0 g
Carbohydrate	23.0 g
(of which sugars)	5.0 g
Fat	17.0 g
(of which saturates)	4.0 g
Fibre	2.0 g

SUITABLE FOR:
NUT-FREE, LOW-CALORIE AND
DIABETIC DIETS.

125 g (4 oz) feta cheese, cut into large dice
1 tbsp olive oil
1 tbsp chopped fresh thyme
freshly ground black pepper
toasted pitta bread, to serve

HOT FETA PITTA TOPPER

SERVES 2 • PREPARATION: 5 MINUTES • COOKING TIME: 7 MINUTES

1 Place the cheese in a shallow heatproof dish just large enough to hold it in a single layer. Sprinkle over the oil and scatter with the thyme and black pepper.

2 Put under a hot grill for 5–7 minutes or until beginning to colour. Serve spread on pitta bread.

NUTRITIONAL ANALYSIS (per portion)	
Energy	205 cals
Protein	10.0 g
Carbohydrate	0.9 g
(of which sugars)	0.9 g
Fat	18.0 g
(of which saturates)	9.0 g
Fibre	0.0 g

SUITABLE FOR:
NUT-FREE, LOW-CALORIE AND DIABETIC DIETS.

---

75 g (3 oz) reduced-fat Cheddar cheese, coarsely grated
2 rashers thinly cut lean bacon, grilled until crisp
1 small red onion, peeled and chopped
2 tsp chopped fresh chives
1 small French baguette, halved and toasted

CHEESE AND CHIVE MELTS

SERVES 2 • PREPARATION: 10 MINUTES • COOKING TIME: 5 MINUTES

1 Put the first 4 ingredients in a food processor and blend together for about 30 seconds.

2 Spread on to the warm toasted baguette and return to the grill until bubbling and deep golden. Serve at once.

NUTRITIONAL ANALYSIS (per portion)	
Energy	360 cals
Protein	25.0 g
Carbohydrate	47.0 g
(of which sugars)	3.0 g
Fat	10.0 g
(of which saturates)	5.0 g
Fibre	1.5 g

SUITABLE FOR:
LOW-CALORIE AND DIABETIC DIETS.

---

75 g (3 oz) plain flour
140 g (4½ oz) finely grated fresh Parmesan cheese
75 g (3 oz) butter
salt and freshly ground black pepper
¼ tsp cayenne pepper
4 tbsp sun-dried tomato paste
15 g (½ oz) fresh breadcrumbs
900 g (2 lb) tomatoes, preferably plum, thickly sliced
1 tbsp chopped fresh thyme
fresh thyme sprigs, to garnish

COUNTRY TOMATO TART

SERVES 6 • PREPARATION: 40 MINUTES, PLUS CHILLING • COOKING TIME: 40 MINUTES

1 In a food processor, blend the plain flour with 75 g (3 oz) Parmesan cheese, the butter, ½ tsp salt and the cayenne pepper until the mixture resembles rough breadcrumbs. Set aside one-third of the crumb mixture, cover and refrigerate. Press the remaining crumb mixture into the base of a 21 cm (8¼ inch) square, loose-based flan tin, spreading it out to the edges. Chill for 10 minutes.

2 Cook the crumb base at 180°C (350°F) Mark 4 for 15–20 minutes or until light golden. Cool.

3 Spread the sun-dried tomato paste all over the cooled crumb base, then sprinkle with half the fresh breadcrumbs. Layer the tomato slices and chopped fresh thyme on top and sprinkle with the remaining fresh breadcrumbs, the remaining Parmesan cheese and the reserved pastry crumb mixture; season with salt and pepper.

4 Cook the tart in the oven for a further 15–20 minutes or until golden. Cool slightly, then cut into portions and serve warm, garnished with thyme.

NUTRITIONAL ANALYSIS (per portion)	
Energy	285 cals
Protein	12.0 g
Carbohydrate	18.0 g
(of which sugars)	6.0 g
Fat	18.5 g
(of which saturates)	12.0 g
Fibre	2.0 g

SUITABLE FOR:
NUT-FREE, LOW-CALORIE AND DIABETIC DIETS.

1 tbsp lemon juice

3 tbsp olive oil

3 tbsp spring onion tops, chopped

salt and freshly ground black pepper

3 ripe tomatoes, skinned, deseeded and chopped

200 g (7 oz) baby leeks, trimmed and cut into 2.5 cm (1 inch) pieces

125 g (4 oz) young fresh spinach

6 large eggs

4 tbsp semi-skimmed milk

freshly grated nutmeg

125 g (4 oz) feta cheese, diced

fresh basil sprigs, to garnish

SPINACH FRITTATAS

SERVES 4 • PREPARATION: 20 MINUTES • COOKING TIME: 12 MINUTES

1 For the dressing, whisk together the lemon juice, 2 tbsp olive oil and spring onion tops; season with salt and pepper. Add the tomatoes and set aside.

2 Blanch the leeks in boiling, salted water for 2 minutes. Add the spinach to the pan just before draining the leeks. Drain, refresh with cold water, drain again and dry on kitchen paper.

3 Whisk the eggs, milk, seasoning and nutmeg to taste. Stir in the feta cheese, leeks and spinach.

4 Heat the remaining oil in a non-stick frying pan. Place four 10 cm (4 inch) poaching rings in the pan and pour a quarter of the egg mixture into each one. Fry gently for 4–5 minutes. Finish under a hot grill for 4–5 minutes until the tops are golden and just firm to the touch.

5 Turn the frittatas out of the poaching rings, garnish with basil and serve with the dressing.

NUTRITIONAL ANALYSIS (per portion)	
Energy	260 cals
Protein	16.0 g
Carbohydrate	4.2 g
(of which sugars)	3.8 g
Fat	20.0 g
(of which saturates)	7.0 g
Fibre	2.5 g

SUITABLE FOR:

GLUTEN-FREE, NUT-FREE, LOW-CALORIE AND DIABETIC DIETS.

125 g (4 oz) plain flour

pinch of salt

75 g (3 oz) butter, diced

1 egg yolk

1 tbsp olive oil

700 g (1½ lb) onions, peeled and finely sliced

2 garlic cloves, peeled and sliced

1 sprig rosemary or 1 tsp dried

175 g (6 oz) salmon fillet, roughly chopped

125 g (4 oz) soft goat's cheese, crumbled

4 anchovy fillets, chopped

rosemary sprigs and sea salt, to sprinkle

SALMON PISSALADIÈRE

SERVES 4 • PREPARATION: 15 MINUTES, PLUS CHILLING • COOKING TIME: ABOUT 1¼ HOURS

1 Sift the flour into a food processor, then add the salt, butter and egg yolk. Process for 30 seconds to combine, then add 1 tbsp water and process for another 30 seconds. Turn out on to a lightly floured surface and knead together. Roll out to a thin circle about 25 cm (10 inches) in diameter. Place on a baking sheet and chill for 30 minutes.

2 Prick the pastry with a fork. Cook at 200°C (400°F) Mark 6 for 12–15 minutes or until golden.

3 Heat the oil in non-stick frying pan and add the onions, garlic and rosemary. Lay greaseproof paper over the onions and cover the pan with a tight-fitting lid. Simmer over a low heat for 45 minutes until very soft and tender (add a little water if the pan looks dry).

4 Stir the salmon into the onions and drain off any liquid that may be in the pan. Cool the onion mixture, then stir in the cheese and anchovies.

5 Spread the onion mixture over the pastry base. Sprinkle with rosemary and salt. Cook at 200°C (400°F) Mark 6 for 20 minutes; cover loosely with foil if browning too quickly. Cool for 5 minutes before serving.

NUTRITIONAL ANALYSIS (per portion)	
Energy	495 cals
Protein	19.0 g
Carbohydrate	38.0 g
(of which sugars)	11.0 g
Fat	31.0 g
(of which saturates)	15.0 g
Fibre	3.5 g

SUITABLE FOR:
NUT-FREE AND DIABETIC DIETS.

4 large baking potatoes

salt and freshly ground black pepper

200 ml (7 fl oz) half-fat crème fraîche

2 tbsp wholegrain mustard

4 tbsp chopped fresh parsley or chives

225 g (8 oz) smoked mackerel fillets

squeeze of lemon juice, to taste

NOTE: Do not season with salt as mackerel is salty enough.

BAKED POTATOES WITH MACKEREL AND MUSTARD

SERVES 4 • PREPARATION: ABOUT 20 MINUTES • COOKING TIME: 1 HOUR 20 MINUTES

1 Wash the potatoes well, then prick all over with a fork or skewer. Rub lightly with salt and pepper while still damp. Bake at 200°C (400°F) Mark 6 for about 1¼ hours or until very tender.

2 Split open the potatoes and spoon the flesh into a bowl. Mash with the crème fraîche and mustard. Stir in the parsley or chives.

3 Ease the smoked mackerel flesh from the skin and lightly stir into the potato, taking care not to break up the fish too much. Adjust the seasoning (see Note) and add a squeeze of lemon juice.

4 Pile the mixture back into the potato skins and brown under a hot grill for 3–4 minutes.

NUTRITIONAL ANALYSIS (per portion)	
Energy	536 cals
Protein	16.0 g
Carbohydrate	37.0 g
(of which sugars)	16.0 g
Fat	36.0 g
(of which saturates)	3.0 g
Fibre	3.0 g

SUITABLE FOR:
GLUTEN-FREE, NUT-FREE, AND DIABETIC DIETS.

2 tbsp olive oil

50 g (2 oz) cashew nuts, roughly chopped

700 g (1½ lb) large, raw prawns, peeled and de-veined

1 bunch spring onions, trimmed and finely chopped

3 garlic cloves, peeled and crushed

2.5 cm (1 inch) piece fresh root ginger, peeled and grated

1 red chilli, deseeded and finely chopped

grated rind and juice of 2 limes

4 tbsp Thai fish sauce

4 tbsp very roughly chopped fresh mint

a handful of fresh basil, roughly torn

QUICK-FRIED PRAWNS WITH CASHEWS, LIME AND MINT

SERVES 4 • PREPARATION: 15 MINUTES • COOKING TIME: 15 MINUTES

1 Heat 1 tbsp oil in a large wok or non-stick frying pan. Add the cashew nuts and stir-fry for 1–2 minutes until golden. Remove from the pan with a slotted spoon and set aside. Add the prawns to the wok, in two batches, and cook for 3–4 minutes until they turn opaque and just begin to brown. Turn all the prawns on to a warm plate and set aside.

2 Add the remaining oil to the wok and return to the heat. When smoking hot, add the spring onions, garlic, ginger and chilli and stir-fry for 1–2 minutes.

3 Return the prawns, with any juices, to the pan. Add the cashew nuts and stir in the remaining ingredients. Toss over the heat for about 30 seconds or until the pan juices begin to bubble, then serve immediately.

NUTRITIONAL ANALYSIS (per portion)	
Energy	260 cals
Protein	33.5 g
Carbohydrate	3.0 g
(of which sugars)	1.5 g
Fat	13.0 g
(of which saturates)	2.0 g
Fibre	1.0 g

SUITABLE FOR:
GLUTEN-FREE, LOW-CALORIE, DAIRY PRODUCE-FREE AND DIABETIC DIETS.

4 chicken breast fillets,
cut into bite-sized strips

2 sticks lemon grass,
finely chopped

finely grated rind of 1 lime
and the juice of 2 limes

4 fat garlic cloves, peeled
and crushed

225 g (8 oz) shallots,
peeled and thinly sliced

2 tbsp Thai fish sauce

2 tsp light brown
(muscovado) sugar

1 small red chilli,
deseeded and finely
chopped

2 tbsp oil

1 tbsp sesame oil

1 tbsp sesame seeds

a little extra oil, for stir-
.frying

chilli curls, to garnish
(optional)

lime wedges and Chinese
pancakes or steamed
rice, to serve

LIME AND SESAME CHICKEN

*SERVES 4 • PREPARATION: 15 MINUTES, PLUS
MARINATING • COOKING TIME: 10 MINUTES*

1 Mix together all the ingredients in a large non-metallic bowl. Cover and leave to marinate in the refrigerator for 2–3 hours.

2 Wipe the surface of a large wok with a little oil and place over a high heat until smoking hot.

3 Stir-fry the chicken mixture, a few pieces at a time, for 3–4 minutes until golden brown and cooked through. Return all the chicken to the wok and toss together over the heat for 1 minute.

4 Garnish with chilli, if wished. Serve immediately, with lime wedges and warm Chinese pancakes or plain steamed rice.

NUTRITIONAL ANALYSIS (per portion)	
Energy	270 cals
Protein	37.0 g
Carbohydrate	3.5 g
(of which sugars)	3.0 g
Fat	12.0 g
(of which saturates)	2.0 g
Fibre	0.5 g

SUITABLE FOR:

GLUTEN-FREE, NUT-FREE, LOW-CHOLESTEROL, LOW-CALORIE, DAIRY PRODUCE-FREE AND DIABETIC DIETS.

Lime juice... useful and healthy

The juice of fresh limes is an excellent source of vitamin C, and a good tenderising marinade for meat and fish. Lime juice also acts as a seasoning, so where it is included in a recipe, little extra salt is needed – useful for a low-sodium diet.

VIETNAMESE NOODLE SOUP WITH TERIYAKI CHICKEN

350 g (12 oz) skinned chicken breast fillets, cut lengthways into thin strips

3 tbsp grated fresh root ginger

2 tbsp soy sauce

1.4 litres (2½ pints) chicken stock

1 tbsp sunflower oil

125 g (4 oz) rice noodles

2 spring onions, trimmed and finely sliced

12 mangetout, trimmed and finely shredded

125 g (4 oz) bean sprouts, rinsed and drained

2 Chinese leaves, finely shredded

1 tsp sesame oil

SERVES 4 • PREPARATION: 15 MINUTES, PLUS MARINATING • COOKING TIME: 20 MINUTES

1 Place the chicken strips in a non-metallic bowl with 1 tbsp ginger and 1 tbsp soy sauce and mix to coat well. Cover and marinate for 30 minutes.

2 Put the chicken stock in a large saucepan with the remaining ginger and soy sauce. Bring to the boil over a moderate heat, then reduce the heat to very low and continue to simmer very gently.

3 Meanwhile, heat the oil in a wok or non-stick frying pan until hot and stir-fry the chicken for 5–7 minutes or until cooked through. Keep warm.

4 Place the noodles in a large bowl, cover with boiling water and leave to stand for 4 minutes. Drain the noodles and divide between 4 bowls.

5 Ladle the broth into the bowls, top with the chicken and sprinkle over the spring onions, mangetout, bean sprouts and Chinese leaves. Sprinkle with a few drops of sesame oil and serve.

NUTRITIONAL ANALYSIS (per portion)	
Energy	280 cals
Protein	23.0 g
Carbohydrate	28.0 g
(of which sugars)	2.0 g
Fat	8.0 g
(of which saturates)	2.0 g
Fibre	1.0 g

SUITABLE FOR:
GLUTEN-FREE, NUT-FREE, LOW-CHOLESTEROL, LOW-CALORIE, DAIRY PRODUCE-FREE AND DIABETIC DIETS.

NOTE: The secret of this dish lies in the rich home-made chicken stock, skimmed of all the fat.

ROASTED VEGETABLES AND TURKEY WITH FOCACCIA

900 g (2 lb) red onions, peeled, quartered and separated into 'petals'

6 tbsp olive oil

3 red and 3 yellow peppers, halved, deseeded and cut into wedges

6 large garlic cloves, skins left on

200 g (7 oz) red cherry tomatoes

2 tbsp balsamic vinegar

sea salt flakes and freshly ground black pepper

1 tbsp white wine vinegar

1 Italian loaf, such as focaccia or ciabatta, thickly sliced

300 g (11 oz) cooked turkey, cut into thick strips

fresh basil sprigs and crushed black peppercorns, to garnish

SERVES 6 • PREPARATION: 30 MINUTES • COOKING TIME: 1 HOUR 10 MINUTES

1 Place the red onions in a large roasting tin and toss in 2 tbsp of the olive oil. Cook at 220°C (425°F) Mark 7 for 10 minutes, add the peppers and garlic cloves, mix together thoroughly and return to the oven for about 50 minutes or until the vegetables are charred and soft. Add the cherry tomatoes and return to the oven for 10 minutes. Remove from the oven and mix in the balsamic vinegar and seasoning. Set aside and keep warm.

2 Pour the white wine vinegar and 3 tbsp olive oil into a small bowl, then season and whisk thoroughly to form a dressing. Set aside.

3 Toast the bread slices on one side, turn and brush the second side with the remaining oil and toast until brown and crisp. Sprinkle with sea salt.

4 Add the cooked turkey to the warm vegetables, then toss in the dressing. Garnish with basil and crushed peppercorns and serve with the focaccia.

NUTRITIONAL ANALYSIS (per portion)	
Energy	305 cals
Protein	19.0 g
Carbohydrate	29.0 g
(of which sugars)	10.0 g
Fat	13.5 g
(of which saturates)	2.0 g
Fibre	3.0 g

SUITABLE FOR:
NUT-FREE, LOW-CHOLESTEROL, LOW-CALORIE, DAIRY PRODUCE-FREE AND DIABETIC DIETS.

550 g (1¼ lb) rump steak, cut into wafer-thin, bite-sized pieces

5 cm (2 inch) piece fresh root ginger, peeled and finely chopped

1 large red chilli, deseeded and thinly sliced

2 tbsp dark brown (muscovado) sugar

3 tbsp light oil

1 tsp cumin seeds

225 g (8 oz) onions, peeled and thinly sliced

pinch of ground turmeric

3 tbsp lemon juice

75 ml (3 fl oz) beef stock

1 large crusty baguette, cut into 6 lengths

RAITA

300 ml (½ pint) low-fat natural yogurt

⅛ cucumber, finely chopped or grated

1 garlic clove, peeled and crushed

3 tbsp chopped fresh mint

salt and freshly ground black pepper

GINGER BEEF BAGUETTE

SERVES 6 • PREPARATION: 20 MINUTES, PLUS MARINATING • COOKING TIME: 35 MINUTES

1 To make the raita, beat the yogurt, then mix in the cucumber and garlic. Add the mint and season with salt and pepper to taste. Cover and leave to stand for 30 minutes for the flavours to develop.

2 For the ginger beef, mix together the beef, ginger, chilli and sugar.

3 Brush the base of a non-stick wok with a little of the oil and fry the cumin seeds for about a minute, until lightly toasted. Stir into the beef mixture.

4 Heat half the remaining oil in the wok or non-stick frying pan and stir-fry the onions for 7–10 minutes until soft and a deep golden brown. Stir in the turmeric and cook for a further 2 minutes. Remove the onions and set aside.

5 Add the remaining oil to the wok and stir-fry the beef strips in 2 batches for about 4 minutes until well browned and tender. Return all the beef to the wok and stir in 3 tbsp lemon juice and the stock. Bring to the boil and bubble until the liquid has evaporated. Return the onions to the wok and stir over the heat for 1 minute. Season well.

6 Split the baguette pieces down the middle and open out like a book. Toast the cut side. Spread one half of the bread generously with raita, then top with the hot beef mixture. Sandwich together and serve at once, with the raita.

NUTRITIONAL ANALYSIS (per portion)	
Energy	359 cals
Protein	28.0 g
Carbohydrate	37.0 g
(of which sugars)	14.0 g
Fat	12.0 g
(of which saturates)	3.0 g
Fibre	1.0 g

SUITABLE FOR:
NUT-FREE, LOW-CHOLESTEROL, LOW-CALORIE AND DIABETIC DIETS.

---

700 g (1½ lb) lean lamb, cut into bite-sized pieces

450 g (1 lb) small onions, peeled and quartered

3 tbsp lemon juice

1 garlic clove, crushed

½ tsp ground cumin

pinch of ground paprika

large pinch of oregano

2 tbsp olive oil

½ tsp salt

freshly ground black pepper

HUMMUS SAUCE

75 g (3 oz) reduced-fat hummus

150 ml (¼ pint) Greek yogurt

SPICED LAMB KEBABS

SERVES 4 • PREPARATION: 10 MINUTES, PLUS MARINATING • COOKING TIME: 15 MINUTES

1 To make the sauce, stir the hummus into the yogurt until thoroughly combined. Cover and chill.

2 To make the kebabs, mix together the lamb pieces, onions, lemon juice, garlic, cumin, paprika, oregano and oil. Cover and marinate overnight.

3 Thread the lamb and onions, not too tightly, on to 8 skewers. Season with salt and pepper.

4 Cook the kebabs under a hot grill for 12–15 minutes or until the lamb is well charred but still pink in the middle. Serve the kebabs with the hummus sauce.

NUTRITIONAL ANALYSIS (per portion)	
Energy	425 cals
Protein	40.0 g
Carbohydrate	12.5 g
(of which sugars)	8.6 g
Fat	24.5 g
(of which saturates)	9.0 g
Fibre	2.0 g

SUITABLE FOR:
GLUTEN-FREE, NUT-FREE, LOW-CHOLESTEROL, LOW-CALORIE AND DIABETIC DIETS.

about 4 tbsp olive oil

450 g (1 lb) courgettes, thickly sliced diagonally

1 red or white onion, peeled and sliced into thick wedges

2 fennel bulbs, each about 175 g (6 oz), trimmed and thinly sliced

salt and freshly ground black pepper

3 ripe tomatoes or plum tomatoes, quartered and deseeded

pinch of sugar

225 g (8 oz) halloumi cheese, thickly sliced

about 20 black olives, stoned and halved

4 tbsp chopped fresh basil

4 tbsp chopped fresh chives

grated rind and juice of 1 lemon

CHARRED GARDEN SALAD WITH HALLOUMI

SERVES 6 • PREPARATION: 10 MINUTES • COOKING TIME: 20 MINUTES

1 Heat 1 tbsp oil in a ridged griddle pan and cook the courgettes, onion and fennel over a high heat in batches, adding more oil after each batch – they will need 2–3 minutes on each side and should be just charred on the outside but still retain their crispness. Transfer to a bowl and keep warm.

2 Season the tomatoes with salt and pepper, then add a pinch of sugar. Add the tomatoes to the pan and cook quickly for 1–2 minutes, taking care not to overcook. Add to the cooked vegetables; keep warm.

3 Add a little of the remaining oil to the pan and cook the halloumi for about 30 seconds on each side until browned and slightly softened. Add to the vegetables with the olives, herbs and lemon rind and juice. Season well and toss until well combined. Drizzle with a little olive oil and serve.

NUTRITIONAL ANALYSIS
(per portion)

Energy	225 cals
Protein	12.0 g
Carbohydrate	6.5 g
(of which sugars)	5.5 g
Fat	17.0 g
(of which saturates)	6.0 g
Fibre	3.0 g

SUITABLE FOR:
GLUTEN-FREE, NUT-FREE, LOW-CALORIE AND DIABETIC DIETS.

NOTE: Halloumi cheese is best served freshly cooked as it tends to toughen when cooled. If you can't find it, use feta cheese instead – but omit the salt in the recipe.

2 garlic cloves, crushed

1 red chilli, deseeded and thinly sliced

2 tsp light soy sauce

1 tbsp rice wine

2 tsp demerara sugar

½ tsp Chinese five-spice powder

125 g (4 oz) basmati rice

1 tbsp oil

125 g (4 oz) red pepper, deseeded, cut into strips

4 spring onions, sliced

125 g (4 oz) baby corn, halved lengthways

450 g (1 lb) mixed Chinese greens, roughly chopped

50 g (2 oz) bean sprouts

5 tbsp torn coriander

salt and freshly ground black pepper

coriander, to garnish

PEANUT SAUCE

1 tbsp oil

125 g (4 oz) shallots, peeled and finely chopped

1 stick lemon grass, finely chopped

3 garlic cloves, crushed

1 cm (½ inch) piece fresh root ginger, finely grated

1 tsp red curry paste

150 g (5 oz) smooth peanut butter

2 tbsp chopped coriander

STIR-FRIED GREENS WITH FRAGRANT PEANUT SAUCE

SERVES 4 • PREPARATION: 25 MINUTES • COOKING TIME: 25 MINUTES

1 To make the peanut sauce, heat the oil in a small saucepan and add the shallots, lemon grass, garlic and ginger. Stir over a moderate heat until very lightly browned.

2 Stir in the curry paste and continue to cook for a further 2 minutes before adding the peanut butter and 300 ml (½ pint) water. Bring to the boil, then simmer gently for about 5 minutes. Cool slightly, then blend in a blender or food processor with the coriander. Set aside.

3 For the stir-fry, mix together the garlic, chilli, soy sauce, rice wine, sugar and five-spice powder. Set aside.

4 Cook the rice according to packet instructions. Drain well and rinse with cold water.

5 Heat the oil until smoking hot in a large wok. Add the pepper, spring onions, corn and Chinese greens and stir-fry for about 2 minutes. Add the rice and soy mixture and stir-fry for a further 2–3 minutes. Stir in the beans sprouts and coriander and season with salt and pepper. Garnish with coriander and serve with the peanut sauce.

NUTRITIONAL ANALYSIS (per portion)	
Energy	476 cals
Protein	14.0 g
Carbohydrate	43.0 g
(of which sugars)	5.0 g
Fat	26.0 g
(of which saturates)	5.0 g
Fibre	7.0 g

SUITABLE FOR:

HIGH-FIBRE, GLUTEN-FREE, LOW-CHOLESTEROL, DAIRY PRODUCE-FREE AND DIABETIC DIETS.

NOTE: Most major supermarkets now offer a wide range of Chinese leaves. Look out for pak choi which has tender green tops and a white fleshy stem, or try the long slender leaves of ung choi, which is Chinese water spinach.

25 g (1 oz) dried shiitake mushrooms

2 tbsp groundnut oil

2 shallots, peeled and finely chopped

2 small red chillies, deseeded and chopped

2 garlic cloves, peeled and crushed

2 ripe tomatoes, chopped

2 tbsp lemon juice

1 tsp sugar

1.2 litres (2 pints) vegetable stock

1 stick lemon grass, sliced

4 kaffir lime leaves, finely shredded

225 g (8 oz) oyster or button mushrooms, sliced

1 tbsp light soy sauce

2 tbsp chopped coriander

MUSHROOM TOM YAM

SERVES 4 • PREPARATION: 10 MINUTES, PLUS SOAKING • COOKING TIME: 40 MINUTES

1 Cover the dried mushrooms with 150 ml (¼ pint) boiling water and soak for 20 minutes. Strain and reserve the liquid. Chop the mushrooms; reserve.

2 Heat the oil in a saucepan, add the shallots, chillies and garlic and fry gently for 5 minutes. Add the tomatoes with the lemon juice and sugar. Fry for 5 minutes until the tomatoes are pulpy.

3 Pour in the stock and reserved mushroom liquid, then add the lemon grass and lime leaves. Bring to the boil, cover and simmer for 20 minutes.

4 Add all the mushrooms and the soy sauce. Simmer gently for a further 5–10 minutes until tender. Stir in the coriander and serve.

NUTRITIONAL ANALYSIS (per portion)	
Energy	80 cals
Protein	1.9 g
Carbohydrate	7.0 g
(of which sugars)	3.0 g
Fat	6.0 g
(of which saturates)	0.7 g
Fibre	0.5 g

SUITABLE FOR:

GLUTEN-FREE, NUT-FREE, LOW-CHOLESTEROL, LOW-CALORIE, DAIRY PRODUCE-FREE AND DIABETIC DIETS.

Right: Stir-fried Greens with Fragrant Peanut Sauce

2 x 400 g (14 oz) cans chick peas, well-drained

1 red chilli, deseeded and finely chopped

2 ripe tomatoes, skinned, deseeded and finely chopped

4 small spring onions, trimmed and roughly chopped

50 g (2 oz) stoned black olives, roughly chopped

2 garlic cloves, peeled and crushed

4 tbsp chopped fresh coriander

salt and freshly ground black pepper

1 egg, beaten

125 g (4 oz) fine fresh white breadcrumbs

oil, for brushing

lemon aioli, to serve (see Note)

CHILLI CHICK PEA CAKES

SERVES 4 • PREPARATION: 10 MINUTES, PLUS CHILLING • COOKING TIME: 20 MINUTES

1 Place the chick peas in a food processor and process for about 30 seconds or until roughly chopped.

2 Turn the chick peas into a bowl and stir in the chilli, tomatoes, spring onions, olives, garlic and coriander. Season well with salt and pepper.

3 Divide the mixture into 12 and squeeze firmly into 5 cm (2 inch) diameter cakes. Brush with the beaten egg and roll in the breadcrumbs. Cover and chill overnight.

4 Place the chick pea cakes on a baking sheet and brush lightly with oil. Cook at 200°C (400°F) Mark 6 for 20 minutes or until hot through and golden brown. Serve hot with lemon aioli.

NUTRITIONAL ANALYSIS (per portion)	
Energy	410 cals
Protein	20.5 g
Carbohydrate	58.0 g
(of which sugars)	3.0 g
Fat	12.0 g
(of which saturates)	2.0 g
Fibre	10.0 g

SUITABLE FOR:
HIGH-FIBRE, NUT-FREE, LOW-CHOLESTEROL, LOW-CALORIE, DAIRY PRODUCE-FREE AND DIABETIC DIETS.

4 tsp dark soy sauce

2 tbsp rice wine or dry sherry

1 tsp cornflour

1 tsp sugar

175 g (6 oz) egg noodles

1 tbsp sunflower oil

1 tsp sesame oil

350 g (12 oz) small mixed mushrooms, such as oyster, brown-cap and field

225 g (8 oz) pak choi or tatsoi, roughly sliced (see Note)

shredded egg omelette and spring onions, to serve

MUSHROOM CHOW MEIN

SERVES 4 • PREPARATION: 15 MINUTES •
COOKING TIME: 12 MINUTES

1 Whisk together the first 4 ingredients in a bowl.

2 Cook the noodles according to the packet instructions, then rinse thoroughly in cold water and leave to drain.

3 Heat the oils in a wok or large non-stick frying pan and fry the mushrooms for 2 minutes. Add the pak choi or tatsoi and cook for 3–4 minutes or until the mushrooms are golden brown and the excess liquid has evaporated.

4 Stir in the cooked noodles and soy mixture and bring to the boil. Bubble for 1–2 minutes, then serve immediately, topped with shredded egg omelette and spring onions.

NUTRITIONAL ANALYSIS (per portion)	
Energy	250 cals
Protein	8.0 g
Carbohydrate	37.0 g
(of which sugars)	5.0 g
Fat	8.0 g
(of which saturates)	1.5 g
Fibre	3.5 g

SUITABLE FOR:
NUT-FREE, LOW-CHOLESTEROL, LOW-CALORIE, DAIRY PRODUCE-FREE AND DIABETIC DIETS.

NOTE: Tatsoi is similar to pak choi (Chinese greens), but it has smaller leaves and a delicate flavour.

3 tbsp extra-virgin olive oil

2 sprigs fresh rosemary

3 garlic cloves, peeled and finely chopped

3 canned anchovy fillets, finely chopped

1 tbsp lemon juice

4 tbsp chopped fresh flat-leaf parsley

salt and freshly ground black pepper

400 g (14 oz) can cannellini beans, rinsed and drained

400 g (14 oz) can borlotti beans, rinsed and drained

2 ciabatta rolls, halved and sliced lengthways to give 4 pieces

125 g (4 oz) low-fat soft cheese with garlic and herbs

rocket salad, to serve

WARM MIXED BEAN SALAD ON BRUSCHETTA

SERVES 4 • PREPARATION: 15 MINUTES •
COOKING TIME: ABOUT 10 MINUTES

1 Heat the oil in a large non-stick frying pan and fry the rosemary sprigs over a medium heat for 1 minute. Remove the rosemary. Add the garlic to the pan and fry for 1 minute.

2 In a bowl or mortar, pound the anchovies to a paste. Slowly pound in the garlic oil from the pan, with the lemon juice and parsley. Season well with salt and pepper.

3 Tip the beans into the frying pan (it will still have a light coating of oil from frying the garlic) and stir over a medium heat for about 3–4 minutes, until hot through. Stir in the garlic and herb mixture and remove from the heat.

4 Meanwhile, toast the ciabatta on the cut side only. Spread with a little of the soft cheese, spoon on the warm beans and serve immediately with a rocket salad.

NUTRITIONAL ANALYSIS (per portion)	
Energy	365 cals
Protein	16.5 g
Carbohydrate	30.5 g
(of which sugars)	5.0 g
Fat	20.0 g
(of which saturates)	8.0 g
Fibre	6.0 g

SUITABLE FOR:
HIGH-FIBRE, NUT-FREE, LOW-CALORIE AND DIABETIC DIETS.

6 large red onions, each 175-225 g (6-8 oz) (see Note)

salt and freshly ground black pepper

25 g (1 oz) butter

25 g (1 oz) fresh breadcrumbs

125 g (4 oz) cooked ham, diced

25 g (1 oz) sun-dried tomatoes, chopped

1 tbsp grainy mustard

1 tsp chopped fresh sage

125 g (4 oz) leftover hard cheese, such as Cheddar, Emmenthal or Gouda, grated

1 tbsp balsamic vinegar

4 tbsp olive oil

lettuce, fresh sage leaves and crushed black peppercorns, to garnish

NOTE: Instead of large onions, you can always use 12 small onions, each 75–125 g (3–4 oz): allow 10–15 minutes simmering and 30–35 minutes baking.

WARM STUFFED ONION SALAD

SERVES 6 • PREPARATION: 30 MINUTES, PLUS DRAINING • COOKING TIME: 1¼ HOURS

1 Peel the onions carefully. Remove all the thin outer layers, making sure you leave the root intact, but trimming away the root hairs. Slice off the stalk end of the onion about 2 cm (¾ inch) from the top. Scoop out the middles with a teaspoon or apple corer. Chop and reserve the flesh.

2 Place the hollowed-out onions in a large saucepan, then cover with cold, salted water, bring to the boil and simmer for 15–20 minutes or until beginning to soften. Drain, then place, cut-side down, on kitchen paper for about 20 minutes.

3 Melt the butter in a medium-sized frying pan, add the reserved, chopped onion and cook for 10 minutes or until soft and golden brown. Mix the chopped onion with the breadcrumbs, ham, sun-dried tomatoes, mustard, sage, half the cheese and seasoning. Season the inside of the onions and fill with the breadcrumb mixture.

4 Place the onions in a large, ovenproof dish and sprinkle the remaining cheese over the top. Cover with foil and bake at 190°C (375°F) Mark 5 for 40–45 minutes or until the onions are soft and golden brown. Remove foil after 20 minutes. Keep warm.

5 Mix together the balsamic vinegar, olive oil and seasoning, then drizzle over the warm onions on serving plates. Garnish and serve at once.

NUTRITIONAL ANALYSIS (per portion)	
Energy	305 cals
Protein	12.0 g
Carbohydrate	17.0 g
(of which sugars)	10.0 g
Fat	21.0 g
(of which saturates)	8.5 g
Fibre	2.5 g

SUITABLE FOR:
NUT-FREE, LOW-CALORIE AND DIABETIC DIETS.

Onions... a valuable vegetable

Onions are valued for the sulphur compounds they contain. These appear to offer some protection from tumour formation and may possibly reduce the risk of stomach cancer. Apart from being a reasonable source of soluble fibre, baked onions are a surprisingly good source of energy-giving natural sugars, such as glucose and fructose.

pasta, rice and grains

6 tbsp olive oil, plus extra for brushing

2 garlic cloves, peeled and crushed

400 g (14 oz) can chopped tomatoes

450 g (1 lb) tomatoes, preferably plum, skinned, deseeded and roughly chopped

3 tbsp sun-dried tomato paste

500 g (1 lb 2 oz) dried linguine pasta

salt and freshly ground black pepper

1 tsp dried chilli flakes

700 g (1½ lb) cooked mixed seafood, such as peeled prawns, mussels and crab meat

225 g (8 oz) can or jar clams, drained

2 tbsp chopped fresh flat-leaf parsley

flat-leaf parsley sprigs and grated, toasted Parmesan cheese (optional), to serve

SEAFOOD LINGUINE PARCELS

SERVES 6 • PREPARATION: 30 MINUTES • COOKING TIME: 35 MINUTES

1 Heat 4 tbsp olive oil in a large, heavy-based saucepan, add the garlic and cook for 30 seconds. Add the canned tomatoes, chopped fresh tomatoes and sun-dried tomato paste and cook for a further 5 minutes.

2 Meanwhile, cook the linguine pasta in boiling, salted water for about 5 minutes, stirring to prevent it from sticking. Drain well, place in a bowl and stir through the remaining olive oil. Add the tomato sauce, dried chilli flakes, seafood, drained clams and chopped fresh parsley. Season well.

3 Place 6 pieces greaseproof paper, each about 35 cm (14 inches) square, on a work surface. Brush lightly with oil. Divide the pasta mixture among the squares of paper. Wrap up in a bundle, secure with string, then place on a baking sheet.

4 Cook the seafood parcels at 190°C (375°F) Mark 5 for 20–25 minutes or until heated through. Allow your guests to open each package at the table, then sprinkle with flat-leaf parsley sprigs and toasted Parmesan cheese, if wished.

NUTRITIONAL ANALYSIS (per portion)	
Energy	570 cals
Protein	38.0 g
Carbohydrate	69.0 g
(of which sugars)	7.0 g
Fat	15.0 g
(of which saturates)	2.0 g
Fibre	4.0 g

SUITABLE FOR:
NUT-FREE, DAIRY PRODUCE-FREE AND DIABETIC DIETS.

NOTE: To toast Parmesan cheese, sprinkle the grated cheese on to a baking sheet, then place under a hot grill until golden brown. Use a fish slice to scrape up the cheese from the baking sheet, then sprinkle it over pasta or salads.

225 g (8 oz) pasta shapes

450 g (1 lb) smoked haddock, skinned

salt and freshly ground black pepper

15 g (½ oz) butter

450 g (1 lb) baby spinach

150 ml (¼ pint) carton soured cream

2 tbsp fresh chives, snipped

1 tbsp lemon juice

pinch of freshly grated nutmeg

lemon wedges, to serve

PASTA WITH SMOKED HADDOCK AND SPINACH

SERVES 4 • PREPARATION: 10 MINUTES • COOKING TIME: ABOUT 15 MINUTES

1 Cook the pasta in a large saucepan of water according to the packet instructions.

2 Meanwhile, season the haddock with black pepper, then slice diagonally into 4 cm (1½ inch) pieces. Melt the butter in a frying pan, add half the haddock and cook over a medium heat for about 4–5 minutes. Set aside and cook the remaining haddock in the same way.

3 Drain the pasta. Place the spinach in the pan and cook for 1–2 minutes or until just wilted. Return the pasta to the pan, then stir in the soured cream, chives, lemon juice, salt and nutmeg and stir well. Gently stir the haddock into the pasta and serve immediately with lemon wedges.

NUTRITIONAL ANALYSIS (per portion)	
Energy	370 cals
Protein	30.0 g
Carbohydrate	41.0 g
(of which sugars)	4.0 g
Fat	13.0 g
(of which saturates)	7.0 g
Fibre	4.0 g

SUITABLE FOR:
NUT-FREE, LOW-CALORIE AND DIABETIC DIETS.

NOTE: To reduce the fat content further, use half-fat crème fraîche instead of soured cream.

Right: Seafood Linguine Parcels

150 g (5 oz) fresh or dried lasagnette

salt and freshly ground black pepper

2 tbsp sunflower oil

225 g (8 oz) baby carrots, halved lengthways

125 g (4 oz) baby courgettes, halved lengthways

1 bunch spring onions, trimmed and sliced

4 garlic cloves, peeled and thinly sliced

1 red chilli, deseeded and chopped

175 g (6 oz) Chinese leaves, shredded

350 g (12 oz) cooked peeled prawns

4 tbsp fresh parsley or coriander, roughly chopped

2 tbsp toasted sesame seeds, to garnish

DRESSING

1 piece preserved stem ginger, finely chopped, plus 2 tbsp syrup from jar

1 tbsp soy sauce

1 tbsp sesame oil

GINGERED PRAWNS AND LASAGNETTE SALAD

SERVES 4 • PREPARATION: 20 MINUTES • COOKING TIME: 15 MINUTES

1 To make the dressing, combine the ginger, ginger syrup, soy sauce and sesame oil.

2 Cook the pasta in a large saucepan of water according to the packet instructions until just tender. Drain the pasta and place in a bowl. Add the dressing and toss to coat evenly.

3 Heat the oil in a large wok or frying pan. Add the carrots and the courgettes and fry very quickly over a high heat until lightly charred. Remove the vegetables with a slotted spoon and set aside. Add the spring onions, garlic, chilli and Chinese leaves to the frying pan, then fry quickly until the leaves are just wilted. Add the prawns and heat through briefly.

4 Add all the vegetables to the pasta, then stir in the parsley or coriander and season to taste. Serve the salad warm, scattered with toasted sesame seeds to garnish.

NUTRITIONAL ANALYSIS (per portion)	
Energy	385 cals
Protein	28.0 g
Carbohydrate	35.0 g
(of which sugars)	7.0 g
Fat	15.0 g
(of which saturates)	2.0 g
Fibre	5.0 g

SUITABLE FOR:
NUT-FREE, LOW-CALORIE, DAIRY PRODUCE-FREE AND DIABETIC DIETS.

175 g (6 oz) pasta shapes

3 tbsp olive oil

1 tbsp rice wine vinegar

grated rind and juice of 2 limes

2 red chillies, deseeded and finely chopped

salt and freshly ground black pepper

350 g (12 oz) cooked peeled prawns

225 g (8 oz) yellow cherry tomatoes, halved

1 large avocado, peeled and thickly sliced

1 red onion, peeled and finely sliced

50 g (2 oz) large green olives, cut into quarters

3 tbsp chopped coriander

WARM PRAWN, AVOCADO AND PASTA SALAD

SERVES 4 • PREPARATION: 10 MINUTES • COOKING TIME: 10 MINUTES

1 Cook the pasta in a large saucepan of water according to the packet instructions until just tender. Drain and transfer to a serving dish.

2 Whisk together the olive oil and vinegar, then whisk in the lime rind and juice and chillies. Season to taste with salt and pepper.

3 Stir the dressing into the pasta with the prawns, tomatoes, avocado, onion, olives and coriander. Serve immediately.

NUTRITIONAL ANALYSIS (per portion)	
Energy	444 cals
Protein	27.0 g
Carbohydrate	38.0 g
(of which sugars)	4.0 g
Fat	22.0 g
(of which saturates)	4.0 g
Fibre	4.0 g

SUITABLE FOR:
NUT-FREE, LOW-CALORIE, DAIRY PRODUCE-FREE AND DIABETIC DIETS.

Pasta... carbohydrate-rich and low-fat

Nutritionally, pasta is comparable with other main carbohydrate-rich staples such as rice and potatoes, but has a higher protein and iron content. Wholewheat pasta contains more insoluble fibre than the plain type. Since pasta has very little fat, it can be eaten by calorie-counters – the danger area fat-wise is the accompanying sauce.

2 large chicken breasts

salt and freshly ground black pepper

250 g (9 oz) penne

2 tbsp olive oil

1 onion, peeled and thinly sliced

2 garlic cloves, peeled and crushed

40 g (1½ oz) pine nuts, lightly toasted

125 g (4 oz) rocket or watercress

1 tbsp light brown (muscovado) sugar

1 tbsp grainy mustard

1 tbsp white wine vinegar

5 tbsp Greek yogurt

CHICKEN, PINE NUT AND ROCKET PASTA

SERVES 4 • PREPARATION: 10 MINUTES • COOKING TIME: ABOUT 20 MINUTES

1 Slice each chicken breast in half horizontally, then cut each piece into three. Season lightly with salt and pepper and place between two layers of cling film. Beat with a rolling pin to flatten.

2 Cook the pasta in a large pan of water according to the packet instructions.

3 Meanwhile, heat the oil in a frying pan. Add the chicken pieces and fry for about 3 minutes on each side until cooked through. Drain and keep warm. Add the onion to the pan and cook gently for 3 minutes until softened. Stir in the garlic and pine nuts and cook for a further 1 minute.

4 Drain the pasta and return to the saucepan. Add the contents of the frying pan, the chicken and the rocket and toss lightly together. Transfer to warmed serving plates.

5 Stir the brown sugar, mustard, vinegar and yogurt into the pan with 100 ml (3½ fl oz) water. Heat through, stirring, for 1 minute without boiling, then spoon over the pasta.

NUTRITIONAL ANALYSIS (per portion)	
Energy	480 cals
Protein	27.0 g
Carbohydrate	54.0 g
(of which sugars)	8.0 g
Fat	19.0 g
(of which saturates)	4.0 g
Fibre	3.0 g

SUITABLE FOR:
LOW-CHOLESTEROL AND DIABETIC DIETS.

3 tbsp olive oil

450 g (1 lb) chicken livers, rinsed and chopped, with any fibrous bits discarded

125 g (4 oz) mixed red and yellow cherry tomatoes

75 g (3 oz) smoked back bacon, cut into thin strips

2 red onions, peeled and sliced into thick wedges

4 garlic cloves, peeled and crushed

2 tbsp sun-dried tomato paste

150 ml (¼ pint) sherry

150 ml (¼ pint) chicken stock

2 tbsp balsamic vinegar

salt and freshly ground black pepper

300 g (10 oz) dried tagliatelle

350 g (12 oz) fresh young spinach

TAGLIATELLE WITH CHICKEN LIVERS

SERVES 6 • PREPARATION: 25 MINUTES • COOKING TIME: 30 MINUTES

1 Heat 1 tbsp oil in a large non-stick frying pan. When hot, fry the livers in batches over a high heat, stirring, for 5 minutes or until just browned. Using a slotted spoon, remove the livers from the pan and set aside. Add the tomatoes and cook, stirring, for 1–2 minutes. Remove and set aside.

2 Add the remaining oil with the bacon and fry until it starts to become crisp. Add the onions and garlic and cook, stirring frequently, for 10–15 minutes or until the onion is soft.

3 Add the tomato paste, sherry, chicken stock and the balsamic vinegar. Bring to the boil and bubble for 5 minutes or until syrupy. Return the chicken livers and tomatoes to the pan, season to taste with salt and pepper and stir for 1–2 minutes or until the mixture is heated through.

4 Meanwhile, cook the pasta in a large pan of water according to the packet instructions, then drain well. Before serving, stir the spinach into the sauce and heat to wilt. Serve with the pasta.

NUTRITIONAL ANALYSIS (per portion)	
Energy	395 cals
Protein	25.0 g
Carbohydrate	42.0 g
(of which sugars)	5.0 g
Fat	13.0 g
(of which saturates)	3.0 g
Fibre	3.0 g

SUITABLE FOR:
NUT-FREE, LOW-CALORIE, DAIRY PRODUCE-FREE AND DIABETIC DIETS.

NOTE: Many women have low iron stores – and the good news is that just one serving of this dish will provide over half your recommended daily intake (14.8 mg).

2 tbsp olive oil

4 bay leaves

several sprigs of thyme

1 garlic clove, peeled and halved

150 g (5 oz) stoned black olives

50 g (2 oz) can anchovy fillets, drained

3 tbsp sun-dried tomato paste

finely grated rind and juice of 1 lime

salt and freshly ground black pepper

300 g (10 oz) pasta shapes or tagliatelle

4 tbsp roughly chopped flat-leaf parsley

40 g (1½ oz) freshly grated Parmesan cheese

PASTA WITH OLIVE AND ANCHOVY PASTE

SERVES 4 • PREPARATION: 10 MINUTES • COOKING TIME: ABOUT 15 MINUTES

1 Put the oil, bay leaves, thyme and garlic in a frying pan and heat gently for 2 minutes to bring out the flavours of the herbs. Add the olives, anchovy fillets and tomato paste and cook for a further minute. Remove the bay leaves.

2 Transfer the mixture to a food processor and add the lime rind and juice and a little seasoning. Blend briefly until fairly coarsely chopped.

3 Cook the pasta in a large saucepan of water according to the packet instructions until just tender. Drain lightly, so that a little water still clings to the pasta, and return to the saucepan.

4 Stir in the olive paste and parsley and heat through gently for 1 minute. Turn onto warmed serving plates and serve scattered with Parmesan.

NUTRITIONAL ANALYSIS (per portion)	
Energy	475 cals
Protein	18.0 g
Carbohydrate	68.0 g
(of which sugars)	3.0 g
Fat	17.0 g
(of which saturates)	3.5 g
Fibre	4.0 g

SUITABLE FOR:
NUT-FREE, LOW-CHOLESTEROL AND DIABETIC DIETS.

NOTE: The olive and anchovy paste can be made in advance, then simply added to the cooked pasta. It keeps well in the refrigerator for several days.

350 g (12 oz) baby leeks, or 2 large leeks, trimmed

75 g (3 oz) sugarsnap peas or mangetout, trimmed

300 g (10 oz) fettuccine or tagliatelle pasta

15 g (½ oz) butter

2 tbsp olive oil

2 garlic cloves, peeled and crushed

salt and freshly ground black pepper

¼ tsp freshly grated nutmeg

1 tsp chopped fresh thyme

175 g (6 oz) firm goat's cheese, rind removed

3 tbsp capers, rinsed

coarsely chopped flat-leaf parsley, to garnish

FETTUCCINE WITH GREEN VEGETABLES AND GOAT'S CHEESE

SERVES 4 • PREPARATION: 10 MINUTES • COOKING TIME: ABOUT 10 MINUTES

1 Wash the leeks well, then halve each one lengthways. If using large leeks, cut lengthways into long thin ribbons, then across into 7.5 cm (3 inch) strips. Cut the sugarsnap peas or mangetout in half lengthways.

2 Cook the pasta in a large saucepan of water according to the packet instructions.

3 Meanwhile, heat the butter and 1 tbsp oil in a frying pan. Add the leeks, garlic, seasoning and nutmeg and sauté gently for 3–5 minutes until the leeks are softened but still retain a little texture. Add the sugarsnap peas or mangetout and thyme and cook for a further 30 seconds.

4 Lightly drain the pasta so that some of the water still clings to it and return to the saucepan. Stir in the leek mixture, then crumble the cheese on top. Scatter with the capers and fold together lightly. Turn on to serving plates and drizzle with the remaining oil. Garnish with parsley and serve.

NUTRITIONAL ANALYSIS (per portion)	
Energy	465 cals
Protein	17.0 g
Carbohydrate	61.0 g
(of which sugars)	5.0 g
Fat	18.5 g
(of which saturates)	7.5 g
Fibre	5.0 g

SUITABLE FOR:
NUT-FREE AND DIABETIC DIETS.

1 tbsp oil

3 garlic cloves, peeled and crushed

500 g (1 lb 2 oz) carton creamed tomatoes or passata

1 bay leaf

1 sprig fresh thyme

salt and freshly ground black pepper

large pinch of caster sugar

300 g (10 oz) dried tagliatelle or spaghetti

3 tbsp chopped fresh basil

TOMATO AND BASIL SAUCE WITH PASTA

SERVES 4 • PREPARATION: 5 MINUTES • COOKING TIME: 15 MINUTES

1 To make the sauce, heat the oil in a saucepan, add the garlic and cook for 30 seconds (cook it very briefly; if it browns it will taste bitter).

2 Immediately add the creamed tomatoes or passata, bay leaf and fresh thyme. Season to taste with salt and pepper and a large pinch of caster sugar. Bring to the boil and simmer, uncovered, for 5–10 minutes.

3 Meanwhile, cook the pasta in a large pan of water according to the packet instructions. Drain well and transfer to a serving dish.

4 Remove the bay leaf and thyme from the sauce, then add the chopped fresh basil. Toss the sauce into the pasta and serve immediately.

NUTRITIONAL ANALYSIS (per portion)	
Energy	305 cals
Protein	10.0 g
Carbohydrate	60.0 g
(of which sugars)	5.0 g
Fat	4.0 g
(of which saturates)	0.5 g
Fibre	3.0 g

SUITABLE FOR:
NUT-FREE, LOW-CHOLESTEROL, LOW-CALORIE, DAIRY PRODUCE-FREE AND DIABETIC DIETS.

2 lemons

50 g (2 oz) butter

75 g (3 oz) toasted hazelnuts, roughly chopped

6 garlic cloves, peeled and thinly sliced

450 g (1 lb) fresh spaghetti or 225 g (8 oz) dried

4 tbsp chopped fresh basil

4 tbsp chopped fresh parsley

2 tbsp single cream (optional)

salt and freshly ground black pepper

SPAGHETTI WITH LEMON AND NUT BUTTER

SERVES 4 • PREPARATION: 10 MINUTES • COOKING TIME: 15 MINUTES

1 Coarsely grate the rind and squeeze the juice from the lemons.

2 Melt the butter in a medium-sized pan until it turns a pale golden brown. Add the chopped hazelnuts and the garlic, then cook for about 30 seconds. Add the lemon rind and set aside.

3 Cook the spaghetti in a large pan of water according to the packet instructions. Drain well and stir into the butter mixture.

4 Stir the spaghetti mixture over a low heat for 2–3 minutes. Stir in the herbs, 4 tbsp lemon juice and single cream, if using. Season with plenty of salt and pepper and serve immediately.

NUTRITIONAL ANALYSIS (per portion)	
Energy	420 cals
Protein	9.5 g
Carbohydrate	44.0 g
(of which sugars)	2.0 g
Fat	23.0 g
(of which saturates)	7.5 g
Fibre	3.0 g

SUITABLE FOR:
LOW-CALORIE AND DIABETIC DIETS.

VARIATION:
Blanched asparagus tips, broccoli florets or other spring vegetables can be added to this dish very successfully.

Nuts... protein packed

Nuts are a valuable source of protein in a vegetarian diet. However, they are deficient in the amino acid lysine, and therefore, in a vegetarian diet, they are best eaten with foods that contain lysine, such as pulses. With the exception of chestnuts, nuts are high in fat, although it is the healthier unsaturated kind.

15 g (½ oz) dried mushrooms

15 g (½ oz) butter, plus a little extra for greasing

225 g (8 oz) brown-cap mushrooms, finely chopped

250 g (9 oz) ricotta cheese

1 tsp anchovy essence

salt and freshly ground black pepper

4 sheets fresh lasagne, each measuring 11.5 x 16.5 cm (4½ x 6½ inches)

2 x 300 ml (½ pint) tubs fresh tomato sauce

50 g (2 oz) Parmesan cheese shavings

black pepper and basil sprigs, to garnish

NOTE: If you want to use dried lasagne instead of the fresh version, cook it according to the packet instructions but reduce the overall cooking time by 15 minutes.

MUSHROOM AND RICOTTA CANNELLONI WITH TOMATO SAUCE

SERVES 4 • PREPARATION: 15 MINUTES • COOKING TIME: 50 MINUTES

1 Wash the dried mushrooms, then pour 150 ml (¼ pint) boiling water over and leave to stand for 15 minutes. Drain and finely chop. Lightly grease a large, shallow, ovenproof dish with butter.

2 Heat the butter in a large frying pan, add the fresh and soaked dried mushrooms and cook for 10–15 minutes or until they are beginning to brown and any liquid has evaporated. Leave to cool.

3 Place the ricotta cheese in a bowl, add the mushrooms, anchovy essence and seasoning, then mix until thoroughly combined.

4 Cook the lasagne according to the packet instructions, then halve widthways. Place about 3 tbsp mushroom mixture along one edge of the lasagne, then roll up to enclose the filling. Repeat this process with the remaining lasagne. Arrange the filled pasta seam-side down in the prepared dish. Pour the tomato sauce over and sprinkle with the Parmesan. Cook at 200°C (400°F) Mark 6 for 35–40 minutes. Garnish with pepper and basil.

NUTRITIONAL ANALYSIS (per portion)	
Energy	240 cals
Protein	15.0 g
Carbohydrate	17.0 g
(of which sugars)	6.0 g
Fat	14.0 g
(of which saturates)	9.0 g
Fibre	2.0 g

SUITABLE FOR:
NUT-FREE, LOW-CALORIE AND DIABETIC DIETS.

125 g (4 oz) pasta shapes

75 g (3 oz) baby carrots, washed and trimmed

75 g (3 oz) asparagus, trimmed and cut into 7.5 cm (3 inch) pieces

175 g (6 oz) broccoli, cut into small florets

200 g (7 oz) can artichoke hearts in water, drained and roughly chopped

350 ml (12 fl oz) cheese sauce

salt and freshly ground black pepper

1 tbsp olive oil

25 g (1 oz) Gruyère cheese, grated

15 g (½ oz) sunflower seeds, toasted

50 g (2 oz) fresh breadcrumbs

SUMMER VEGETABLE AND PASTA BAKE

SERVES 4 • PREPARATION: 10 MINUTES • COOKING TIME: 30 MINUTES

1 Cook the pasta shapes according to the packet instructions until just tender. Drain; transfer to an ovenproof dish.

2 Place the carrots in a pan of boiling water and cook for 3 minutes. Add the asparagus and broccoli and cook until just tender. Drain well.

3 Stir the cooked vegetables, artichoke hearts and cheese sauce into the pasta and season. Mix the oil, cheese and sunflower seeds into the breadcrumbs, then sprinkle over the vegetables.

4 Cook at 200°C (400°F) Mark 6 for 20 minutes. Serve immediately.

NUTRITIONAL ANALYSIS (per portion)	
Energy	360 cals
Protein	16.0 g
Carbohydrate	42.0 g
(of which sugars)	6.0 g
Fat	15.0 g
(of which saturates)	5.0 g
Fibre	4.0 g

SUITABLE FOR:
NUT-FREE, LOW-CALORIE AND DIABETIC DIETS.

4 tbsp extra-virgin olive oil, plus extra for brushing

2 small red onions, peeled and thinly sliced

1 garlic clove, peeled and crushed

1 tbsp chopped fresh thyme

pinch of sugar

2 heads of radicchio

400 g (14 oz) dried buckwheat tagliatelle

salt and freshly ground black pepper

2 tbsp balsamic vinegar

25 g (1 oz) capers in wine vinegar, drained

50 g (2 oz) pine nuts, toasted

2 tbsp chopped fresh basil

freshly grated Parmesan cheese, to serve (optional)

BUCKWHEAT PASTA WITH GRILLED RADICCHIO

SERVES 4 • PREPARATION: 15 MINUTES • COOKING TIME: 15 MINUTES

1 Heat the oil in a deep frying pan. Add the onions, garlic, thyme and sugar and cook for 10–15 minutes until golden and tender.

2 Meanwhile, cut the radicchio into wedges and lay on the grill rack. Brush with a little oil and grill for 2–3 minutes. Turn, brush with oil and grill for a further 2–3 minutes until charred and tender; keep warm.

3 Cook the buckwheat pasta in a large pan of boiling salted water until just tender.

4 Add the balsamic vinegar, capers, nuts and basil to the onions and stir well; keep warm.

5 Drain the pasta, reserving 4 tbsp cooking water. Add both to the caramelised onions with the radicchio. Stir briefly over a medium heat, then season with salt and pepper and serve at once, with Parmesan, if wished.

NUTRITIONAL ANALYSIS
(per portion)

Energy	565 cals
Protein	15.0 g
Carbohydrate	80.0 g
(of which sugars)	6.0 g
Fat	22.0 g
(of which saturates)	2.5 g
Fibre	5.0 g

SUITABLE FOR:
LOW-CHOLESTEROL, DAIRY PRODUCE-FREE AND DIABETIC DIETS.

1 stick lemon grass, trimmed and finely chopped

100 g (3½ oz) medium egg noodles (one layer)

100 g (3½ oz) sugarsnap peas, cut in half diagonally

salt and freshly ground black pepper

4 tbsp oil

4 garlic cloves, peeled and crushed

3 large eggs, beaten

juice of 2 lemons

3 tbsp Thai fish sauce

2 tbsp light soy sauce

½ tsp caster sugar

50 g (2 oz) roasted salted peanuts

½ tsp chilli powder

12 spring onions, trimmed and roughly chopped

150 g (5 oz) bean sprouts

2 tbsp chopped fresh coriander

coriander sprigs, to garnish

THAI EGG NOODLES

SERVES 4 • PREPARATION: 20 MINUTES, PLUS SOAKING • COOKING TIME: 12 MINUTES

1 Place the lemon grass in a bowl with the noodles. Pour 600 ml (1 pint) boiling water over, set aside for 20 minutes, stirring from time to time.

2 Cook the sugarsnap peas in boiling, salted water for 1 minute, then drain and plunge into ice-cold water.

3 Heat the oil in a wok or frying pan, add the garlic and stir-fry for 30 seconds. Add the beaten eggs and cook gently until lightly scrambled. Add the lemon juice, fish sauce, soy sauce, sugar, peanuts, chilli powder, spring onions and bean sprouts to the eggs. Pour the noodles, lemon grass and soaking liquid into the wok. Bring to the boil and bubble for 4–5 minutes, stirring from time to time.

4 Drain the sugarsnap peas, then add to the noodle mixture with the chopped coriander; warm through and season to taste. Garnish with coriander sprigs and serve.

NUTRITIONAL ANALYSIS
(per portion)

Energy	365 cals
Protein	14.5 g
Carbohydrate	23.0 g
(of which sugars)	4.0 g
Fat	25.0 g
(of which saturates)	5.0 g
Fibre	3.0 g

SUITABLE FOR:
LOW-CHOLESTEROL, LOW-CALORIE, DAIRY PRODUCE-FREE AND DIABETIC DIETS.

225 g (8 oz) fresh chicken livers

50 g (2 oz) Italian salami, sliced

175 g (6 oz) lean back bacon rashers, thinly sliced

100 g (3½ oz) butter

225 g (8 oz) onions, peeled and roughly chopped

375 g (12 oz) risotto (arborio) rice

2 tbsp tomato paste

1.4-1.7 litres (2½-3 pints) chicken or vegetable stock

200 ml (7 fl oz) white wine

2 tbsp finely chopped fresh rosemary

salt and freshly ground black pepper

freshly grated Parmesan cheese, to serve (optional)

rosemary sprigs, to garnish

CRISP CHICKEN LIVER RISOTTO

SERVES 4 • PREPARATION: 15 MINUTES • COOKING TIME: 40 MINUTES

1 Halve the chicken livers, if very large. Place the salami and bacon in a layer in a large roasting tin. Cook at 200°C (400°F) Mark 6 for 15–20 minutes or until crisp, then drain on kitchen paper.

2 Meanwhile, melt 25 g (1 oz) butter in a large pan, add the livers and fry briskly for 2–3 minutes. Drain and set aside, then wipe out the pan. Add the remaining butter to the pan and cook the onions over medium heat for 10 minutes until soft.

3 Stir in the rice and tomato paste and cook for 1 minute. Bring the stock and wine to the boil together and pour a ladleful of hot liquid into the rice. Bubble gently until absorbed, stirring. Keep adding stock in ladlefuls, stirring until each one is absorbed; this should take about 20 minutes – the risotto will become thick and creamy.

4 To serve, discard any juices from the chicken livers, then add to the risotto with the chopped rosemary, crisp salami, bacon and seasoning. Stir for 1 minute over the heat, then sprinkle with Parmesan, if using, and garnish with rosemary.

NUTRITIONAL ANALYSIS (per portion)	
Energy	682 cals
Protein	30.0 g
Carbohydrate	79.0 g
(of which sugars)	3.0 g
Fat	23.0 g
(of which saturates)	9.0 g
Fibre	0.5 g

SUITABLE FOR:
NUT-FREE AND DIABETIC DIETS.

NOTE: Keep a close watch on the risotto as it cooks – if the liquid evaporates too quickly it may stick to the pan.

750-900 ml (1¼-1½ pints) light vegetable stock with a splash of white wine (optional)

50 g (2 oz) butter

175 g (6 oz) onion, peeled and finely chopped

3 garlic cloves, peeled and crushed

225 g (8 oz) risotto (arborio) rice

50 g (2 oz) grated Parmesan cheese

salt and freshly ground black pepper

4-5 tbsp chopped fresh parsley

GARLIC AND PARMESAN RISOTTO

SERVES 4 • PREPARATION: 5 MINUTES • COOKING TIME: 35 MINUTES

1 Heat the stock and keep it hot over a low heat. Meanwhile, melt half the butter in a large heavy-based saucepan and stir in the onion. Cook for 8–10 minutes until very soft but not too coloured, then stir in the garlic and rice. Stir over the heat to fry the rice lightly in the butter for 2–3 minutes.

2 Pour in a ladleful of the hot stock and let it simmer gently, stirring frequently until the rice has absorbed most of it. Keep adding the stock in this way for 20–25 minutes until the rice is tender but still has a little bite to it; the end result should look creamy and soft.

3 Stir in the remaining butter, along with the Parmesan cheese, seasoning and parsley.

NUTRITIONAL ANALYSIS (per portion)	
Energy	290 cals
Protein	8.5 g
Carbohydrate	38.0 g
(of which sugars)	2.0 g
Fat	11.5 g
(of which saturates)	7.0 g
Fibre	0.5 g

SUITABLE FOR:
GLUTEN-FREE, NUT-FREE, LOW-CALORIE AND DIABETIC DIETS.

NOTE: Always use risotto or arborio rice – the grains are thick, short and starchy, giving the risotto its wonderful texture.

350 g (12 oz) frozen broad beans

salt and freshly ground black pepper

25 g (1 oz) butter

1 onion, peeled and finely chopped

200 g (7 oz) risotto (arborio) rice

1 litre (1¾ pints) hot vegetable stock

grated rind and juice of 1 lemon

75 g (3 oz) freshly grated Parmesan cheese

freshly grated Parmesan cheese and lemon rind, to garnish

BROAD BEAN AND LEMON RISOTTO

SERVES 4 • PREPARATION: 25 MINUTES • COOKING TIME: 35 MINUTES

1 Cook the broad beans in a large pan of boiling salted water for 3–5 minutes or until just tender. Plunge into ice-cold water to cool. Drain, peel off the outer skin (optional) and set aside.

2 Melt the butter in large pan, add the onion and cook over a medium heat for 5 minutes or until beginning to soften. Add the rice and continue to cook, stirring, for 1–2 minutes. Pour in a ladleful of the hot stock and simmer gently, stirring frequently until the rice has absorbed most of it. Keep adding the stock in this way until the rice is tender but still has bite to it; this will take about 15–20 minutes. The risotto should look creamy and soft.

3 Add the broad beans, lemon rind and juice and warm through. Stir in the Parmesan and season with salt and pepper to taste.

4 Serve the risotto immediately, garnished with grated Parmesan and lemon rind.

NUTRITIONAL ANALYSIS (per portion)	
Energy	380 cals
Protein	17.0 g
Carbohydrate	49.0 g
(of which sugars)	3.0 g
Fat	12.0 g
(of which saturates)	7.0 g
Fibre	6.0 g

SUITABLE FOR:

GLUTEN-FREE, NUT-FREE, LOW-CALORIE AND DIABETIC DIETS.

Broad beans ... full of goodness

Broad beans contain vitamin B1 and iron, and are a good source of soluble fibre, which can help reduce high blood cholesterol levels.

4-6 tbsp olive oil

300 g (10 oz) aubergine, roughly chopped

225 g (8 oz) onions, peeled and finely chopped

25 g (1 oz) butter

½ tsp cumin seeds

175 g (6 oz) long-grain rice

600 ml (1 pint) vegetable or chicken stock

salt and freshly ground black pepper

400 g (14 oz) can chick peas, drained and rinsed

225 g (8 oz) baby spinach

AUBERGINE AND CHICK PEA PILAFF

SERVES 6 • PREPARATION: 10 MINUTES •
COOKING TIME: 20 MINUTES, PLUS STANDING

1 Heat half the olive oil in a large pan or flameproof casserole. Fry the aubergine for 4–5 minutes in batches until deep golden brown. Remove from the pan with a slotted spoon and set aside. Add the remaining oil to the pan and cook the onions for 5 minutes or until golden and soft.

2 Add the butter, then stir in the cumin seeds and rice. Fry for 1–2 minutes, pour the stock over, season and bring to the boil. Reduce the heat, then simmer, uncovered, for 10–12 minutes or until most of the liquid has evaporated and the rice is tender.

3 Remove the pan from the heat. Stir in the chick peas, spinach and reserved, cooked aubergine. Cover with a tight-fitting lid and leave to stand for 5 minutes until the spinach is wilted and the chick peas are heated through. Adjust the seasoning to taste. Fork through the rice grains before serving.

NUTRITIONAL ANALYSIS (per portion)	
Energy	300 cals
Protein	9.0 g
Carbohydrate	39.0 g
(of which sugars)	4.0 g
Fat	13.0 g
(of which saturates)	4.0 g
Fibre	5.0 g

SUITABLE FOR:

GLUTEN-FREE, NUT-FREE, LOW-CHOLESTEROL, LOW-CALORIE AND DIABETIC DIETS.

225 g (8 oz) spinach

400 g (14 oz) can beans, such as pinto, chick peas, kidney beans or mixed pulses

2 tbsp oil

225 g (8 oz) onions, peeled and chopped

2 garlic cloves, peeled and crushed

75 g (3 oz) red rice (see Note)

75 g (3 oz) long-grain rice

450 ml (¾ pint) vegetable or chicken stock

salt and freshly ground black pepper

RED RICE, SPINACH AND BEAN PILAFF

SERVES 6 • PREPARATION: 20 MINUTES •
COOKING TIME: 1 HOUR 20 MINUTES

1 If the spinach leaves are large, remove the stalks. Wash well in cold water, drain and roughly chop. Drain and rinse the beans.

2 Heat the oil in a large flameproof casserole, add the onions and cook, stirring, for 10 minutes or until they are golden and soft.

3 Add the garlic and the red rice to the onions; cook, stirring, for a further minute. Add the stock, bring to the boil and season, then cover and simmer for 10 minutes. Cook at 200°C (400°F) Mark 6 for 30 minutes. Add the long-grain rice to the casserole and bring back to the boil. Return to the oven for 25 minutes or until the rice is just tender.

4 Stir in the beans and return to the oven for 5 minutes. Just before serving, stir the spinach through the pilaff until wilted. Season and serve.

NUTRITIONAL ANALYSIS (per portion)	
Energy	227 cals
Protein	8.5 g
Carbohydrate	34.0 g
(of which sugars)	3.0 g
Fat	6.5 g
(of which saturates)	1.0 g
Fibre	4.0 g

SUITABLE FOR:

GLUTEN-FREE, NUT-FREE, LOW-CHOLESTEROL, LOW-CALORIE, DAIRY PRODUCE-FREE AND DIABETIC DIETS.

NOTE: Red rice, which has a firm, nutty texture, is now available in most major supermarkets but if you can't find it, use wild rice instead.

50 g (2 oz) wild rice

3 tbsp olive oil

100 g (3½ oz) blanched almonds, roughly chopped

2 onions, peeled and chopped

300 g (10 oz) brown rice

3 garlic cloves, peeled and crushed

4 cm (1½ inch) piece fresh root ginger, peeled and grated

1 red chilli, deseeded and sliced

2 tsp ground coriander

1 stick cinnamon, halved

½ tsp ground turmeric

750 ml (1¼ pints) vegetable stock

150 g (5 oz) French beans, halved

large handful of coriander, roughly chopped

salt and freshly ground black pepper

chopped fresh coriander, to garnish

Greek yogurt and spiced fruit chutney (optional), to serve

MIXED RICE AND ALMOND PILAFF

SERVES 6 • PREPARATION: 15 MINUTES • COOKING TIME: ABOUT 45 MINUTES

1 Cook the wild rice in plenty of water for about 30 minutes until the grains are tender and just beginning to split.

2 Meanwhile, heat the olive oil in a large, heavy-based saucepan. Add the almonds and fry gently until golden; remove with a slotted spoon. Add the onions to the pan and fry for 3 minutes. Stir in the brown rice, garlic, ginger, chilli, coriander, cinnamon and turmeric and cook, stirring, for 1 minute.

3 Add the stock and bring to the boil. Cover with a lid and cook gently for about 30 minutes until the rice is tender and the stock has been absorbed. Stir in the beans, drained wild rice and coriander and cook gently for a further 5 minutes or until the beans are softened, adding a little water to the pan if the pilaff becomes too dry.

4 Season to taste, then spoon on to serving plates. Garnish with coriander and serve with spoonfuls of yogurt and chutney, if wished.

NUTRITIONAL ANALYSIS (per portion)	
Energy	380 cals
Protein	9.0 g
Carbohydrate	50.0 g
(of which sugars)	3.0 g
Fat	16.5 g
(of which saturates)	2.0 g
Fibre	3.0 g

SUITABLE FOR:

GLUTEN-FREE, LOW-CHOLESTEROL, LOW-CALORIE, DAIRY PRODUCE-FREE AND DIABETIC DIETS.

CHESTNUT RISOTTO CAKES

4 tbsp olive oil

200 g (7 oz) chestnut mushrooms, chopped

1 onion, peeled and finely chopped

3 garlic cloves, peeled and crushed

175 g (6 oz) risotto (arborio) rice

750 ml (1¼ pint) hot vegetable stock

240 g (8½ oz) can cooked whole chestnuts, or vacuum packed, chopped

25 g (1 oz) Parmesan cheese, grated

3 tbsp roughly chopped parsley

1 tbsp chopped fresh sage

salt and freshly ground black pepper

1 egg

50 g (2 oz) polenta

a little flour, for dusting

SERVES 6 • PREPARATION: 30 MINUTES • COOKING TIME: 40 MINUTES

1 Heat 1 tbsp olive oil in a frying pan. Add the mushrooms and fry gently for about 5 minutes until the mushroom juices have evaporated.

2 Heat another 1 tbsp oil in a heavy-based saucepan. Add the onion and fry gently for 2 minutes. Add the garlic and rice and cook for a further 1 minute.

3 Add a ladleful of the hot stock, stirring until the stock is almost absorbed. Continue cooking for about 15–20 minutes, adding a little more of the stock as it becomes absorbed, until the mixture is creamy and thick. Stir in the cooked mushrooms, chestnuts, Parmesan, herbs and a little salt and pepper. Transfer to a bowl; cool completely.

4 Beat the egg in a shallow bowl. Put the polenta on a large plate. Mark the risotto mixture into 12 wedges. Using floured hands, shape each wedge into a small cake and coat in egg, then polenta.

5 Heat the remaining oil in the frying pan and fry the cakes, in 2 batches if necessary, for 2–3 minutes on each side until golden and crisp. Drain on kitchen paper and serve hot.

NUTRITIONAL ANALYSIS (per portion)	
Energy	316 cals
Protein	8.0 g
Carbohydrate	45.0 g
(of which sugars)	4.0 g
Fat	11.5 g
(of which saturates)	2.5 g
Fibre	2.5 g

SUITABLE FOR:
GLUTEN-FREE, NUT-FREE, LOW-CHOLESTEROL, LOW-CALORIE AND DIABETIC DIETS.

NOTE: These risotto cakes freeze well, making a perfect prepare-ahead starter or light supper dish with a mixed, leafy salad. Freeze them before frying and interleave with greaseproof paper.

DRIED FRUIT TABBOULEH

200 g (7 oz) bulghar wheat

4 tbsp olive oil

1 bay leaf

25 g (1 oz) mixture of fresh mint and parsley

2 garlic cloves, peeled and halved

4 spring onions, trimmed and roughly chopped

75 g (3 oz) unblanched hazelnuts, lightly toasted

finely grated rind and juice of 1 lemon

50 g (2 oz) no-soak dried apricots, roughly chopped

50 g (2 oz) no-soak dried prunes, roughly chopped

salt and freshly ground black pepper

SERVES 4 • PREPARATION: 10 MINUTES, PLUS SOAKING • COOKING TIME: 2 MINUTES

1 Cover the bulghar wheat with plenty of boiling water. Leave for 30–35 minutes or until tender.

2 Meanwhile, put the oil, herbs, garlic and spring onions in a frying pan. Heat gently for 2 minutes until bay leaves start to curl. Remove from heat.

3 Blend the hazelnuts in a food processor until roughly chopped. Remove the bay leaves from the herb mixture, then transfer the pan contents to the food processor with the hazelnuts. Add the lime rind and juice and blend briefly until the herbs are coarsely chopped.

4 Thoroughly drain the bulghar wheat and transfer to a large bowl. Add the apricots and prunes to the bowl with the blended mixture and a little seasoning. Toss together and chill before serving.

NUTRITIONAL ANALYSIS (per portion)	
Energy	440 cals
Protein	8.5 g
Carbohydrate	48.0 g
(of which sugars)	10.0 g
Fat	24.0 g
(of which saturates)	2.5 g
Fibre	3.0 g

SUITABLE FOR:
LOW-CHOLESTEROL, LOW-CALORIE, DAIRY PRODUCE-FREE AND DIABETIC DIETS.

NOTE: This salad is best served chilled. Make it several hours in advance so the flavours can develop.

25 g (1 oz) dried shiitake or porcini mushrooms

50 g (2 oz) butter

2 garlic cloves, peeled and finely chopped

4 shallots, peeled and finely chopped

225 g (8 oz) fresh mixed wild mushrooms, finely sliced

225 g (8 oz) button mushrooms, finely sliced

225 g (8 oz) pearl barley, rinsed and drained

120 ml (4 fl oz) dry white wine or dry sherry

salt and freshly ground black pepper

2 tbsp finely chopped fresh parsley

2 tbsp finely chopped fresh coriander

WILD MUSHROOM AND BARLEY RISOTTO

SERVES 4 • PREPARATION: 15 MINUTES, PLUS SOAKING • COOKING TIME: 1 HOUR

1 Soak the dried mushrooms in 450 ml (¾ pint) boiling water for 30 minutes, then drain, reserving the soaking liquid. Thinly slice the mushrooms, discarding the stalks.

2 Melt the butter in a large saucepan, add the garlic and shallots and cook for 3 minutes, stirring constantly.

3 Add all the fresh sliced mushrooms to the pan and cook for 5 minutes over low heat, turning constantly. Stir in the barley with the soaked dried mushrooms and reserved liquid. Pour in 600 ml (1 pint) water and bring to the boil. Reduce the heat to low, cover the pan and simmer for 35 minutes.

4 Add the wine and season with salt and pepper. Cook for a further 15–20 minutes over low heat, stirring occasionally to prevent sticking

5 Just before serving, adjust the seasoning and fork in the parsley and coriander.

NUTRITIONAL ANALYSIS (per portion)	
Energy	350 cals
Protein	7.0 g
Carbohydrate	52.0 g
(of which sugars)	1.0 g
Fat	12.0 g
(of which saturates)	7.0 g
Fibre	1.0 g

SUITABLE FOR:
NUT-FREE, LOW-CALORIE AND DIABETIC DIETS.

NOTE: This barley dish makes a delicious alternative to the more traditional rice risotto.

finely grated rind of 1 lemon

1 large garlic clove, peeled and crushed

3 tbsp chopped fresh parsley

1 tbsp olive oil

1 onion, peeled and chopped

2 sticks celery, trimmed and sliced

50 g (2 oz) bacon lardons

75 g (3 oz) pearl barley

1.2 litres (2 pints) chicken stock

500 g (1 lb 2 oz) baby potatoes

2 large leeks, trimmed and sliced

200 g (7 oz) baby spinach

freshly grated nutmeg

NOTE: Barley contains very little gluten.

PEARL BARLEY BROTH WITH SPINACH AND POTATOES

SERVES 4 • PREPARATION: 10 MINUTES • COOKING TIME: ABOUT 1 HOUR

1 Mix together the lemon rind, garlic and parsley. Cover with cling film and reserve.

2 Heat the oil in a large saucepan. Add the onion, celery and bacon and cook gently for 5 minutes until lightly coloured. Add the pearl barley and stock and bring just to the boil. Reduce the heat, cover with a lid and simmer gently for 30 minutes.

3 Add the potatoes and leeks and cook, covered, for a further 20 minutes until the potatoes and barley are tender.

4 Stir in the spinach and nutmeg and season lightly to taste. Cook for 2–3 minutes until the spinach has wilted. Ladle into bowls and serve hot with the reserved lemon and garlic scattered over the broth.

NUTRITIONAL ANALYSIS (per portion)	
Energy	279 cals
Protein	9.0 g
Carbohydrate	42.0 g
(of which sugars)	4.0 g
Fat	9.0 g
(of which saturates)	2.5 g
Fibre	4.0 g

SUITABLE FOR:
NUT-FREE, LOW-CHOLESTEROL, LOW-CALORIE, DAIRY PRODUCE-FREE AND DIABETIC DIETS.

---

225 g (8 oz) couscous

300 ml (½ pint) chicken or vegetable stock

400 g (14 oz) can cherry tomatoes (see Note)

small handful basil leaves, torn into pieces

2 tsp white wine vinegar

3 tbsp olive oil

few drops of tabasco sauce

1 tsp caster sugar

salt and freshly ground black pepper

2 small red onions, peeled and sliced

200 g (7 oz) feta cheese, diced

3 tbsp capers, rinsed

basil leaves, to garnish

NOTE: If you can't get canned cherry tomatoes, use a can of plum tomatoes instead. Once drained, roughly chop the tomatoes before adding to the couscous.

COUSCOUS WITH FETA AND CHERRY TOMATOES

SERVES 4 • PREPARATION: 15 MINUTES • COOKING TIME: ABOUT 30 MINUTES

1 Put the couscous in an ovenproof dish and pour over the stock. Leave for 5 minutes. Drain the can of tomatoes, reserving the juice. Gently fold the tomatoes into the couscous with the basil. Cover and transfer to the oven and cook at 190°C (375°F) Mark 5 for 20 minutes.

2 Meanwhile, make the dressing. Blend the reserved tomato juice with the vinegar, 1 tbsp oil, the tabasco sauce and sugar. Season with salt and pepper and reserve.

3 Heat the remaining oil in a frying pan. Add the onions and fry gently for 6–8 minutes until deep golden. Add the feta and capers and cook for a further 2 minutes.

4 Spoon the couscous on to serving plates and top with the onions and feta. Spoon over the dressing and serve scattered with basil leaves.

NUTRITIONAL ANALYSIS (per portion)	
Energy	366 cals
Protein	12.5 g
Carbohydrate	35.0 g
(of which sugars)	6.0 g
Fat	20.0 g
(of which saturates)	8.0 g
Fibre	1.5 g

SUITABLE FOR:
NUT-FREE, LOW-CALORIE AND DIABETIC DIETS.

Right: Couscous with Feta and Cherry Tomatoes

125 g (4 oz) rocket or watercress

120 ml (4 fl oz) lemon juice

150 ml (¼ pint) olive oil

salt and freshly ground black pepper

450 g (1 lb) couscous

2 bunches spring onions, trimmed and chopped

1 cucumber, halved, deseeded and roughly chopped

GREEN COUSCOUS WITH LEMON DRESSING

SERVES 6 • PREPARATION: 15 MINUTES • COOKING TIME: 25 MINUTES

1 Remove any tough stalks from the rocket or watercress, then roughly chop. For the dressing, mix together the lemon juice and olive oil, then season with salt and pepper; set aside.

2 Place the couscous in a bowl and cover with 600 ml (1 pint) cold water. Strain and return the couscous to the bowl; leave for 5–10 minutes to allow the couscous grains to swell. Lightly rake the grains to remove any lumps.

3 Place the couscous in the top compartment of an oiled steamer (see Note). Steam over boiling water for 20–25 minutes, separating the grains occasionally with a fork.

4 Place the couscous in a warmed serving bowl, stir in the rocket or watercress, spring onions, cucumber and lemon dressing, then serve immediately.

NUTRITIONAL ANALYSIS (per portion)	
Energy	350 cals
Protein	6.0 g
Carbohydrate	41.0 g
(of which sugars)	2.0 g
Fat	19.0 g
(of which saturates)	3.0 g
Fibre	1.0 g

SUITABLE FOR:
NUT-FREE, LOW-CHOLESTEROL, LOW-CALORIE, DAIRY PRODUCE-FREE AND DIABETIC DIETS.

NOTE: If you don't have a steamer or couscoussière use a metal colander that fits tightly over a large saucepan. Line the base with a clean J-cloth or muslin.

MILLET AND PEPPER SALAD

SERVES 4 • PREPARATION: 15 MINUTES •
COOKING TIME: 30 MINUTES

225 g (8 oz) millet

600 ml (1 pint) vegetable stock

1 red pepper

1 yellow pepper

1 orange pepper

6 tbsp extra-virgin olive oil

1 onion, peeled and finely chopped

2 garlic cloves, peeled and finely chopped

1 small red chilli, deseeded and finely chopped

1 tsp ground mixed spice

2 ripe tomatoes, skinned and diced

2 tbsp balsamic vinegar

2 tbsp chopped fresh basil

salt and freshly ground black pepper

1 Dry-fry the millet in a large frying pan for 3–4 minutes until golden and releasing a smoky aroma, then transfer to a saucepan. Add the stock, bring to the boil, cover and simmer gently for about 20–25 minutes until the grains are swollen and the stock is absorbed. Transfer to a large bowl.

2 Meanwhile, grill the peppers under a high heat for 15–20 minutes turning frequently until charred. Put in a bowl, cover and leave until cool enough to handle. Remove the pepper skins, core and seeds over a bowl to catch the juice. Slice the flesh.

3 Heat 1 tbsp oil in a frying pan, add the onion, garlic, chilli and mixed spice and fry gently for 5 minutes. Add the tomatoes and remove from heat.

4 Whisk the remaining oil with the vinegar and reserved pepper juices. Add to the cooked millet with the spiced mixture and basil. Toss to mix and season with salt and pepper to taste. Serve warm.

NUTRITIONAL ANALYSIS
(per portion)

Energy	400 cals
Protein	7.0 g
Carbohydrate	56.0 g
(of which sugars)	8.0 g
Fat	18.0 g
(of which saturates)	2.5 g
Fibre	2.3 g

SUITABLE FOR:
GLUTEN-FREE, NUT-FREE, LOW-CHOLESTEROL, LOW-CALORIE, DAIRY PRODUCE-FREE AND DIABETIC DIETS.

POLENTA WITH CHORIZO

SERVES 4 • PREPARATION: 20 MINUTES •
COOKING TIME: ABOUT 15 MINUTES

350 g (12 oz) broccoli, divided into small florets (with stalks cut off, sliced and reserved)

2 tbsp olive oil

70 g (2¾ oz) chorizo sausage, sliced very thinly

1 large onion, peeled and chopped

1 tbsp balsamic vinegar

2 tsp runny honey

2 tsp chopped fresh rosemary

1 litre (1¾ pints) vegetable or chicken stock

salt and freshly ground black pepper

200 g (7 oz) quick-cook polenta

finely grated rind of 1 lemon

1 tsp ground paprika

4 tbsp roughly chopped flat-leaf parsley

1 Cook the broccoli stalks in boiling water for 30 seconds. Add the florets and cook for 1 minute. Drain, refresh under cold water and leave to drain.

2 Heat 1 tbsp oil in a frying pan and fry the chorizo very gently for 2 minutes. Remove from the pan. Add the broccoli to the pan and fry quickly for 4–5 minutes until beginning to colour; remove from the pan. Add the remaining oil and fry the onion for 5 minutes until golden. Return chorizo to pan with the broccoli, vinegar, honey and rosemary; stand.

3 Bring the stock to the boil with ½ tsp salt. Pour in the polenta in a steady stream, whisking well so that lumps do not form. Cook over a very gentle heat for about 5 minutes, stirring with a wooden spoon until soft and smooth. Stir in the lemon rind, paprika and parsley; season with black pepper.

4 Warm the chorizo mixture through for 2 minutes. Spoon the polenta on to serving plates, then add the chorizo topping and pour over any pan juices.

NUTRITIONAL ANALYSIS
(per portion)

Energy	375 cals
Protein	13.0 g
Carbohydrate	45.0 g
(of which sugars)	6.5 g
Fat	16.0 g
(of which saturates)	1.0 g
Fibre	4.0 g

SUITABLE FOR:
NUT-FREE, LOW-CHOLESTEROL, LOW-CALORIE, DAIRY PRODUCE-FREE AND DIABETIC DIETS.

750 ml (1¼ pints) vegetable stock

salt and freshly ground black pepper

175 g (6 oz) quick-cook polenta

2 tbsp chopped fresh mixed herbs

75 g (3 oz) freshly grated Parmesan cheese

olive oil, for brushing and greasing

TOPPING

1 tbsp olive oil

1 garlic clove, peeled and crushed

250 g (9 oz) trimmed baby leeks, sliced diagonally

200 g (7 oz) mixed green and black olives, stoned

flat-leaf parsley, to garnish

GRILLED POLENTA WITH WARM LEEKS AND OLIVES

SERVES 4 • PREPARATION: 10 MINUTES, PLUS COOLING • COOKING TIME: 25 MINUTES

1 Bring the stock to the boil with ½ tsp salt. Pour in the polenta in a steady stream, whisking well so that no lumps form. Cook over a very gentle heat for about 5 minutes, stirring with a wooden spoon until soft and smooth. Stir in the herbs and cheese; add black pepper to taste.

2 Spoon the polenta in a thick layer into a greased rectangular tin, about 18 x 25 cm (7 x 10 inches); smooth the top. Cool, cover and chill for 30 minutes until firm. Cut into 8 triangular slices. Brush both sides with oil, place on a baking sheet and cook under a moderately hot grill for 4 minutes on each side or until golden.

3 For the topping, heat the oil in a saucepan, add the garlic and cook for 30 seconds. Add the leeks and cook for 4–5 minutes. Add the olives and cook for a further 5 minutes. Season and spoon over the polenta. Garnish with parsley and serve.

NUTRITIONAL ANALYSIS (per portion)	
Energy	350 cals
Protein	13.0 g
Carbohydrate	34.0 g
(of which sugars)	1.5 g
Fat	17.0 g
(of which saturates)	5.0 g
Fibre	4.0 g

SUITABLE FOR:
GLUTEN-FREE, NUT-FREE, LOW-CALORIE AND DIABETIC DIETS.

vegetable accompaniments

700 g (1½ lb) summer vegetables (see Note)

salt and freshly ground black pepper

1 tbsp Japanese rice vinegar

grated rind and juice of 1 lime

1 tsp light soft brown (muscovado) sugar

4 tbsp grapeseed oil

4 tbsp coconut cream

2 tbsp chopped coriander

coriander sprigs, to garnish

SUMMER VEGETABLES WITH LIME DRESSING

SERVES 6 • PREPARATION: 25 MINUTES • COOKING TIME: 4 MINUTES

1 Trim the vegetables, and cut the courgettes into batons. Cook the broad beans in boiling, salted water for 1 minute, then drain and refresh in cold water. Cook the rest of the vegetables for 3 minutes, then drain and refresh in cold water. Drain all the vegetables again.

2 Whisk together the vinegar, lime rind, 2 tsp lime juice, seasoning and sugar, then whisk in the oil and coconut cream. Pour over the vegetables. Toss in the chopped coriander and garnish with coriander sprigs.

NUTRITIONAL ANALYSIS (per portion)	
Energy	142 cals
Protein	5.8 g
Carbohydrate	8.0 g
(of which sugars)	4.5 g
Fat	10.0 g
(of which saturates)	2.5 g
Fibre	5.0 g

SUITABLE FOR:
GLUTEN-FREE, NUT-FREE, LOW-CHOLESTEROL, LOW-CALORIE, DAIRY PRODUCE-FREE AND DIABETIC DIETS.

PEAS WITH PESTO

SERVES 4 • PREPARATION: 5 MINUTES •
COOKING TIME: 5 MINUTES

350 g (12 oz) frozen peas
salt and freshly ground
black pepper
1 garlic clove, peeled and
crushed
3 tbsp pesto sauce
fresh basil leaves, to
garnish

1 Place the peas in a pan of boiling, salted water and boil for 2 minutes.
2 Drain, reserving 6 tbsp of the cooking liquid. Add the crushed garlic to the liquid with the pesto and peas. Bring to the boil, season with salt and pepper, and bubble for 1–2 minutes. Serve immediately, garnished with basil leaves.

NUTRITIONAL ANALYSIS	
(per portion)	
Energy	100 cals
Protein	6.5 g
Carbohydrate	9.0 g
(of which sugars)	2.5 g
Fat	5.0 g
(of which saturates)	1.5 g
Fibre	4.5 g

SUITABLE FOR:
GLUTEN-FREE, LOW-FAT LOW-CHOLESTEROL, LOW-CALORIE AND DIABETIC DIETS.

CURLY KALE WITH CRISPY BACON

SERVES 6 • PREPARATION: 10 MINUTES, PLUS
DRAINING • COOKING TIME: 5 MINUTES

1 kg (2½ lb) curly kale
salt and freshly ground
black pepper
25 g (1 oz) butter
6 rashers lean back
bacon, cut into strips

1 Remove and discard any tough or discoloured outer leaves from the curly kale.
2 Blanch the curly kale for 20 seconds in boiling, salted water. Drain and immediately plunge into cold water to stop further cooking. Drain again and tip out on to kitchen paper to dry. Set aside.
3 Melt the butter in a wok or large frying pan. Add the bacon and fry gently for 3–4 minutes or until turning golden brown. Toss in the curly kale and stir-fry for 3–4 minutes until coated with butter and heated through. Season well and serve.

NUTRITIONAL ANALYSIS	
(per portion)	
Energy	130 cals
Protein	11.0 g
Carbohydrate	2.0 g
(of which sugars)	2.0 g
Fat	8.0 g
(of which saturates)	3.0 g
Fibre	5.0 g

SUITABLE FOR:
GLUTEN-FREE, NUT-FREE, LOW-CALORIE AND DIABETIC DIETS.

MINTED PEAS WITH SPRING ONIONS AND CUCUMBER

SERVES 6 • PREPARATION: 5 MINUTES •
COOKING TIME: 10 MINUTES

175 g (6 oz) cucumber
450 g (1 lb) shelled fresh
peas
salt and freshly ground
black pepper
50 g (2 oz) butter
1 bunch spring onions,
trimmed and sliced
150 ml (¼ pint) half-fat
creme fraîche
3 tbsp dry vermouth
2 tbsp chopped fresh mint
pinch of sugar
mint sprigs, to garnish

1 Halve the cucumber lengthways, scrape out the seeds and slice thickly.
2 Add the peas to a pan of boiling salted water and cook for 5–10 minutes until tender; drain.
3 Meanwhile, heat the butter in a frying pan, add the spring onions and cucumber and sauté for 3 minutes. Add the crème fraîche and vermouth and bring to the boil. Alow to bubble for 2–3 minutes.
4 Add the peas, mint and sugar. Season with salt and pepper and toss to mix. Serve at once, garnished with mint.

NUTRITIONAL ANALYSIS	
(per portion)	
Energy	175 cals
Protein	5.5 g
Carbohydrate	9.0 g
(of which sugars)	4.0 g
Fat	12.0 g
(of which saturates)	7.5 g
Fibre	4.3 g

SUITABLE FOR:
GLUTEN-FREE, NUT-FREE, LOW-CALORIE AND DIABETIC DIETS.

279

½ small white cabbage,
about 400 g (14 oz)

200 g (7 oz) spring greens,
stalks removed

15 g (½ oz) butter

1 tbsp olive oil

1 bunch spring onions,
trimmed and sliced

65 g (2½ oz) piece
horseradish, peeled and
finely grated (see Note)

salt

MIXED CABBAGE WITH HORSERADISH

SERVES 4 • PREPARATION: 10 MINUTES •
COOKING TIME: 5 MINUTES

1 Cut the white cabbage into wedges, discarding the core. Finely shred the cabbage and spring greens in a food processor.

2 Melt the butter in a large wok or frying pan with the oil. Add the cabbage and greens and fry gently for 2 minutes until softened.

3 Add the spring onions, grated horseradish and a little salt and cook for a further 3 minutes, stirring, until softened but still retaining texture.

4 Transfer to a warming serving bowl and serve at once.

NUTRITIONAL ANALYSIS (per portion)	
Energy	110 cals
Protein	4.5 g
Carbohydrate	8.0 g
(of which sugars)	7.0 g
Fat	7.0 g
(of which saturates)	2.5 g
Fibre	5.5 g

SUITABLE FOR:

GLUTEN-FREE, NUT-FREE, LOW-CHOLESTEROL, LOW-CALORIE AND DIABETIC DIETS.

BAKED RED CABBAGE WITH WALNUTS AND RAISINS

500 g (1lb 2 oz) red cabbage

1 tbsp olive oil

1 onion, peeled and sliced

75 g (3 oz) walnuts, roughly chopped

75 g (3 oz) raisins

finely grated rind of 1 lemon, plus 1 tbsp juice

40 g (1½ oz) dark brown (muscovado) sugar

3 tbsp sherry vinegar

salt and freshly ground black pepper

SERVES 4 • PREPARATION: 10 MINUTES • COOKING TIME: ABOUT 1 HOUR

1 Finely shred the cabbage, discarding the core. Heat the oil in a flameproof casserole, add the onion and fry gently for 3 minutes. Stir in the walnuts and cook for 1 minute.

2 Add the raisins and shredded cabbage to the casserole. Mix together the lemon rind, juice, sugar, vinegar and a little salt and pepper. Add to the casserole and mix the ingredients together.

3 Bake in the oven at 180°C (350°F) Mark 4 for 50-60 minutes until the cabbage has softened but still retains texture. Adjust the seasoning and serve at once.

NUTRITIONAL ANALYSIS (per portion)	
Energy	279 cals
Protein	5.0 g
Carbohydrate	31.0 g
(of which sugars)	29.0 g
Fat	16.0 g
(of which saturates)	1.5 g
Fibre	4.5 g

SUITABLE FOR:
GLUTEN-FREE, LOW-CHOLESTEROL, LOW-CALORIE, DAIRY PRODUCE-FREE AND DIABETIC DIETS.

MIXED VEGETABLE STEW

350 g (12 oz) new potatoes

2 tbsp olive oil

1 large onion, peeled and chopped

500 g (1 lb 2 oz) plum tomatoes, skinned and roughly chopped

2 tsp ground paprika

1 garlic clove, peeled and crushed

½ tsp caster sugar

2 tbsp sun-dried tomato paste

salt and freshly ground black pepper

200 g (7 oz) frozen peas

2 tbsp chopped flat-leaf parsley

SERVES 4 • PREPARATION: 15 MINUTES • COOKING TIME: ABOUT 35 MINUTES

1 Quarter the potatoes lengthways. Heat the oil in a heavy-based saucepan and fry the onion for 5 minutes.

2 Add the potatoes, tomatoes, paprika, garlic, sugar and tomato paste. Season with salt and pepper. Cover and simmer gently for about 25–30 minutes, until the potatoes are tender, stirring occasionally.

3 Add the peas and cook, uncovered, for a further 2 minutes until tender, and the sauce is pulpy. Stir in the parsley and season to taste. Serve hot or cold.

NUTRITIONAL ANALYSIS (per portion)	
Energy	200 cals
Protein	6.6 g
Carbohydrate	30.0 g
(of which sugars)	10.5 g
Fat	6.5 g
(of which saturates)	1.0 g
Fibre	6.0 g

SUITABLE FOR:
HIGH-FIBRE, GLUTEN-FREE, NUT-FREE, LOW-CHOLESTEROL, LOW-CALORIE, DAIRY PRODUCE-FREE AND DIABETIC DIETS.

Cabbage and greens... really are good for you

Cabbages and other leafy greens, such as kale, are nutritionally outstanding. They contain a whole string of cancer-fighting phytochemicals, and they are also rich in vitamins C and E – both antioxidants known to fight disease. In addition, cabbages contain high levels of folic acid and potassium, as well as useful amounts of calcium.

350 g (12 oz) broccoli

40 g (1½ oz) quick-cook polenta

½ tsp crushed dried chillies

2 tsp cumin seeds, lightly crushed

½ tsp ground turmeric

salt and freshly ground black pepper

1 small onion, peeled and thinly sliced

3 tbsp olive oil

NOTE: The broccoli can be tossed in the spice mixture in advance ready for last-minute cooking.

SPICED BROCCOLI

SERVES 4 • PREPARATION: 10 MINUTES • COOKING TIME: ABOUT 10 MINUTES

1 Cut the broccoli florets from the stalks and halve if large. Thinly slice the stalks. Bring a pan of salted water to the boil, add the broccoli, return to the boil and cook for 30 seconds. Drain and refresh under cold water. Leave to drain thoroughly.

2 Mix together the polenta, crushed chillies, cumin seeds, turmeric and a little seasoning in a polythene bag. Add the broccoli and toss the ingredients in the bag until coated.

3 Heat 1 tbsp of the oil in a large non-stick frying pan. Add the onion and fry gently for 3 minutes. Add the remaining oil and the broccoli mixture and fry gently for about 3–4 minutes until turning crisp. Drain and serve at once.

NUTRITIONAL ANALYSIS (per portion)	
Energy	145 cals
Protein	5.0 g
Carbohydrate	10.0 g
(of which sugars)	2.0 g
Fat	9.5 g
(of which saturates)	1.3 g
Fibre	2.5 g

SUITABLE FOR:
GLUTEN-FREE, NUT-FREE, LOW-CHOLESTEROL, LOW-CALORIE, DAIRY PRODUCE-FREE AND DIABETIC DIETS.

---

450 g (1 lb) shallots, peeled

25 g (1 oz) butter

1 tbsp runny honey

juice of ½ lemon

1 tbsp Worcestershire sauce

1 tbsp balsamic vinegar

salt and freshly ground black pepper

NOTE: Served with one small roast chicken breast, green vegetables and two heaped tbsp mashed potatoes, the total calorie count is 375.

HONEY-GLAZED SHALLOTS

SERVES 4 • PREPARATION: 15 MINUTES • COOKING TIME: 25 MINUTES

1 Place the shallots in a pan with just enough cold water to cover. Bring to the boil, then simmer for 5 minutes. Drain well.

2 Add the butter to the pan with all the remaining ingredients.

3 Stir until the shallots are coated with the glaze. Cover and cook over a low heat, stirring from time to time, for about 20 minutes or until the shallots are tender. Remove the lid and continue to cook for a further 2–3 minutes until any remaining liquid is thick and syrupy.

NUTRITIONAL ANALYSIS (per portion)	
Energy	95 cals
Protein	1.5 g
Carbohydrate	13.0 g
(of which sugars)	11.0 g
Fat	5.0 g
(of which saturates)	3.5 g
Fibre	1.5 g

SUITABLE FOR:
GLUTEN-FREE, LOW-FAT, NUT-FREE, LOW-CALORIE AND DIABETIC DIETS.

700 g (1½ lb) fennel, about 3 bulbs
3 tbsp olive oil
25 g (1 oz) butter, melted
1 lemon
1 tsp caster sugar
salt and freshly ground black pepper
2 large sprigs thyme

NOTE: This is a good dish to serve with grilled trout.

SWEET ROASTED FENNEL

SERVES 6 • PREPARATION: 10 MINUTES • COOKING TIME: 1 HOUR

1 Trim and quarter the fennel, then place in a large roasting tin.

2 Drizzle the oil and melted butter over. Halve the lemon; squeeze the juice over. Add the lemon halves to the tin. Sprinkle with sugar and season generously with salt and pepper. Add the thyme; cover with a damp piece of non-stick baking parchment.

3 Cook at 200°C (400°F) Mark 6 for 30 minutes. Remove the baking parchment and cook for 20–30 minutes or until lightly charred and tender.

NUTRITIONAL ANALYSIS (per portion)	
Energy	97 cals
Protein	1.0 g
Carbohydrate	3.0 g
(of which sugars)	3.0 g
Fat	9.0 g
(of which saturates)	3.0 g
Fibre	3.0 g

SUITABLE FOR:
GLUTEN-FREE, NUT-FREE, LOW-CALORIE AND DIABETIC DIETS.

Fennel... digestive powers

The Italians value fennel for its digestive properties, which are attributed to an essential oil responsible for its liquorice-like flavour. Fennel is a useful source of folic acid, one of the most important B vitamins, and its somewhat fibrous texture also provides cellulose, an insoluble form of dietary fibre.

LEEKS WITH TOASTED CHEESE SAUCE

SERVES 4 • PREPARATION: 15 MINUTES • COOKING TIME: 25 MINUTES

700 g (1½ lb) even-sized leeks, trimmed

salt and freshly ground black pepper

25 g (1 oz) butter

25 g (1 oz) plain white flour

125 g (4 oz) reduced-fat soft cheese with garlic and herbs

15 g (½ oz) freshly grated Parmesan cheese

1 Place the leeks in a pan of cold, salted water, bring to the boil and bubble for 2–3 minutes or until just tender. Drain and reserve 300 ml (½ pint) of the cooking liquid.

2 Melt the butter in a saucepan, add the flour and mix until smooth. Blend in the reserved liquid and bring to the boil, stirring continuously. Add the soft cheese, season and return to the boil.

3 Arrange the leeks in a shallow flameproof dish, then spoon the sauce over the top and sprinkle with Parmesan cheese. Place under the grill until golden and bubbling. Serve immediately.

NUTRITIONAL ANALYSIS (per portion)	
Energy	155 cals
Protein	9.0 g
Carbohydrate	10.0 g
(of which sugars)	4.0 g
Fat	9.0 g
(of which saturates)	5.5 g
Fibre	4.0 g

SUITABLE FOR:
NUT-FREE, LOW-CALORIE AND DIABETIC DIETS.

LEEK, POTATO AND GOAT'S CHEESE CAKES

SERVES 8 • PREPARATION: 25 MINUTES, PLUS CHILLING • COOKING TIME: 45 MINUTES

550 g (1¼ lb) potatoes, peeled

salt and freshly ground black pepper

150 g (5 oz) soft goat's cheese

25 g (1 oz) butter

250 g (9 oz) leeks, trimmed and finely chopped

125 g (4 oz) feta cheese, crumbled

50 g (2 oz) fresh breadcrumbs

flour for dusting

oil for brushing

fresh herbs, to garnish

1 Cook the potatoes in boiling, salted water until tender, then drain and dry well. Mash the potato with the soft goat's cheese.

2 Melt the butter in a saucepan, add the leeks and cook for 10 minutes or until very soft. Increase the heat and cook, stirring, until all the liquid has evaporated. Cool, then mix with the potatoes, feta cheese and breadcrumbs. Season well with salt and pepper. Cover and refrigerate for 3–4 hours.

3 Shape the chilled mixture into 16 cakes, each 6.5 cm (2½ inches) across and 1 cm (½ inch) deep.

4 Dust the cakes with flour and brush with oil. Barbecue or grill for 2–3 minutes each side until golden and crisp. Garnish with fresh herbs and serve at once.

NUTRITIONAL ANALYSIS (per portion)	
Energy	195 cals
Protein	7.5 g
Carbohydrate	18.0 g
(of which sugars)	2.0 g
Fat	10.0 g
(of which saturates)	6.0 g
Fibre	2.0 g

SUITABLE FOR:
NUT-FREE, LOW-CALORIE AND DIABETIC DIETS.

Leeks... keep you healthy

An average-sized serving of leeks provides a significant amount of beta-carotene, excellent for fighting off disease. Provided they are not overcooked, leeks also contain a reasonable amount of vitamin C, plus vitamin B6, potassium, calcium and iron.

450 g (1 lb) carrots, peeled and sliced

450 g (1 lb) parsnips, peeled and sliced

salt and freshly ground black pepper

1 tbsp ground coriander

3 tbsp half-fat crème fraîche

4 tbsp chopped fresh coriander

NOTE: Served with an average portion of beef casserole, the total calorie count is 380.

CARROT AND PARSNIP PURÉE WITH CORIANDER

SERVES 4 • PREPARATION: 10 MINUTES • COOKING TIME: 20 MINUTES

1 Place the carrots and parsnips in a pan of cold, salted water. Bring to the boil and cook for 20 minutes until soft. Drain well.

2 Purée the vegetables, coriander and crème fraîche. Season, stir in the fresh coriander and serve.

NUTRITIONAL ANALYSIS (per portion)	
Energy	130 cals
Protein	3.0 g
Carbohydrate	18.0 g
(of which sugars)	10.0 g
Fat	6.0 g
(of which saturates)	3.0 g
Fibre	7.0 g

SUITABLE FOR:
HIGH-FIBRE, GLUTEN-FREE, NUT-FREE, LOW-CHOLESTEROL, LOW-CALORIE AND DIABETIC DIETS.

1.1 kg (2½ lb) celeriac

salt and freshly ground black pepper

1 tsp lemon juice

450 g (1 lb) eating apples

2 tbsp half-fat crème fraîche

chopped chives, to garnish

CELERIAC WITH APPLES AND CRÈME FRAÎCHE

SERVES 4 • PREPARATION: 15 MINUTES • COOKING TIME: 40 MINUTES

1 Peel the celeriac and cut into chunks. Place immediately in a pan of cold, salted water with the lemon juice. Bring to the boil, cover and simmer for 25–30 minutes.

2 Peel, core and slice the apples, then add to the celeriac. Simmer for 5 minutes. Drain well and mash in the pan over a low heat.

3 Beat in the crème fraîche, season with salt and pepper and serve garnished with chives.

NUTRITIONAL ANALYSIS (per portion)	
Energy	130 cals
Protein	4.0 g
Carbohydrate	20.0 g
(of which sugars)	18.5 g
Fat	4.0 g
(of which saturates)	2.0 g
Fibre	12.0 g

SUITABLE FOR:
HIGH-FIBRE, GLUTEN-FREE, NUT-FREE, LOW-CHOLESTEROL, LOW-CALORIE AND DIABETIC DIETS.

Root vegetables... fibre-rich and very nutritous

Root vegetables, such as celeriac, swedes, turnips and kohlrabi, are useful sources of energy, providing carbohydrates and dietary fibre, particularly the soluble type which is thought to help reduce blood cholesterol levels. They contain important minerals and are surprisingly generous providers of folic acid and vitamin C.

700 g (1½ lb) okra, trimmed (see Note)

salt and freshly ground black pepper

1 tbsp oil

2 tbsp mustard seeds

2 garlic cloves, peeled and crushed

NOTE: Okra, also known as lady's fingers, is available from most major supermarkets. It should be small, firm and bright green. If unavailable, you could use green beans or broccoli for this recipe.

MUSTARD-SEEDED OKRA

SERVES 8 • PREPARATION: 10 MINUTES • COOKING TIME: 5 MINUTES

1 Cook the okra in a large pan of boiling, salted water for 3–4 minutes or until tender; drain.

2 Place the oil, mustard seeds and peeled garlic in a large, dry saucepan and cook until the mustard seeds change colour and become golden brown and pop – take care, as they may splutter! Toss the okra through the flavourings, season well and serve.

NUTRITIONAL ANALYSIS (per portion)	
Energy	40 cals
Protein	2.5 g
Carbohydrate	2.5 g
(of which sugars)	2.0 g
Fat	2.0 g
(of which saturates)	0.5 g
Fibre	3.5 g

SUITABLE FOR:
GLUTEN-FREE, LOW-FAT, NUT-FREE, LOW-CHOLESTEROL, LOW-CALORIE, DAIRY PRODUCE-FREE AND DIABETIC DIETS.

2 butternut squash, each about 650 g (1 lb 7 oz)

salt and freshly ground black pepper

2 medium red onions, peeled

2 tbsp olive or vegetable oil

roughly chopped parsley, to garnish

GLAZE
16 cardamom pods

25 g (1 oz) light muscovado sugar

6 tbsp fresh orange juice

NOTE: This recipe makes a perfect accompaniment to almost any roasted meats or poultry. Use other types of squash or pumpkin if you can't find butternut.

ROASTED BUTTERNUT SQUASH WITH ORANGE AND CARDAMOM

SERVES 4 • PREPARATION: 15 MINUTES • COOKING TIME: 45 MINUTES

1 Halve the squash and scoop out the seeds. Using a vegetable peeler, pare away the skin from each half. Cut each half into 6 chunky pieces.

2 Bring a pan of salted water to the boil. Add the squash and cook for 3 minutes. Drain.

3 Cut each onion into 6 wedges, and place in a roasting tin with the squash and olive oil. Toss to coat well, then roast at 220°C (425°F) Mark 7 for 30 minutes until tender and beginning to colour.

4 Crush the cardamom pods using a pestle and mortar to extract the seeds. Discard the pods and crush the seeds until the consistency of coarse ground black pepper. Mix the seeds with the sugar, orange juice and a little seasoning.

5 Spoon the mixture over the roasted vegetables and toss lightly. Roast for a further 15 minutes, basting two or three times, until lightly charred. Serve hot, scattered with roughly chopped parsley.

NUTRITIONAL ANALYSIS (per portion)	
Energy	220 cals
Protein	4.0 g
Carbohydrate	40.0 g
(of which sugars)	1.0 g
Fat	6.0 g
(of which saturates)	1.0 g
Fibre	6.0 g

SUITABLE FOR:
HIGH-FIBRE, GLUTEN-FREE, NUT-FREE, LOW-CHOLESTEROL, LOW-CALORIE, DAIRY PRODUCE-FREE AND DIABETIC DIETS.

450 g (1 lb) orange-fleshed sweet potatoes

450 g (1 lb) old floury potatoes

salt and freshly ground black pepper

50 g (2 oz) butter

3 tbsp chopped fresh thyme (optional)

NOTE: If you have time, boil both types of potato whole in their skins, then peel. This will stop the potatoes absorbing water while they cook and give a lighter result.

PURÉE OF SWEET POTATOES

SERVES 6 • PREPARATION: 15 MINUTES • COOKING TIME: 25 MINUTES

1 Peel the sweet potatoes, making sure you peel them deeply enough to expose the orange flesh, otherwise the purée will be stringy. Cut into chunks. Peel the floury potatoes and cut into chunks.

2 Place both types of potato in a large saucepan and cook in salted water for 20 minutes or until very tender. Drain, return to the pan and dry well over a low heat.

3 Mash the potatoes until smooth. Beat in the butter, season well with salt and pepper and stir in the fresh thyme, if wished. Serve immediately.

NUTRITIONAL ANALYSIS (per portion)	
Energy	185 cals
Protein	2.5 g
Carbohydrate	29.0 g
(of which sugars)	5.0 g
Fat	7.0 g
(of which saturates)	4.5 g
Fibre	3.0 g

SUITABLE FOR:
GLUTEN-FREE, NUT-FREE, LOW-CALORIE AND DIABETIC DIETS.

900 g (2 lb) small new potatoes

12 garlic cloves, peeled

2 tbsp olive oil

50 g (2 oz) Parmesan cheese, finely grated

coarse sea salt

rosemary sprigs, to garnish

ROAST NEW POTATOES WITH GARLIC AND PARMESAN

SERVES 6 • PREPARATION: 5 MINUTES • COOKING TIME: 40 MINUTES

1 Place the new potatoes in a large roasting tin with the garlic cloves. Toss in the olive oil and Parmesan cheese.

2 Roast at 220°C (425°F) Mark 7 for 30–40 minutes. Season with coarse sea salt and garnish with rosemary sprigs just before serving.

NUTRITIONAL ANALYSIS (per portion)	
Energy	180 cals
Protein	6.0 g
Carbohydrate	26.0 g
(of which sugars)	1.0 g
Fat	7.0 g
(of which saturates)	2.0 g
Fibre	2.0 g

SUITABLE FOR:
GLUTEN-FREE, NUT-FREE AND DIABETIC DIETS.

salads

48 live mussels

20 large raw prawns, peeled and de-veined

225 g (8 oz) monkfish fillet, skinned and cut into 5 mm (¼ inch) slices

225 g (8 oz) small squid, cleaned

5 tbsp extra-virgin olive oil

2 tbsp lemon juice

1 garlic clove, peeled and crushed

salt and freshly ground black pepper

125 g (4 oz) French beans, trimmed

2 shallots, peeled and thinly sliced

2 sticks celery, trimmed and roughly chopped

25 g (1 oz) canned anchovy fillets, drained and roughly chopped

2 tbsp chopped fresh parsley

1 tbsp chopped fresh basil

1 tbsp chopped fresh chervil

50 g (2 oz) Italian olives

chervil sprigs, to garnish

ITALIAN SEAFOOD SALAD

SERVES 4 • PREPARATION: 30 MINUTES, PLUS CHILLING • COOKING TIME: 15 MINUTES

1 Scrub the mussels and pull any 'beards' from the shells. Discard any open mussels that do not close when you tap them. Wash the mussels well.

2 Place the mussels in a saucepan with about 100 ml (3½ fl oz) water. Cover and cook over a high heat for 4–5 minutes until the shells have steamed open. Discard any that remain closed. Strain off the cooking liquid; reserve. Immediately refresh the mussels in cold water. Place in a bowl.

3 Return the cooking liquid to the pan and bring to the boil, adding a little extra water if necessary. Add the prawns and cook for 4 minutes; add the monkfish and cook for 1 minute. Add the squid and cook for a further minute. Strain and reserve 2 tbsp of the liquid. Plunge the seafood into cold water, then drain, pat dry and add to the mussels.

4 Whisk the oil with the lemon juice, garlic and reserved cooking liquid. Season with a little salt and pepper and pour over the seafood. Toss well and leave to marinate in the refrigerator for 1 hour.

5 Just before serving, blanch the beans for 3 minutes; drain, then refresh under cold water. Add to the seafood with the shallots, celery, anchovies, herbs and olives. Toss and serve garnished.

NUTRITIONAL ANALYSIS (per portion)	
Energy	324 cals
Protein	35.0 g
Carbohydrate	3.0 g
(of which sugars)	2.0 g
Fat	19.0 g
(of which saturates)	3.0 g
Fibre	1.5 g

SUITABLE FOR:
GLUTEN-FREE, NUT-FREE, LOW-CALORIE, DAIRY PRODUCE-FREE AND DIABETIC DIETS.

NOTE: Remove the mussels from their shells, if preferred.

450 g (1 lb) fresh tuna steaks

3 garlic cloves, peeled and crushed

finely grated rind and juice of 1 orange

¼ tsp crushed dried chilli

salt and freshly ground black pepper

1 tbsp vegetable oil

¼ cucumber, cut into thin matchsticks

1 bunch radishes, trimmed and finely sliced

4 spring onions, trimmed and finely chopped

100 g (3 ½ oz) frisée lettuce

5 cm (2 inch) piece fresh root ginger, peeled and grated

3 tbsp mirin

1 tbsp dark brown sugar

2 tbsp lime juice

2 tsp soy sauce

crusty bread, to serve

CITRUS TUNA SALAD

SERVES 4 • PREPARATION: 15 MINUTES • COOKING TIME: ABOUT 8 MINUTES

1 Pat the tuna dry on kitchen paper. Mix together the garlic, orange rind, chilli and seasoning and spread half over one side of the tuna.

2 Heat the oil in a frying pan. Add the tuna, seasoned side down, and fry gently for 2–3 minutes until golden. Spread the remaining garlic mixture over the tuna steaks, turn and cook for a further 2–3 minutes until cooked through to the centre. (Test by piercing with a knife).

3 Meanwhile, put the cucumber sticks in a bowl with the radishes, spring onions and frisée.

4 Drain the tuna. Mix together the ginger, mirin, sugar, lime juice, soy sauce and orange juice and add to the frying pan. Heat through for 1 minute, scraping up the pan juices.

5 Arrange the salad on 4 individual serving plates and flake the tuna over the salad. Spoon over the dressing and serve with crusty bread.

NUTRITIONAL ANALYSIS (per portion)	
Energy	215 cals
Protein	28.0 g
Carbohydrate	7.5 g
(of which sugars)	7.0 g
Fat	8.0 g
(of which saturates)	2.0 g
Fibre	1.0 g

SUITABLE FOR:
GLUTEN-FREE, NUT-FREE, LOW-CHOLESTEROL, LOW-CALORIE, DAIRY PRODUCE-FREE AND DIABETIC DIETS.

450 g (1 lb) prepared squid, cut into 1 cm (½ inch) rings

2 tbsp olive oil

salt and freshly ground black pepper

450 g (1 lb) ripe plum tomatoes, skinned and sliced

dill sprigs and flat-leaf parsley, to garnish

DRESSING
2 garlic cloves, peeled

1-2 tsp salt

4 tbsp olive oil

juice of 1 lemon

2 tbsp chopped fresh dill

1 tbsp chopped flat-leaf parsley

SEAFOOD AND TOMATO SALAD

SERVES 6 • PREPARATION: 25 MINUTES, PLUS CHILLING • COOKING TIME: 4 MINUTES

1 To make the dressing, place the garlic and salt in a pestle and mortar and pound to a paste. Mix in the olive oil, lemon juice and chopped herbs.

2 For the salad, heat the olive oil in a large frying pan or wok and cook the squid in batches for 1–2 minutes or until just tender. Mix the squid with the garlic dressing, then cool, cover and chill for up to 4 hours.

3 Season the tomatoes. Place the dressed squid in the middle of a large serving plate and arrange the sliced tomatoes around it. Garnish with dill and parsley to serve.

NUTRITIONAL ANALYSIS (per portion)	
Energy	175 cals
Protein	12.0 g
Carbohydrate	3.0 g
(of which sugars)	2.5 g
Fat	12.0 g
(of which saturates)	2.0 g
Fibre	1.0 g

SUITABLE FOR:
GLUTEN-FREE, NUT-FREE, LOW-CHOLESTEROL, LOW-CALORIE, DAIRY PRODUCE-FREE AND DIABETIC DIETS.

VARIATION:
You can always replace the squid with 450 g (1 lb) large raw shelled prawns or 700 g (1½ lb) scrubbed mussels and cook for 1–2 minutes as in step 2. If using a combination of all three shellfish, you'll need 175 g (6 oz) of each one.

1 large cucumber

4 long thin green chillies, deseeded and chopped (see Note)

salt

4 tbsp Thai fish sauce

4 tsp caster sugar

4 small plaice or sole fillets, skinned, about 350 g (12 oz)

oil, for grilling

1 large mango, peeled and sliced

125 g (4 oz) shallots or red onions, peeled and finely chopped

1 red pepper, deseeded and finely chopped

handful of fresh coriander

25 g (1 oz) large, roasted peanuts

WARM THAI FISH SALAD

SERVES 4 • PREPARATION: 10 MINUTES • COOKING TIME: 10 MINUTES

1 Cut the cucumber in half lengthways, remove the seeds. Using a vegetable peeler, shave off lengths of cucumber in long strips. Set aside in a cool place.

2 To make the dressing, mix the chillies with a pinch of salt, the fish sauce and sugar. Set aside.

3 Place the fish on a lightly oiled, foil-lined baking sheet and cook under a hot grill for 2–3 minutes on each side or until firm to the touch.

4 Meanwhile, arrange the mango, shallots or red onions, red pepper, coriander sprigs, cucumber, peanuts and cooked fish on 4 individual serving plates. Drizzle the dressing over and serve immediately.

NUTRITIONAL ANALYSIS (per portion)	
Energy	200 cals
Protein	17.0 g
Carbohydrate	15.0 g
(of which sugars)	14.0 g
Fat	7.0 g
(of which saturates)	1.5 g
Fibre	3.5 g

SUITABLE FOR:

GLUTEN-FREE, LOW-CHOLESTEROL, LOW-CALORIE, DAIRY PRODUCE-FREE AND DIABETIC DIETS.

NOTE: Use long, thin, green chillies as they are milder than the extremely hot tiny red or green Thai chillies.

2 tbsp white wine vinegar

150 ml (¼ pint) olive oil

salt and freshly ground black pepper

2 tbsp pickled ginger, chopped

2.5 cm (1 inch) piece fresh root ginger, peeled and grated

225 g (8 oz) fresh white crab meat, flaked, with claws if available

1 large head chicory, trimmed and leaves separated

½ cucumber, about 300 g (10 oz), pared into ribbons with a peeler

1 charentais melon, cut into quarters, each about 175 g (6 oz)

chives, to garnish

CRAB, MELON AND CUCUMBER SALAD

SERVES 4 • PREPARATION: 20 MINUTES

1 Mix together the vinegar, oil and seasoning in a bowl. Add the pickled ginger and root ginger. Toss the crab meat in half the dressing.

2 On each plate, arrange a few chicory leaves, cucumber ribbons and a melon quarter. Spoon over the crab meat and remaining dressing and garnish with chives to serve.

NUTRITIONAL ANALYSIS (per portion)	
Energy	340 cals
Protein	12.0 g
Carbohydrate	6.0 g
(of which sugars)	5.5 g
Fat	30.0 g
(of which saturates)	4.0 g
Fibre	1.0 g

SUITABLE FOR:

GLUTEN-FREE, NUT-FREE, LOW-CALORIE, DAIRY PRODUCE-FREE AND DIABETIC DIETS.

Shellfish... low-fat and nutrient packed

This wide-ranging group provides delicious flavours and important nutrients. Shellfish are low in fat and are generous providers of easily digestible protein, B vitamins and essential minerals. However, since they contain varying amounts of cholesterol, it is best to avoid shellfish if you are on a low-cholesterol diet.

150 g (5 oz) French beans, halved

150 g (5 oz) courgettes, trimmed and cut into thin matchsticks

150 g (5 oz) fennel, trimmed and cut into thin matchsticks

200 g (7 oz) cherry tomatoes, halved if large

25 g (1 oz) roughly chopped fresh basil

4 slices Parma ham

1 tbsp soft brown sugar

25 g (1 oz) flaked almonds, lightly toasted

Parmesan cheese shavings and basil sprigs, to garnish

DRESSING
2 tbsp lemon juice

120 ml (4 fl oz) olive oil

salt and freshly ground black pepper

SUMMER CRUNCH SALAD

SERVES 4 • PREPARATION: 15 MINUTES

1 To make the dressing, place the lemon juice in a small bowl and whisk in the olive oil. Season with salt and pepper, then cover and set aside.

2 For the salad, blanch the French beans in boiling, salted water for 1 minute, drain, refresh in cold water and drain again. Mix all the vegetables together in a large bowl, toss the chopped basil through and season.

3 Place the Parma ham on a baking sheet, sprinkle with the sugar and place under a hot grill for 2–3 minutes or until golden: watch the ham carefully while grilling as the sugar tends to burn quickly. The ham will become crisp as it cools.

4 Mix the dressing and almonds into the salad and serve with the Parma ham, garnished with Parmesan shavings and basil sprigs.

NUTRITIONAL ANALYSIS (per portion)	
Energy	260 cals
Protein	4.5 g
Carbohydrate	5.6 g
(of which sugars)	5.0 g
Fat	22.5 g
(of which saturates)	3.0 g
Fibre	3.0 g

SUITABLE FOR:
GLUTEN-FREE, LOW-CHOLESTEROL, LOW-CALORIE, DAIRY PRODUCE-FREE AND DIABETIC DIETS.

450 g (1 lb) fennel, trimmed

2 large Braeburn or Cox's apples, about 450 g (1 lb)

75 g (3 oz) shelled pecan nuts

300 g (10 oz) cooked ham, cut into wide strips

1 head chicory, divided into leaves

flat-leaf parsley sprigs, to garnish

DRESSING

1 tsp runny honey

2 tsp German or Dijon mustard

3 tbsp cider vinegar

salt and freshly ground black pepper

9 tbsp vegetable oil

2 tsp poppy seeds

APPLE, FENNEL, HAM AND PECAN SALAD

SERVES 6 • PREPARATION: 30 MINUTES

1 To make the dressing, whisk together the honey, mustard, vinegar and seasoning in a small bowl. Whisk in the vegetable oil, then the poppy seeds. Set aside.

2 Halve the fennel, then remove the central cores and slice thinly lengthways. Quarter the apples, then core and slice.

3 Place the fennel in a large bowl with the apples, nuts, ham and chicory. Toss with the dressing and correct the seasoning, if necessary. Garnish with parsley sprigs and serve.

NUTRITIONAL ANALYSIS (per portion)	
Energy	280 cals
Protein	12.5 g
Carbohydrate	12.5 g
(of which sugars)	12.0 g
Fat	23.0 g
(of which saturates)	3.0 g
Fibre	4.0 g

SUITABLE FOR:
GLUTEN-FREE, LOW-CHOLESTEROL, LOW-CALORIE, DAIRY PRODUCE-FREE AND DIABETIC DIETS.

NOTE: Low in calories, this refreshing, crunchy winter salad is simple to prepare and makes a substantial meal.

GRILLED CHICKEN AND SWEET POTATO SALAD

SERVES 4 • PREPARATION: 20 MINUTES • COOKING TIME: ABOUT 20 MINUTES

650 g (1 lb 7 oz) sweet potatoes, peeled and cut into 5 mm (¼ inch) thick pieces

2 large boneless chicken breasts, skinned and cut into 5 mm (¼ inch) wide slices

100 g (3½ oz) watercress

2 spring onions, trimmed and finely chopped

sea salt

DRESSING

6 tbsp light olive oil

3 tbsp runny honey

2 tbsp lemon juice

1 tsp chopped thyme

1½ tsp black onion seeds

1 tsp cumin seeds

¼ tsp crushed dried chillies

1 To make the dressing, whisk all the ingredients together and set aside.

2 Bring a large pan of lightly salted water to the boil. Add the sweet potatoes, return to the boil and boil for 1–2 minutes until softened. Drain well.

3 Pat the chicken dry on kitchen paper, then place the pieces, spaced slightly apart, between two layers of cling film. Beat with a rolling pin until flattened.

4 Line the grill rack with lightly oiled foil and place the potato slices in a single layer on the foil. Transfer 2 tbsp of the dressing to a separate bowl to use as a baste for grilling. Baste the potatoes and grill for about 6–8 minutes on each side until turning deep golden around the edges. Remove the potato slices and grill the chicken slices for about 1–2 minutes on each side, basting lightly.

5 Toss the watercress with the spring onions and place on individual serving plates. Arrange the sweet potatoes, then the chicken on top of the salad. Spoon over the reserved dressing, scatter with sea salt and serve warm.

NUTRITIONAL ANALYSIS (per portion)	
Energy	410 cals
Protein	19.0 g
Carbohydrate	40.0 g
(of which sugars)	14.0 g
Fat	21.0 g
(of which saturates)	4.0 g
Fibre	4.0 g

SUITABLE FOR:
GLUTEN-FREE, NUT-FREE, LOW-CHOLESTEROL, LOW-CALORIE, DAIRY PRODUCE-FREE AND DIABETIC DIETS.

PEASANT BREAD AND CHEESE SALAD

SERVES 6 • PREPARATION: 25 MINUTES

175 g (6 oz) ciabatta or pugliese bread

700 g (1½ lb) plum tomatoes, cut into chunks

175 g (6 oz) soft cheese, such as mozzarella or Brie, cut into chunks

450 g (1 lb) cucumber, cut into chunks

50 g (2 oz) sun-dried tomatoes in oil, sliced

50 g (2 oz) stoned black olives, such as Kalamata

125 g (4 oz) washed baby spinach or lamb's lettuce

basil leaves, to garnish

DRESSING

2 tbsp red wine vinegar

4 tbsp olive oil

2 tbsp chopped fresh basil

salt and freshly ground black pepper

1 Cut the ciabatta or pugliese bread into 2.5 cm (1 inch) dice. Cover with 150 ml (5 fl oz) water and leave to soak for 5 minutes. Gently squeeze the bread to remove excess water. Set the bread aside and discard the liquid.

2 To make the dressing, mix together the red wine vinegar, olive oil and chopped basil, then season with salt and pepper.

3 Place the bread, plum tomatoes, cheese, cucumber, sun-dried tomatoes, olives and spinach in a large bowl. Add the dressing and toss well together. Garnish with basil leaves and serve.

NUTRITIONAL ANALYSIS (per portion)	
Energy	295 cals
Protein	12.0 g
Carbohydrate	20.0 g
(of which sugars)	6.0 g
Fat	20.0 g
(of which saturates)	6.0 g
Fibre	3.0 g

SUITABLE FOR:
NUT-FREE, LOW-CALORIE AND DIABETIC DIETS.

550 g (1¼ lb) baby new potatoes

salt

12 quail eggs

½ bunch radishes, trimmed and halved

100 g (3½ oz) endive salad

2 tbsp olive oil

2 tsp lemon juice

toasted walnut bread, to serve

TAPENADE

1 tbsp capers, rinsed

100 g (3½ oz) black olives, stoned

25 g (1 oz) anchovy fillets (½ drained can)

1 garlic clove, peeled and sliced

75 ml (3 fl oz) olive oil

freshly ground black pepper

MIXED SALAD WITH BABY POTATOES, TAPENADE AND QUAIL EGGS

SERVES 4 • PREPARATION: 20 MINUTES • COOKING TIME: ABOUT 20 MINUTES

1 To make the tapenade, put the capers, olives, anchovy fillets and garlic in a food processor and blend lightly until chopped. With the motor running, gradually add the olive oil in a steady stream to make a coarse paste. Season with pepper and transfer to a bowl.

2 Cook the potatoes in plenty of lightly salted water for 15–20 minutes or until tender. Drain. Cook the quail eggs in a separate pan of simmering water for 2 minutes. Drain, rinse under cold water, then peel and halve.

3 Toss the endive salad with the olive oil, lemon juice and a little seasoning, then arrange on individual serving plates. Pile the potatoes, quail eggs and radishes over the salad. Top with spoonfuls of the tapenade and serve with bread.

NUTRITIONAL ANALYSIS (per portion)	
Energy	450 cals
Protein	16.0 g
Carbohydrate	26.0 g
(of which sugars)	1.5 g
Fat	32.0 g
(of which saturates)	6.0 g
Fibre	3.0 g

SUITABLE FOR:
LOW-CALORIE, DAIRY PRODUCE-FREE AND DIABETIC DIETS.

175 g (6 oz) brown rice

salt and freshly ground black pepper

2 tbsp sesame oil

4 tbsp sunflower oil

2 tbsp dark soy sauce

juice of ½ orange

2 cm (½ inch) piece fresh root ginger, peeled and finely chopped

3 ripe tomatoes, deseeded and diced

2 spring onions, trimmed and chopped

1 red pepper, deseeded and thinly sliced

½ cucumber, halved, deseeded and diced

1 tbsp sesame seeds

3 tbsp chopped fresh coriander

1 tbsp chopped fresh mint

GINGERED RICE SALAD

SERVES 6 • PREPARATION: 15 MINUTES • COOKING TIME: 45 MINUTES

1 Cook the rice in twice its volume of boiling salted water for about 45 minutes until all the water is absorbed.

2 Turn the rice into a sieve and rinse under cold running water. Drain thoroughly and turn into a large bowl. Add the oils, soy sauce and orange juice; toss well. Leave to cool

3 Add the ginger, tomatoes, spring onions, red pepper and cucumber to the rice and stir to mix together.

4 Dry-fry the sesame seeds in a small frying pan, stirring, until golden. Add to the salad with the coriander, mint and salt and pepper to taste. Toss before serving.

NUTRITIONAL ANALYSIS
(per portion)

Energy	300 cals
Protein	4.5 g
Carbohydrate	41.0 g
(of which sugars)	4.0 g
Fat	13.5 g
(of which saturates)	2.0 g
Fibre	2.0 g

SUITABLE FOR:
GLUTEN-FREE, NUT-FREE, LOW-CHOLESTEROL, LOW-CALORIE, DAIRY PRODUCE-FREE AND DIABETIC DIETS.

175 g (6 oz) pasta shapes

1 tbsp extra-virgin olive oil

4 sun-dried tomatoes in oil, drained and sliced

225 g (8 oz) cherry tomatoes, halved

4-5 spring onions, trimmed and shredded

8-12 basil leaves, torn into pieces

8-12 black olives

DRESSING

2 sun-dried tomatoes in oil, drained

2 tbsp oil, from the sun-dried tomato jar

2 tbsp red wine vinegar

1 garlic clove, peeled and crushed

1 tbsp tomato paste

pinch of sugar (optional)

coarse sea salt and freshly ground black pepper

2 tbsp extra-virgin olive oil

MEDITERRANEAN PASTA SALAD

SERVES 4 • PREPARATION: 15 MINUTES, PLUS STANDING • COOKING TIME: 10 MINUTES

1 Cook the pasta in a large pan of water according to the packet instructions until just tender. Drain, refresh under cold water, then drain again thoroughly and transfer to a large bowl. Stir in 1 tbsp oil.

2 Add the sun-dried and cherry tomatoes to the pasta, together with the spring onions, basil and olives. Toss to mix.

3 To make the dressing, put the sun-dried tomatoes, oil, vinegar, garlic and tomato paste in a blender or food processor. Add the sugar, if using, and salt and pepper. With the motor running, gradually add the olive oil through the feeder tube and process briefly to make a fairly thick dressing.

4 Pour the dressing over the pasta and toss well. Cover and leave to stand for 1–2 hours before serving, to allow the flavours to mingle.

NUTRITIONAL ANALYSIS
(per portion)

Energy	340 cals
Protein	6.5 g
Carbohydrate	36.0 g
(of which sugars)	4.0 g
Fat	20.0 g
(of which saturates)	3.0 g
Fibre	2.5 g

SUITABLE FOR:
NUT-FREE, LOW-CHOLESTEROL, LOW-CALORIE, DAIRY PRODUCE-FREE AND DIABETIC DIETS.

150 g (5 oz) brown lentils

3 whole cardamom pods

1 bay leaf (optional)

50 g (2 oz) bulghar wheat

1 small red chilli, deseeded and finely chopped

50 ml (2 fl oz) olive oil

1 tsp runny honey

1½ tsp balsamic vinegar

salt and freshly ground black pepper

1 small bunch spring onions, trimmed and chopped

225 g (8 oz) broccoli, divided into small florets

75 g (3 oz) feta cheese, crumbled

HOT LENTIL AND FETA SALAD

SERVES 4 • PREPARATION: 15 MINUTES • COOKING TIME: 30 MINUTES

1 Rinse and pick over the lentils to remove any small stones. Split the cardamom pods, extract the seeds and place in a saucepan with the lentils and bay leaf, if using. Cover with plenty of water, bring to the boil and simmer, uncovered, for about 20–30 minutes or until tender.

2 Meanwhile, cover the bulghar wheat with boiling water. Leave to stand for 20–30 minutes or until the grains are soft.

3 Mix the chilli with the oil, honey, vinegar and salt and pepper. Add the chopped spring onions to the dressing.

4 About 3 minutes before the lentils are due to finish cooking, add the broccoli to the saucepan. Cover and cook until just tender.

5 Drain the lentil mixture well; remove the bay leaf. Add the drained bulghar wheat and mix with the dressing. Adjust the seasoning. Serve hot, sprinkled with crumbled feta cheese.

NUTRITIONAL ANALYSIS (per portion)	
Energy	315 cals
Protein	16.0 g
Carbohydrate	31.5 g
(of which sugars)	4.0 g
Fat	14.5 g
(of which saturates)	4.0 g
Fibre	5.0 g

SUITABLE FOR:
NUT-FREE, LOW-CALORIE AND DIABETIC DIETS.

225 g (8 oz) couscous

300 ml (½ pint) vegetable stock

200 ml (7 fl oz) tomato juice

1 small red onion, peeled and finely chopped

juice of ½ lemon

1 tbsp cider vinegar

2 tbsp olive oil

2 tsp soy sauce

2 tbsp finely chopped fresh mint

2 tbsp finely chopped fresh parsley

2 tbsp finely chopped fresh coriander

2 tbsp finely chopped fresh dill

2 firm tomatoes, finely diced

¼ cucumber, finely diced

50 g (2 oz) toasted pine nuts

HERB COUSCOUS SALAD WITH PINE NUTS

SERVES 6 • PREPARATION: 20 MINUTES

1 Put the couscous into a large bowl. Heat the stock and tomato juice until boiling, pour over the couscous and set aside for about 10 minutes, or until the liquid has been absorbed.

2 Add all the remaining ingredients to the couscous and stir well to combine.

NUTRITIONAL ANALYSIS (per portion)	
Energy	200 cals
Protein	5.0 g
Carbohydrate	23.0 g
(of which sugars)	3.0 g
Fat	10.0 g
(of which saturates)	1.0 g
Fibre	1.0 g

SUITABLE FOR:

LOW-CHOLESTEROL, LOW-CALORIE, DAIRY PRODUCE-FREE AND DIABETIC DIETS.

Herbs... enhance your life

Eaten in quantity, leafy herbs such as parsley, mint and coriander, can be a useful source of vitamins and minerals. A good handful of parsley provides plenty of vitamin C, beta-carotene, iron and calcium, while basil and rocket offer useful amounts of iron and vitamin C. Prolonged exposure to heat tends to destroy the flavour of these herbs, so they are best used raw or added to cooked dishes just before serving.

50 g (2 oz) raisins

4 tbsp orange juice

125 g (4 oz) cracked wheat or bulghar wheat

1 large avocado, peeled and sliced

4 cm (1½ inch) piece fresh root ginger, peeled and finely chopped

6 spring onions, trimmed and sliced

25 g (1 oz) sunflower seeds

2 tsp soy sauce

salt and freshly ground black pepper

CRACKED WHEAT AND AVOCADO SALAD

SERVES 4 • PREPARATION: 25 MINUTES, PLUS SOAKING

1 Place the raisins in a small bowl, pour in the orange juice and leave to soak for 30 minutes; reserve the orange juice after soaking.

2 Pour 600 ml (1 pint) boiling water over the cracked wheat, then cover and allow to stand for 15 minutes.

3 Drain the cracked wheat and transfer to a large serving bowl. Add the avocado, ginger, spring onions, sunflower seeds, raisins and reserved orange juice. Stir in the soy sauce, season with salt and pepper and mix well. Serve immediately.

NUTRITIONAL ANALYSIS (per portion)	
Energy	270 cals
Protein	6.0 g
Carbohydrate	36.0 g
(of which sugars)	11.0 g
Fat	13.0 g
(of which saturates)	2.0 g
Fibre	2.0 g

SUITABLE FOR:

NUT-FREE, LOW-CALORIE, DAIRY PRODUCE-FREE AND DIABETIC DIETS.

NOTE: If you're worried about the high fat content in avocados, bear in mind that it is made up of 'healthy' monounsaturated fat.

2 medium aubergines, thinly sliced

2 large courgettes, thinly sliced

2 tbsp olive oil

50 g (2 oz) Italian salami, cut into paper-thin slices

150 g (5 oz) ricotta cheese

basil leaves, black olives and sea salt, to garnish

DRESSING
large handful of basil leaves

1 small garlic clove, peeled and chopped

4 tbsp extra-virgin olive oil

1 tbsp balsamic vinegar

salt and freshly ground black pepper

BASIL DRESSED AUBERGINE AND RICOTTA SALAD

SERVES 4 • PREPARATION: 20 MINUTES •
COOKING TIME: ABOUT 20 MINUTES

1 To make the dressing, put all the ingredients in a blender or food processor and blend until smooth. Transfer to a small dish and reserve.

2 Brush the aubergine and courgette slices with oil and season lightly with salt and pepper. Grill in batches under a high heat for 8–10 minutes on each side or until softened and slightly charred.

3 Pile the vegetables on to 4 individual serving plates. Crumple the salami slices on top, then add spoonfuls of the ricotta. Spoon over the dressing and scatter with the basil leaves, black olives and sea salt.

NUTRITIONAL ANALYSIS	
(per portion)	
Energy	300 cals
Protein	9.0 g
Carbohydrate	5.0 g
(of which sugars)	4.5 g
Fat	27.0 g
(of which saturates)	5.0 g
Fibre	3.0 g

SUITABLE FOR:

NUT-FREE, LOW-CALORIE AND DIABETIC DIETS.

NOTE: Accompanied with warmed bread this dish makes a light all-in-one meal.

900 g (2 lb) mixed vegetables such as fennel, courgettes, leeks, aubergines, baby turnips, new potatoes and red onions, prepared and cut into chunks

2 garlic cloves, unpeeled

4-5 sprigs fresh marjoram or rosemary

5 tbsp olive oil

1 tsp flaked sea-salt

mixed crushed peppercorns, to taste

4 tsp balsamic vinegar

marjoram sprigs and green olives, to garnish

warm crusty bread to accompany

MUSTARD MAYONNAISE

150 ml (¼ pint) low-calorie mayonnaise

2 tbsp Dijon mustard

salt and freshly ground black pepper

ROASTED VEGETABLE SALAD WITH MUSTARD MAYONNAISE

SERVES 6 • PREPARATION:10 MINUTES • COOKING TIME: 40 MINUTES

1 Place the vegetables, garlic, marjoram, oil, salt and peppercorns in a roasting tin. The vegetables should fit in a single layer: use 2 roasting tins if necessary. Toss well to coat in the oil.

2 Cook at 220°C (425°F) Mark 7 for 30–35 minutes or until the vegetables are golden, tossing frequently. Sprinkle over the balsamic vinegar and return to the oven for a further 5 minutes.

3 To make the mustard mayonnaise, mix together the mayonnaise and mustard, then season with salt and pepper and set aside.

4 Transfer the roasted vegetables to a serving dish and garnish with marjoram sprigs and green olives. Serve with the mustard mayonnaise and crusty bread.

NUTRITIONAL ANALYSIS (per portion)	
Energy	205 cals
Protein	2.2 g
Carbohydrate	13.0 g
(of which sugars)	3.0 g
Fat	6.5 g
(of which saturates)	1.5 g
Fibre	3.0 g

SUITABLE FOR:

GLUTEN-FREE, NUT-FREE, LOW-CALORIE, DAIRY PRODUCE-FREE AND DIABETIC DIETS.

---

900 g (2 lb) fresh spinach, washed (see Note)

1 garlic clove, peeled and crushed

1 tsp salt

450 ml (¾ pint) Greek yogurt

1 tbsp tomato paste

2 tbsp olive oil

1 tsp chilli powder

flat-leaf parsley sprigs, to garnish

NOTE: Older spinach is best for this salad as it has more flavour.

SPINACH AND CHILLI YOGURT SALAD

SERVES 8 • PREPARATION: 20 MINUTES • COOKING TIME: 2 MINUTES

1 Steam the spinach in a large saucepan until it has just wilted, then dry on a clean tea-towel and place in a large bowl.

2 Mix the garlic with the salt and add to the yogurt. Toss the spinach in the yogurt dressing and place in a shallow serving dish. Mix the tomato paste, oil and chilli powder and drizzle over the spinach. Cover and chill. Garnish with parsley sprigs to serve.

NUTRITIONAL ANALYSIS (per portion)	
Energy	115 cals
Protein	6.0 g
Carbohydrate	5.0 g
(of which sugars)	5.0 g
Fat	8.0 g
(of which saturates)	3.0 g
Fibre	2.0 g

SUITABLE FOR:

GLUTEN-FREE, NUT-FREE, LOW-CALORIE AND DIABETIC DIETS.

1.8 kg (4 lb) broad beans, shelled (about 450 g (1 lb) shelled weight)

3-4 heads of red chicory, trimmed and separated into leaves

50 g (2 oz) hard Pecorino cheese, finely pared (see Note)

½ small red onion, peeled and thinly sliced

25 g (1 oz) hazelnuts, toasted and roughly chopped

DRESSING
2 tsp raspberry vinegar

½ tsp runny honey

salt and freshly ground black pepper

4 tbsp hazelnut oil

BROAD BEAN AND PECORINO SALAD

SERVES 4 • PREPARATION: 30 MINUTES • COOKING TIME: 1 MINUTE

1 Bring a large pan of lightly salted water to a rolling boil, add the broad beans, return to the boil and cook for 1 minute. Drain and immediately refresh under cold water. Drain and pat dry.

2 Slip the broad beans out of their tough outer skins and place in a large bowl. Add the chicory.

3 To make the dressing, place the vinegar, honey and seasoning in a small jug and gradually whisk in the oil until blended. Pour half of the dressing over the beans and chicory and toss to coat.

4 Arrange the beans and chicory on individual serving plates, top with the cheese, onion and nuts and drizzle over the remaining dressing. Serve at once.

NUTRITIONAL ANALYSIS (per portion)	
Energy	280 cals
Protein	13.0 g
Carbohydrate	13.0 g
(of which sugars)	4.0 g
Fat	21.0 g
(of which saturates)	4.5 g
Fibre	8.0 g

SUITABLE FOR:
HIGH-FIBRE, LOW-CALORIE AND DIABETIC DIETS.

NOTE: Pecorino is a ewe's milk cheese which hardens as it ages, in a similar way to Parmesan. A young, softer Pecorino or Parmesan can be substituted if preferred.

2 tsp hoisin sauce

4 tsp rice wine vinegar

2 tsp soy sauce

1 tbsp peanut oil

1 tsp sesame oil

2 tsp runny honey

225 g (8 oz) each carrot and celeriac or mooli

75 g (3 oz) roasted, salted peanuts, finely chopped

50 g (2 oz) alfalfa or 125 g (4 oz) bean sprouts

CARROT AND CELERIAC SALAD

SERVES 4 • PREPARATION: 20 MINUTES

1 Whisk the first 6 ingredients together in a small bowl.

2 Peel and coarsely grate or shred the carrot and celeriac. Place in a large bowl with the peanuts. Pour the dressing over and mix well. Stir in the alfalfa or bean sprouts and serve immediately.

NUTRITIONAL ANALYSIS (per portion)	
Energy	185 cals
Protein	6.0 g
Carbohydrate	9.5 g
(of which sugars)	9.0 g
Fat	14.0 g
(of which saturates)	2.0 g
Fibre	3.0 g

UNSUITABLE FOR:
HIGH-FIBRE, LOW-FAT AND NUT-FREE DIETS.

---

225 g (8 oz) carrots, peeled

150 g (5 oz) courgettes, trimmed

25 g (1 oz) raisins

25 g (1 oz) lightly toasted sunflower seeds

DRESSING
salt and freshly ground black pepper

4 tbsp orange juice

1 tbsp white wine vinegar

1 tbsp olive oil

1 small garlic clove, peeled and crushed

3 tbsp chives, chopped

SUNSHINE CARROT AND COURGETTE SALAD

SERVES 4 • PREPARATION: 10 MINUTES

1 Coarsely grate the carrots and courgettes and transfer to a serving bowl: if you use a food processor to grate the carrots and courgettes, put them in a sieve and allow the excess liquid to drain off before transferring to the serving bowl.

2 To make the dressing, whisk all the ingredients together in a small bowl.

3 Stir the raisins into the grated vegetables with the sunflower seeds. Pour the dressing over, toss well and serve.

NUTRITIONAL ANALYSIS (per portion)	
Energy	80 cals
Protein	1.5 g
Carbohydrate	10.0 g
(of which sugars)	9.5 g
Fat	4.0 g
(of which saturates)	0.5 g
Fibre	2.0 g

SUITABLE FOR:
GLUTEN-FREE, LOW-FAT, NUT-FREE, LOW-CHOLESTEROL, LOW-CALORIE, DAIRY PRODUCE-FREE AND DIABETIC DIETS.

---

3 tbsp mango chutney

grated rind and juice of 1 lime

2 tbsp olive oil

salt and freshly ground black pepper

150 g (5 oz) sprouted beans

1 small red onion, peeled and finely chopped

4 plum tomatoes, deseeded and diced

1 red pepper, deseeded and finely diced

1 yellow pepper, deseeded and finely diced

1 mango, peeled and finely diced

4 tbsp chopped fresh coriander

SPROUTED BEAN AND MANGO SALAD

SERVES 6 • PREPARATION: 15 MINUTES

1 Place the mango chutney in a small bowl and add the lime rind and juice. Whisk in the oil and season with salt and pepper.

2 Place the sprouted beans in a large bowl with the diced onion, tomatoes, peppers, mango and coriander. Pour the dressing over and mix well. Serve the salad immediately.

NUTRITIONAL ANALYSIS (per portion)	
Energy	120 cals
Protein	3.0 g
Carbohydrate	18.0 g
(of which sugars)	1.0 g
Fat	4.5 g
(of which saturates)	1.0 g
Fibre	4.0 g

UNSUITABLE FOR:
HIGH-FIBRE DIET.

Sprouted beans... great for salads

Sprouted beans and seeds are remarkable foods – cheap, nutritious and prolific growers. The sprouting process induces a frenzy of biochemical activity in which enzymes convert to carbohydrates, and proteins are broken down into amino acids which makes them more digestible. Vitamin C concentrations also increase.

2 corn on the cob

2.5 cm (1 inch) piece fresh root ginger, peeled and finely grated

finely grated rind and juice of 1 orange

4 tsp soy sauce

salt and freshly ground black pepper

3 tbsp olive oil

225 g (8 oz) bean sprouts, rinsed

2 Little Gem lettuces, washed and cut into wedges

mixed salad leaves, such as baby spinach and frisée lettuce

GRILLED CORN AND BEAN SPROUT SALAD

SERVES 6 • PREPARATION: 30 MINUTES, PLUS MARINATING • COOKING TIME: 10 MINUTES

1 Place the corn on the cob under a hot grill and cook until golden brown on all sides. Cool, then carefully cut the kernels from the cob with a sharp knife.

2 Whisk together the grated ginger, orange rind, 3 tbsp orange juice and soy sauce. Season with salt and pepper, then whisk in the olive oil.

3 Toss the corn kernels and bean sprouts with the ginger dressing and leave to marinate for at least 10 minutes.

4 Just before serving, toss the dressed mixture into the salad leaves.

NUTRITIONAL ANALYSIS (per portion)	
Energy	105 cals
Protein	3.5 g
Carbohydrate	9.0 g
(of which sugars)	2.4 g
Fat	6.5 g
(of which saturates)	1.0 g
Fibre	1.5 g

SUITABLE FOR:
GLUTEN-FREE, NUT-FREE, LOW-CHOLESTEROL, LOW-CALORIE, DAIRY PRODUCE-FREE AND DIABETIC DIETS.

NOTE: Cooking corn on the cob under the grill gives it a delicious smoky flavour.

2 cucumbers

125 g (4 oz) onion, peeled and thinly sliced

75 g (3 oz) caster sugar

2 tsp salt

50 ml (2 fl oz) white wine vinegar

3 tbsp chopped fresh dill or mint

dill or mint sprigs and crushed pink peppercorns, to garnish

SWEET AND SOUR CUCUMBER SALAD

SERVES 8 • PREPARATION: 15 MINUTES, PLUS CHILLING

1 Peel the cucumbers, cut in half lengthways and remove the seeds with a teaspoon. Slice the cucumber thinly (preferably in a food processor). Cover a tray with kitchen paper and lay the cucumber slices on it. Cover with another layer of kitchen paper and leave to chill for about 30 minutes in the refrigerator.

2 Place the drained cucumber in a bowl with the onion, sugar, salt, vinegar and herbs. Cover and refrigerate for about 30 minutes.

3 Place the cucumber salad in a serving dish and garnish with dill or mint sprigs and crushed pink peppercorns.

NUTRITIONAL ANALYSIS (per portion)	
Energy	50.0 cals
Protein	1.0 g
Carbohydrate	12.0 g
(of which sugars)	12.0 g
Fat	0.1 g
(of which saturates)	0.0 g
Fibre	1.0 g

SUITABLE FOR:
GLUTEN-FREE, LOW-FAT, NUT-FREE, LOW-CHOLESTEROL, LOW-CALORIE AND DAIRY PRODUCE-FREE DIETS.

NOTE: This would also be excellent as a starter with smoked salmon or gravadlax.

450 g (1 lb) plum
tomatoes, skinned,
deseeded and chopped

1 tbsp capers, rinsed

1 garlic clove, peeled and
crushed

1 tsp dried chilli flakes

½ tsp grated lemon rind

3 tbsp olive oil

3 tbsp chopped fresh
parsley

HOT TOMATO SALSA

*SERVES 8 • PREPARATION: 10 MINUTES, PLUS
STANDING*

1   Combine the tomatoes and capers in a bowl.
Add the garlic, chilli flakes, lemon rind, olive oil and
chopped parsley. Stir to mix well.

2   Leave in a cool place for 1 hour before serving.

NUTRITIONAL ANALYSIS (per portion)	
Energy	50 cals
Protein	0.5 g
Carbohydrate	1.5 g
(of which sugars)	1.5 g
Fat	5.0 g
(of which saturates)	1.0 g
Fibre	1.0 g

UNSUITABLE FOR:
HIGH-FIBRE DIET.

900 g (2 lb) ripe plum
tomatoes, skinned and
cut into rough pieces

3 Anaheim chilli peppers,
deseeded and sliced

1 bunch spring onions,
trimmed and finely
chopped

salt and freshly ground
black pepper

4 tbsp olive oil

1 tbsp balsamic vinegar

flat-leaf parsley sprigs, to
garnish

TOMATO SALAD WITH SPRING ONIONS

SERVES 6 • PREPARATION: 15 MINUTES

1   In a bowl, combine the tomatoes with the sliced
chillies and spring onions. Season with salt and
pepper.

2   Whisk together the olive oil and vinegar, then
add to the tomatoes and toss. Garnish with
parsley to serve.

NUTRITIONAL ANALYSIS (per portion)	
Energy	95 cals
Protein	1.5 g
Carbohydrate	5.0 g
(of which sugars)	5.0 g
Fat	8.0 g
(of which saturates)	1.0 g
Fibre	2.0 g

UNSUITABLE FOR:
HIGH-FIBRE AND LOW-FAT DIETS.

1 head of radicchio, torn into bite-sized pieces

1 bunch watercress, stalks removed

½ head fine frisée

50 g (2 oz) baby spinach

50 g (2 oz) rocket

250 g (9 oz) radishes, trimmed and halved or quartered

5 thin slices bread

DRESSING

2 tbsp olive oil

2 tbsp sunflower oil

1½ tsp white wine vinegar

pinch of sugar

1 small garlic clove, peeled and crushed

salt and freshly ground black pepper

MIXED LEAF SALAD WITH TOASTED CROÛTONS

SERVES 8 • PREPARATION: 10 MINUTES • COOKING TIME 4 MINUTES

1 Wash all the salad leaves in cold water, drain and pat dry. Put the salad leaves and radishes in a large polythene bag and chill until needed.

2 Using a heart-shaped cutter, stamp out shapes from the bread. Grill until golden on both sides.

3 To make the dressing, whisk all the ingredients together in a small bowl.

4 To serve, transfer the salad leaves and radishes to a serving bowl, pour on the dressing and toss lightly. Scatter the warm croûtons over the salad and serve at once.

NUTRITIONAL ANALYSIS (per portion)	
Energy	100 cals
Protein	2.5 g
Carbohydrate	9.0 g
(of which sugars)	1.5 g
Fat	6.0 g
(of which saturates)	0.8 g
Fibre	1.0 g

SUITABLE FOR:

NUT-FREE, LOW-CHOLESTEROL, LOW-CALORIE, DAIRY PRODUCE-FREE AND DIABETIC DIETS.

Salad leaves... a source of vitamins

The more robust and flavoursome salad leaves, such as watercress, baby spinach and the slightly bitter chicories and endives, not only bring a salad to life but provide many more nutrients than ordinary lettuce. Vitamin C levels are higher and many of these leaves contain large amounts of beta-carotene. Serve the leaves as fresh as possible.

4 sticks celery, trimmed

6 spring onions, trimmed

150 g (5 oz) prepared frisée salad

extra herb sprigs, to garnish

DRESSING

4 tbsp extra-virgin olive oil

3 tbsp dry white wine

2 tsp lemon juice

1 small garlic clove, peeled and crushed

½ tsp caster sugar

sea salt and freshly ground black pepper

15 g (½ oz) mixed herbs, such as chervil, parsley, tarragon and dill, finely chopped

HERB SALAD WITH CELERY AND ONION RIBBONS

SERVES 4 • PREPARATION: 15 MINUTES, PLUS STANDING

1 To make the dressing, mix together the olive oil, wine, lemon juice, garlic, sugar and salt and pepper. Add the herbs to the bowl and whisk well. Cover and chill until required.

2 For the salad, place the celery sticks flat on the surface and cut horizontally into fine slices using a sharp knife. Cut widthways into 6 cm (2½ inch) lengths. Slice the spring onions lengthways into quarters. Cut widthways into 6 cm (2½ inch) lengths. Place the spring onions and celery in a large bowl of cold water and leave for 30 minutes until curled.

3 Drain the spring onions and celery and mix in a salad bowl with the frisée. Add the dressing and toss well together. Serve scattered with extra herb sprigs.

NUTRITIONAL ANALYSIS (per portion)	
Energy	115 cals
Protein	1.0 g
Carbohydrate	2.0 g
(of which sugars)	2.0 g
Fat	11.0 g
(of which saturates)	1.5 g
Fibre	1.0 g

SUITABLE FOR:

GLUTEN-FREE, NUT-FREE, LOW-CHOLESTEROL, LOW-CALORIE, DAIRY PRODUCE-FREE AND DIABETIC DIETS.

2 tsp pink peppercorns
3 tbsp olive oil
2 tsp balsamic vinegar
½ tsp caster sugar
1 tsp Dijon mustard
125 g (4 oz) radishes,
trimmed and thinly sliced
175 g (6 oz) frisée lettuce
25 g (1 oz) rocket

LEAFY SALAD WITH PINK PEPPERCORNS

SERVES 6 • PREPARATION: 15 MINUTES

1 If using pink peppercorns in brine, drain and rinse the required amount before using to remove all traces of brine. If using dried pink peppercorns, place them in a small bowl, cover with boiling water and leave to stand for 10 minutes. Drain thoroughly before using.

2 Combine the oil, vinegar, caster sugar, mustard and peppercorns in a bowl, then whisk thoroughly.

3 Toss the radishes with the frisée and rocket leaves in a large bowl. Cover and chill.

4 Just before serving, stir the dressing and pour over the leaves. Toss well until evenly mixed, then serve immediately.

NUTRITIONAL ANALYSIS (per portion)	
Energy	60 cals
Protein	0.4 g
Carbohydrate	1.0 g
(of which sugars)	1.0 g
Fat	6.0 g
(of which saturates)	0.8 g
Fibre	0.5 g

SUITABLE FOR:
GLUTEN-FREE, NUT-FREE, LOW-CHOLESTEROL, LOW-CALORIE, DAIRY PRODUCE-FREE AND DIABETIC DIETS.

2 oranges

50 ml (2 fl oz) extra-virgin olive oil

2 tbsp cider vinegar

2 tsp poppy seeds

salt and freshly ground black pepper

1 small avocado, peeled and sliced

4 spring onions, trimmed and sliced

selection of salad leaves, about 100 g (3½ oz)

MIXED GREEN SALAD WITH POPPY SEED AND ORANGE DRESSING

SERVES 4 • PREPARATION: 15 MINUTES

1 Remove the zest from one of the oranges and squeeze the juice, then cut the remaining orange into thin slices. Whisk the juice and zest together with the next 3 ingredients. Season to taste with salt and pepper.

2 Place the avocado and spring onions in a large bowl, together with the salad leaves and sliced orange. Add 3 tbsp dressing to moisten the ingredients (see Note) and toss together lightly. Serve immediately.

NUTRITIONAL ANALYSIS
(per portion)

Energy	155 cals
Protein	2.0 g
Carbohydrate	6.0 g
(of which sugars)	5.5 g
Fat	15.0 g
(of which saturates)	2.5 g
Fibre	2.0 g

SUITABLE FOR:
GLUTEN-FREE, NUT-FREE, LOW-CALORIE, DAIRY PRODUCE-FREE AND DIABETIC DIETS.

NOTE: Any remaining dressing can be stored in a screw-top jar in the refrigerator.

4 large oranges

75 g (3 oz) stoned black olives

125 g (4 oz) lamb's lettuce

1 tbsp balsamic vinegar

3 tbsp olive oil

sea salt flakes and freshly ground black pepper

ORANGE, BLACK OLIVE AND LAMB'S LETTUCE SALAD

SERVES 6 • PREPARATION: 15 MINUTES

1 Peel the oranges, cut the flesh into rounds and arrange in a shallow bowl or serving dish. Sprinkle the black olives over, then carefully mix with 125 g (4 oz) lamb's lettuce.

2 Whisk together the balsamic vinegar and olive oil, then drizzle over the salad. Sprinkle with sea salt flakes and pepper to serve.

NUTRITIONAL ANALYSIS
(per portion)

Energy	95 cals
Protein	1.0 g
Carbohydrate	7.0 g
(of which sugars)	7.0 g
Fat	7.0 g
(of which saturates)	1.0 g
Fibre	2.0 g

SUITABLE FOR:
GLUTEN-FREE, NUT-FREE, LOW-CHOLESTEROL, LOW-CALORIE, DAIRY PRODUCE-FREE AND DIABETIC DIETS.

desserts

900 g (2 lb) cooking apples, peeled and sliced
4 tbsp fruit juice
grated rind of 1 lemon
225 g (8 oz) blackberries
6 tbsp caster sugar
1 large egg white
fresh mint, to decorate

APPLE AND BLACKBERRY SNOW

SERVES 6 • PREPARATION: 15 MINUTES, PLUS CHILLING • COOKING TIME: 12 MINUTES

1 Place the apples and fruit juice in a pan over a low heat and cook, uncovered, for 10 minutes or until soft.

2 Transfer the apples to a food processor and blend until smooth. Stir in the lemon rind, cover and chill for 1 hour.

3 Place the blackberries and 2 tbsp sugar in a pan and heat gently for 2–3 minutes or until the berries begin to soften and the juices run. Cool.

4 Whisk the egg white until stiff, adding the remaining sugar gradually until the mixture forms stiff peaks. Fold into the apple purée. Divide the blackberries and the juice among 6 serving glasses, spoon the apple mixture on top, decorate with mint and serve.

NUTRITIONAL ANALYSIS (per portion)	
Energy	125 cals
Protein	1.0 g
Carbohydrate	35.0 g
(of which sugars)	35.0 g
Fat	0.2 g
(of which saturates)	0.0 g
Fibre	4.0 g

SUITABLE FOR:
GLUTEN-FREE, LOW-FAT, NUT-FREE, LOW-CHOLESTEROL, LOW-CALORIE AND DAIRY PRODUCE-FREE DIETS.

Fresh fruit... vital for healthy living

Fresh fruit is packed with vitamins, minerals and fibre. It's also rich in antioxidants which are believed to reduce the risks of cancer and heart disease. If possible buy organic fruit as it has a more intense flavour and is pesticide free. Most fruits contain between 5–10% sugar, depending on type. These are naturally occurring sugars, such as glucose and fructose, which are contained within the cell structure and therefore do not cause tooth decay.

grated rind and juice of 1 lemon

25 g (1 oz) fresh white breadcrumbs

2 tbsp caster sugar

700 g (1½ lb) cooking apples

6 sheets filo pastry, about 50 g (2 oz)

25 g (1 oz) low-fat spread

icing sugar, to dust

MAPLE FUDGE SAUCE

75 g (3 oz) butter

150 g (5 oz) light brown (muscovado) sugar

2 tbsp maple syrup

75 ml (3 fl oz) half-fat double cream

NOTE: The strudel alone is very low in fat and calories (114 cals per serving), so you can afford to serve it with quite a rich sauce.

APPLE STRUDEL WITH MAPLE FUDGE SAUCE

SERVES 8 • PREPARATION: 30 MINUTES • COOKING TIME: 40 MINUTES

1 Mix the lemon rind with the breadcrumbs and 1 tbsp caster sugar. Peel, quarter and thickly slice the apples. Drizzle the apples with a little lemon juice, then mix with the breadcrumb mixture.

2 Lay 3 pieces of filo pastry side by side on a tea-towel, overlapping the longest edges by 5 cm (2 inches). Brush with a little melted low-fat spread. Place the 3 remaining sheets of filo on top and brush again.

3 Place the apple mixture on the filo pastry. Using the tea-towel to help, roll the filo from the longest edge to form a thick roll. Roll it on to a non-stick baking sheet, seam-side down, curling it slightly, if necessary, to fit the sheet. Brush with remaining spread and sprinkle with the remaining sugar.

4 Bake the strudel at 190°C (375°F) Mark 5 for 40 minutes or until the pastry is golden and the apples are soft. If necessary, cover the pastry loosely with foil to prevent it becoming too brown.

5 Meanwhile, make the maple fudge sauce. Melt the butter in a small, heavy-based pan, then add the sugar and maple syrup and cook gently until the sugar dissolves completely. Stir in the cream and bring to the boil. Allow the sauce to cool slightly before serving with slices of strudel, dusted with icing sugar.

NUTRITIONAL ANALYSIS (per portion)	
Energy	225 cals
Protein	1.0 g
Carbohydrate	36.0 g
(of which sugars)	34.0 g
Fat	9.5 g
(of which saturates)	6.0 g
Fibre	1.5 g

SUITABLE FOR:
NUT-FREE DIET.

50 g (2 oz) ready-to-eat dried apricots, roughly chopped

50 g (2 oz) ground almonds

50 g (2 oz) raisins

50 g (2 oz) caster sugar

1 large egg white

2 large ripe pears

Greek yogurt and a little warm honey, for drizzling (optional)

BAKED PEARS WITH APRICOTS AND ALMONDS

SERVES 4 • PREPARATION: 15 MINUTES • COOKING TIME: 30 MINUTES

1 Place the apricots in a small bowl with the almonds, raisins and sugar. Mix in the egg white.

2 Halve the pears lengthways then, using a teaspoon, remove the core. Pile the almond mixture into the centre of the pears.

3 Place the pears in an ovenproof dish and bake at 180°C (350°F) Mark 4 for 25–30 minutes or until soft. Serve immediately with a spoonful of Greek yogurt drizzled with honey, if wished.

NUTRITIONAL ANALYSIS (per portion)	
Energy	240 cals
Protein	4.5 g
Carbohydrate	38.5 g
(of which sugars)	38.0 g
Fat	7.0 g
(of which saturates)	0.5 g
Fibre	4.5 g

SUITABLE FOR:
GLUTEN-FREE, LOW-CHOLESTEROL AND DAIRY PRODUCE-FREE DIETS.

700 g (1½ lb) dessert plums, stoned and cut into quarters

4 tbsp caster sugar

8 slices fruit or cinnamon bread, about 5 mm (¼ inch) thick

1 large egg

3 tbsp milk

25 g (1 oz) unsalted butter

Greek yogurt, to serve

PLUMS WITH CARAMELISED FRUIT BREAD

SERVES 4 • PREPARATION: 10 MINUTES • COOKING TIME: 16 MINUTES

1 Place the plums in a pan, sprinkle over 2 tbsp caster sugar and cook over a gentle heat, stirring occasionally, for 8–10 minutes or until the plums begin to soften.

2 Meanwhile, using a large plain cutter or an upturned tumbler as a guide, cut the fruit or cinnamon bread into circles. Beat together the egg and the milk.

3 Heat the butter in a non-stick frying pan. Dip the bread into the egg mixture to coat well. Once the butter is hot, add the bread and sprinkle with 1 tbsp caster sugar. Cook over a medium heat for about 3 minutes, turn over and sprinkle with the remaining 1 tbsp sugar; cook for a further 3 minutes or until golden.

4 Arrange the cooked fruit bread on individual plates, then top with the warm plums and a spoonful of Greek yogurt.

NUTRITIONAL ANALYSIS (per portion)	
Energy	250 cals
Protein	5.5 g
Carbohydrate	45.0 g
(of which sugars)	31.0 g
Fat	8.0 g
(of which saturates)	4.0 g
Fibre	3.0 g

SUITABLE FOR:
NUT-FREE DIET.

NOTE: Choose ripe fruit as it will be sweeter and have a better flavour, which means you can cut down on sugar. If you buy unripe fruit in advance, keep it in a dark, warm place to ripen. Or put it with a ripe banana. This gives off ethylene gas which helps fruit ripen.

a little butter for greasing

5 tbsp caster sugar

175 g (6 oz) stoned, ready-to-eat prunes

2 tbsp vegetable oil

75 ml (3 fl oz) unsweetened orange juice

50 g (2 oz) plain chocolate

grated rind of 1 orange

5 egg whites

¼ tsp cream of tartar

pinch of salt

icing sugar, to dust

brandied prunes, to serve (see Note)

NOTE: Brandied prunes make an excellent accompaniment to this dessert. Place 225 g (8 oz) stoned, ready-to-eat prunes in a jar or bowl, then cover with 200 ml (7 fl oz) brandy. Cover with a lid or cling film and leave for 2–3 days (45 cals per serving).

CHOCOLATE, PRUNE AND ORANGE SOUFFLÉS

SERVES 8 • PREPARATION: 20 MINUTES • COOKING TIME: 20 MINUTES

1 Lightly grease eight 150 ml (5 fl oz) ramekins and sprinkle with 1 tbsp caster sugar.

2 Place the prunes, oil and orange juice in a blender and blend for 2-3 minutes to form a purée.

3 Using a sharp knife, chop the plain chocolate into small pieces and mix with the prune purée, 2 tbsp of the remaining caster sugar and the orange rind.

4 Place the egg whites, cream of tartar and salt in a clean bowl and whisk until stiff but not dry. Add the remaining 2 tbsp sugar and continue to whisk until the mixture becomes very stiff and shiny.

5 Using a large metal spoon, beat one-quarter of the egg whites into the prune mixture, then gently fold in the remainder. Spoon into the ramekins.

6 Stand the ramekins in a roasting tin and add enough hot water to come halfway up the sides. Cook at 180°C (350°F) Mark 4 for 20 minutes or until the soufflés are just set. Serve immediately, dusted with icing sugar and accompanied by brandied prunes, if wished.

NUTRITIONAL ANALYSIS
(per portion)

Energy	100 cals
Protein	3.0 g
Carbohydrate	12.0 g
(of which sugars)	12.0 g
Fat	5.0 g
(of which saturates)	1.5 g
Fibre	1.5 g

SUITABLE FOR:

GLUTEN-FREE, LOW-FAT, NUT-FREE, LOW-CHOLESTEROL, LOW-CALORIE AND DAIRY PRODUCE-FREE DIETS.

VARIATION:

If preferred, you can make one large soufflé instead of 8 small ones: place the mixture in a 1.7 litre (3 pint) soufflé dish and cook for 50–55 minutes, covering loosely afer 30 minutes, if necessary, to prevent the soufflé becoming too brown.

---

400 g (14 oz) can apricots in natural juice, drained

200 ml (7 fl oz) Greek yogurt

artificial sweetener, to taste

QUICK APRICOT FOOL

SERVES 4 • PREPARATION: 5 MINUTES, PLUS CHILLING

1 Place the drained apricots in a food processor and blend until smooth. Stir the purée into 200 ml (7 fl oz) Greek yogurt.

2 Sweeten to taste with artificial sweetener and chill for 2 hours.

NUTRITIONAL ANALYSIS
(per portion)

Energy	92 cals
Protein	4.0 g
Carbohydrate	9.0 g
(of which sugars)	9.0 g
Fat	5.0 g
(of which saturates)	2.5 g
Fibre	1.0 g

SUITABLE FOR:

GLUTEN-FREE, LOW-FAT, NUT-FREE, LOW-CHOLESTEROL, LOW-CALORIE AND DIABETIC DIETS.

700 g (1½ lb) fresh apricots, stoned and cut into quarters

2-3 tbsp caster sugar

3-4 green cardamom pods, split, seeds reserved and crushed

50 g (2 oz) plain flour

50 g (2 oz) jumbo rolled oats

50 g (2 oz) light brown sugar

50 g (2 oz) butter, cut into cubes

25 g (1 oz) hazelnuts, browned and roughly chopped

Greek yogurt, to serve (optional)

APRICOT AND CARDAMOM CRUMBLE

SERVES 6 • PREPARATION: 15 MINUTES • COOKING TIME: 30 MINUTES

1 Mix the apricots with the caster sugar and place in a 1.3 litre (2¼ pint) capacity ovenproof dish or divide between 6 individual dishes.

2 Place the crushed cardamom seeds, flour, oats and light brown sugar in a large bowl, then rub in the butter. Mix in the chopped hazelnuts.

3 Spoon the crumble mixture over the fruit. Bake at 190°C (375°F) Mark 5 for 25–30 minutes or until golden brown. Serve warm with a little thick Greek yogurt, if wished.

NUTRITIONAL ANALYSIS (per portion)	
Energy	230 cals
Protein	3.5 g
Carbohydrate	34.0 g
(of which sugars)	22.0 g
Fat	10.5 g
(of which saturates)	5.0 g
Fibre	3.0 g

SUITABLE FOR:
LOW-CHOLESTEROL AND DIABETIC DIETS.

HONEYED APRICOTS

450 g (l lb) ripe apricots
50 g (2 oz) caster sugar
1 tbsp runny honey
2 tbsp lime juice
lime slices and grated
lime rind, to decorate
low-fat yogurt, to serve

*SERVES 4 • PREPARATION: 5 MINUTES •
COOKING TIME: 20 MINUTES*

1 Poach the apricots in 150 ml (¼ pint) water with the sugar for 15–20 minutes or until just soft.

2 Stir in the honey and lime juice. Transfer to a serving dish and decorate with lime slices and grated rind. Serve warm or cold with yogurt.

NUTRITIONAL ANALYSIS (per portion)	
Energy	100 cals
Protein	1.0 g
Carbohydrate	26.0 g
(of which sugars)	26.0 g
Fat	0.1 g
(of which saturates)	0.0 g
Fibre	2.0 g

UNSUITABLE FOR:
HIGH-FIBRE AND DIABETIC DIETS.

RHUBARB AND RASPBERRY MERINGUES

450 g (1 lb) rhubarb, cleaned and cut into 2.5 cm (1 inch) pieces
75 g (3 oz) caster sugar
2.5 cm (1 inch) piece stem ginger, finely chopped (optional)
finely grated rind and juice of 1 orange
75 g (3 oz) frozen raspberries
1 large egg white

*SERVES 4 • PREPARATION: 15 MINUTES •
COOKING TIME: ABOUT 15 MINUTES*

1 Place the rhubarb in a large saucepan with 25 g (1 oz) caster sugar, the chopped stem ginger, if using, and the orange rind. Cover and cook gently for 2–3 minutes, adding a little orange juice if necessary. Add the raspberries. Spoon the mixture into four 150 ml (5 fl oz) ramekins or ovenproof tea cups.

2 Whisk the egg white and remaining sugar together until foamy. Place the bowl over a saucepan of simmering water and continue to whisk for 5 minutes or until stiff and shiny.

3 Place a spoonful of meringue mixture on top of each ramekin and bake at 180°C (350°F) Mark 4 for 5–10 minutes or until lightly golden.

NUTRITIONAL ANALYSIS (per portion)	
Energy	90 cals
Protein	2.0 g
Carbohydrate	21.0 g
(of which sugars)	21.0 g
Fat	0.2 g
(of which saturates)	0.0 g
Fibre	2.0 g

SUITABLE FOR:
GLUTEN-FREE, LOW-FAT, NUT-FREE, LOW-CHOLESTEROL, LOW-CALORIE AND DIABETIC DIETS.

VARIATION:
Rhubarb has a delicate flavour which marries well with ginger, but you could use a pinch of cinnamon as an alternative.

Soft summer fruit... juicy goodness

Luscious soft summer fruit are not only a wonderful seasonal treat but are brimful of nutrients, too. Berries and currants are an excellent source of vitamin C, containing far more than oranges. They are extremely rich in fibre and potassium, and have good levels of folic acid, iron and calcium. Fresh peaches and nectarines also good sources of vitamin C (one fruit contains almost the daily requirement for an adult) while downy-skinned apricots are a useful source of beta-carotene – an important antioxidant necessary for good health.

40 g (1½ oz) caster sugar

1 tbsp oil

200 g (7 oz) packet filo pastry

2 egg yolks

250 g (9 oz) fromage frais

2 tbsp single cream

200 g (7 oz) small strawberries, hulled and thinly sliced

vanilla syrup, to serve, optional (see Note)

NOTE: For an indulgent treat, serve the tartlets with a vanilla syrup. In a small pan, dissolve 50 g (2 oz) sugar in 150 ml (¼ pint) water, add a vanilla pod, split lengthways, and cook gently for about 5 minutes until the liquid is syrupy. Turn into a bowl and leave to cool. Spoon the syrup on and around the tarts. (Bear in mind that this will increase the sugar count of the dish.)

STRAWBERRY AND CUSTARD TARTS

SERVES 6 • PREPARATION: 20 MINUTES • COOKING TIME: ABOUT 20 MINUTES

1 Lightly brush six 9 cm (3½ inch) round, fluted tartlet tins with a little oil. Using a saucer as a guide, cut out sixteen 14 cm (5½ inch) circles from the filo pastry. Line each tin with a circle of pastry, pressing the pastry into the flutes around the sides. Brush lightly with oil and line with a second circle of pastry. Brush with more oil and line with the remaining pastry circles. Bake at 200°C (400°F) Mark 6 for 5 minutes until the pastry is lightly browned.

2 Beat the egg yolks with the fromage frais, cream and remaining sugar. Spoon into the cases and bake for a further 8–10 minutes until very lightly set. Transfer to a wire rack and leave to cool. (The custard still feels soft once baked, but firms up as it cools.)

3 Arrange the strawberries in the centre of each case and chill until required. Transfer the tartlets to individual serving plates and serve with vanilla syrup, if wished.

NUTRITIONAL ANALYSIS (per portion)	
Energy	175 cals
Protein	5.0 g
Carbohydrate	17.2 g
(of which sugars)	13.2 g
Fat	10.0 g
(of which saturates)	5.0 g
Fibre	0.5 g

SUITABLE FOR:
NUT-FREE, LOW-CALORIE AND DIABETIC DIETS.

250 g (9 oz) Madeira cake
12 tbsp fresh orange juice
350 g (12 oz) raspberries
250 g (9 oz) ricotta cheese
artificial sweetener or
caster sugar, to taste
2 tsp powdered gelatine
fresh strawberries or
raspberries, to decorate

RASPBERRY CHEESECAKES

SERVES 6 • PREPARATION: 25 MINUTES, PLUS SOAKING AND CHILLING • COOKING TIME: 3 MINUTES

1 Cut the cake lengthways into 6 slices. Using a round cutter, stamp out six 7 cm (2¾ inch) circles of cake.

2 Make 6 foil collars (see Note). Slip one around each cake circle and transfer to a baking sheet. Spoon 1 tbsp of the orange juice over each cake circle.

3 Blend 225 g (8 oz) of the raspberries in a food processor, then sieve. Mix together the purée and ricotta, then add sweetener or sugar to taste.

4 Put 2 tbsp orange juice in a small heatproof bowl, then sprinkle the gelatine over the top and leave to soak for 5 minutes. Place the bowl over a saucepan of simmering water, stir until melted, allow to cool a little, then stir into the raspberry purée. Spoon the mixture over the cake circles and chill for 2 hours or until set.

5 Blend the remaining raspberries in a food processor with the remaining 4 tbsp orange juice, then sieve and sweeten to taste with artificial sweetener or sugar.

6 Remove the foil collars. Decorate each cheesecake with a few strawberries or raspberries. Serve with the raspberry purée.

NUTRITIONAL ANALYSIS
(per portion)

Energy	210 cals
Protein	6.5 g
Carbohydrate	23.0 g
(of which sugars)	17.0 g
Fat	10.0 g
(of which saturates)	5.5 g
Fibre	2.0 g

SUITABLE FOR:
NUT-FREE AND DIABETIC DIETS.

NOTE: To make the foil collars, take strips of foil 20 x 30 cm (7½ x 11½ inches); fold twice lengthways into bands 5 cm (2 inches) wide. Curl round in circles and secure with a paper clip.

700 g (1½ lb) mixed
summer fruit, such as
strawberries, raspberries
and cherries
2 tbsp Kirsch
2 large egg yolks
25 g (1 oz) caster sugar

WATCHPOINT:
The young, the elderly,
pregnant women and
those suffering from
immune-deficiency
diseases should not eat
raw or lightly cooked
eggs, which may contain
salmonella.

RED FRUIT GRATIN

SERVES 4 • PREPARATION: 10 MINUTES • COOKING TIME: 15 MINUTES

1 In a bowl, toss the fruit with 1 tbsp Kirsch.

2 In another heatproof bowl, combine the egg yolks with the sugar, remaining Kirsch and 1 tbsp water. Place over a pan of simmering water and whisk with an electric whisk for 5–10 minutes or until the mixture is light and pale and leaves a trail when the whisk is lifted

3 Spoon the fruit into 4 shallow, heatproof dishes and spoon the sauce over. Cook under the grill for 1–2 minutes or until the top is a light golden colour. Serve immediately.

NUTRITIONAL ANALYSIS
(per portion)

Energy	115 cals
Protein	3.0 g
Carbohydrate	17.5 g
(of which sugars)	17.5 g
Fat	3.0 g
(of which saturates)	1.0 g
Fibre	2.0 g

SUITABLE FOR:
GLUTEN-FREE, LOW-FAT, NUT-FREE, LOW-CALORIE AND DAIRY PRODUCE-FREE DIETS.

250 g (9 oz) white sliced bread (see Note)

825 g (1 lb 12 oz) mixed summer fruit, such as raspberries, blackberries, cherries and blueberries

4 tbsp caster sugar

NOTE: Using bread that is a day old will give a better result, as it will be slightly drier and therefore able to absorb the fruit juices more easily.

SUMMER PUDDINGS

SERVES 4 • PREPARATION: 20 MINUTES, PLUS CHILLING • COOKING TIME: 3 MINUTES

1 Remove the crusts from the bread. Line four 150 ml (¼ pint) non-metallic moulds with most of the bread, reserving enough slices to make a 'lid' for each one.

2 Place the fruit in a large pan with the sugar. Heat gently, stirring for 2–3 minutes or until the fruit has released its juices and the sugar has dissolved.

3 Fill the lined moulds with three-quarters of the fruit, top with the reserved slices of bread, then cover with cling film. Weigh down with weights or cans and refrigerate overnight.

4 Unmould the summer puddings and spoon the remaining fruit on top to serve.

NUTRITIONAL ANALYSIS (per portion)	
Energy	230 cals
Protein	6.0 g
Carbohydrate	53.0 g
(of which sugars)	29.0 g
Fat	1.0 g
(of which saturates)	0.0 g
Fibre	3.0 g

SUITABLE FOR:
LOW-FAT, NUT-FREE, LOW-CHOLESTEROL, LOW-CALORIE, DAIRY PRODUCE-FREE AND DIABETIC DIETS.

---

225 g (8 oz) raspberries

grated rind of ½ orange

1 tbsp plus 125 g (4 oz) caster sugar

3 large egg whites

1 tbsp cocoa powder

15 g (½ oz) hazelnuts, toasted and roughly chopped

NOTE: If you want a chocolate fix without many calories this is the dessert for you. It's deceptively chocolatey and rich, yet it's low in calories and contains very little fat.

RASPBERRIES WITH CHOCOLATE MALLOW

SERVES 6 • PREPARATION: 15 MINUTES • COOKING TIME: 25 MINUTES

1 Divide the raspberries, grated orange rind and 1 tbsp caster sugar among six 150 ml (¼ pint) ovenproof ramekin dishes.

2 Place the egg whites in a bowl with 125 g (4 oz) caster sugar and set over a saucepan of gently simmering water. Using an electric hand whisk, whisk the egg whites and sugar until very stiff and shiny. Remove the bowl from the heat and whisk for 4–5 minutes or until the bowl is cool. At the last moment, fold in the cocoa powder.

3 Spoon the meringue over the fruit and sprinkle the chopped hazelnuts on top.

4 Bake at 150°C (300°F) Mark 2 for 20–25 minutes or until lightly coloured, crisp on the outside and soft in the middle. Serve immediately.

NUTRITIONAL ANALYSIS (per portion)	
Energy	110 cals
Protein	2.0 g
Carbohydrate	26.0 g
(of which sugars)	26.0 g
Fat	2.0 g
(of which saturates)	0.5 g
Fibre	0.2 g

SUITABLE FOR:
GLUTEN-FREE, LOW-FAT, LOW-CHOLESTEROL AND DAIRY PRODUCE-FREE DIETS.

Right: Summer Puddings

4 eggs

75 g (3 oz) light muscovado sugar

finely grated rind of 1 lemon

50 g (2 oz) wholemeal plain flour

50 g (2 oz) plain flour

25 g (1 oz) unsalted butter, melted

100 g (3½ oz) walnut pieces

100 g (3½ oz) sun-dried dates, roughly chopped

50 g (2 oz) sultanas

half-fat crème fraîche, to serve

DATE AND WALNUT PUDDINGS

SERVES 8 • PREPARATION: 15 MINUTES •
COOKING TIME: 30 MINUTES

1 Lightly grease 8 individual metal pudding moulds and line the bases with greaseproof paper.

2 Place the eggs, sugar and lemon rind in a heatproof bowl set over a pan of gently simmering water and whisk together until pale and thickened and the whisk leaves a trail when lifted from the bowl. Remove from the heat and whisk until cool.

3 Sift the flours over the bowl, then pour the butter around the edges of the bowl and gently fold in, using a large metal spoon. Add the walnuts, dates and sultanas and fold in.

4 Divide between the prepared moulds and place in a roasting tin. Pour a 2 cm (¾ inch) depth of boiling water into the tin. Cover completely with foil and bake at 180°C (350°F) Mark 4 for 25–30 minutes until the puddings feel firm.

5 Loosen the edges with a knife and invert on to individual serving plates. Serve with crème fraîche.

NUTRITIONAL ANALYSIS (per portion)	
Energy	280 cals
Protein	7.5 g
Carbohydrate	32.0 g
(of which sugars)	23.0 g
Fat	15.0 g
(of which saturates)	3.5 g
Fibre	2.0 g

UNSUITABLE FOR THOSE ON SPECIAL DIETS.

VARIATION:
Use other dried fruits such as figs or prunes instead of the dates.

---

50 g (2 oz) pudding rice

600 ml (1 pint) semi-skimmed milk

100 g (3½ oz) caster sugar

100 ml (3½ fl oz) half-fat crème fraîche

1 tsp cornflour

100 ml (3½ fl oz) apple juice

200 g (7 oz) fresh or frozen blackcurrants

¼ tsp ground mixed spice

2 egg whites

1 tbsp slivered or ground almonds

BLACKCURRANT MERINGUE

SERVES 4 • PREPARATION: 15 MINUTES •
COOKING TIME: ABOUT 40 MINUTES

1 Put the rice in a large, heavy-based saucepan with the milk and 25 g (1 oz) sugar. Bring to the boil, reduce the heat and simmer gently for about 30 minutes until thickened and creamy, stirring frequently. Stir in the crème fraîche and turn into a 900 ml (1½ pint) shallow ovenproof dish.

2 Blend the cornflour in a small saucepan with a little of the apple juice. Add the remaining apple juice, the blackcurrants and spice. Cook gently, stirring until slightly thickened. Spoon over the rice.

3 Whisk the egg whites until stiff. Gradually whisk in the remaining sugar, a tablespoonful at a time until stiff and glossy. Spread the meringue over the blackcurrants in the dish, peaking the mixture with the back of the spoon.

4 Sprinkle with the almonds and bake at 190°C (375°F) Mark 5 for about 10 minutes or until the meringue is golden. Serve warm or cold.

NUTRITIONAL ANALYSIS (per portion)	
Energy	260 cals
Protein	8.0 g
Carbohydrate	44.0 g
(of which sugars)	32.0 g
Fat	7.5 g
(of which saturates)	4.5 g
Fibre	1.5 g

SUITABLE FOR:
GLUTEN-FREE DIET.

150 g (5 oz) plain chocolate

100 g (3½ oz) plain flour

1 large egg

pinch of salt

300 ml (½ pint) skimmed milk

25 g (1 oz) butter

1 tbsp light brown sugar

4 medium bananas, thickly sliced

8 tbsp brandy

vegetable oil, for brushing

icing sugar, to dust

chocolate shavings, to decorate

Greek yogurt or quark, to serve

CHOCOLATE AND BANANA PANCAKES

MAKES 12 PANCAKES • PREPARATION: 15 MINUTES, PLUS CHILLING • COOKING TIME: 40 MINUTES

1 Place 50 g (2 oz) chocolate in a food processor and chop. Add the flour, egg, salt and milk and process until smooth. Cover; chill for 30 minutes.

2 Melt the butter and sugar in a frying pan. Add the bananas and stir-fry over a medium heat for 3 minutes. Add the brandy (take care when doing this as it may ignite in the warm pan) and continue to simmer for about 2 minutes until the bananas soften and the liquid is syrupy. Set aside.

3 Lightly brush an 18 cm (7 inch) non-stick crêpe or small frying pan with oil and heat. Stir the batter and coat the base of the pan thinly, with about 4 tbsp batter. Cook for 2 minutes or until golden brown, then turn. Cook for a further 1 minute. Transfer to a plate, cover and keep warm. Cook the remaining batter in the same way.

4 Chop the remaining chocolate. Place 2 spoonfuls of banana filling over one half of each pancake; sprinkle with some of the chocolate. Fold in half, then in half again. Keep warm while filling the remaining pancakes. Dust, decorate and serve warm with yogurt or quark.

NUTRITIONAL ANALYSIS (per pancake)	
Energy	140 cals
Protein	3.0 g
Carbohydrate	23.0 g
(of which sugars)	16.0 g
Fat	4.5 g
(of which saturates)	2.4 g
Fibre	1.0 g

SUITABLE FOR:
NUT-FREE DIET.

VARIATION:
You can use any fruit instead of the banana filling, or serve the pancakes with frozen yogurt.

125 g (4 oz) reduced-fat digestive biscuits

50 g (2 oz) half-fat butter

75 g (3 oz) dark brown sugar, preferably muscovado

250 g (9 oz) ricotta cheese

grated rind and juice of 1 lemon

300 ml (½ pint) low-fat natural yogurt

25 g (1 oz) rice flour

3 large eggs

cocoa powder, to dust

chocolate curls, to decorate (optional)

BAKED RICOTTA TORTE

SERVES 8 • PREPARATION: 20 MINUTES, PLUS CHILLING • COOKING TIME: 40 MINUTES

1 Line the base of a 23 cm (9 inch) spring-release tin with non-stick baking parchment. Crush the biscuits to a fine powder in a food processor. Melt the butter and combine with the biscuits. Press into the tin and chill for 30 minutes.

2 Put the brown sugar in the food processor and process for 1–2 minutes. Add the ricotta cheese and work for 2–3 minutes. Add the lemon rind and 3 tbsp lemon juice, together with the yogurt and rice flour. Pulse to mix well, then add the eggs and combine.

3 Pour the cheese mixture over the prepared base and bake at 180°C (350°F) Mark 4 for 40 minutes or until lightly set. Leave to cool in the tin, then chill.

4 Unmould the torte and serve dusted with cocoa powder. Decorate with chocolate curls, if wished.

NUTRITIONAL ANALYSIS
(per portion)

Energy	230 cals
Protein	9.0 g
Carbohydrate	24.0 g
(of which sugars)	15.0 g
Fat	11.0 g
(of which saturates)	5.0 g
Fibre	0.3 g

SUITABLE FOR:
NUT-FREE DIET.

---

175 g (6 oz) fresh blueberries

2 tbsp caster sugar, plus 1 tsp

25 g (1 oz) medium oatmeal

150 g (5 oz) half-fat crème fraîche

125 g (4 oz) Greek yogurt

2 tsp lemon juice

½ tsp vanilla extract

BLUEBERRY AND OATMEAL FLUMMERY

SERVES 4 • PREPARATION: 10 MINUTES, PLUS COOLING AND CHILLING

1 Put the blueberries in a small bowl with 1 tbsp sugar and crush with a fork until broken up but not puréed. Lightly toast the oatmeal in a frying pan or under the grill. Leave to cool.

2 Mix together the crème fraîche, yogurt, lemon juice, vanilla extract and the remaining sugar. Fold in the toasted oatmeal and blueberries until evenly combined.

3 Spoon into 4 small, long-stemmed glasses and chill for several hours. Serve with fine dessert biscuits, if liked.

NUTRITIONAL ANALYSIS
(per portion)

Energy	150 cals
Protein	4.0 g
Carbohydrate	16.0 g
(of which sugars)	12.0 g
Fat	8.0 g
(of which saturates)	4.5 g
Fibre	2.0 g

SUITABLE FOR:
NUT-FREE, LOW-CALORIE AND DIABETIC DIETS.

NOTE: This quick dessert is best made several hours in advance and chilled so that it thickens up slightly.

4 ripe passionfruit, halved and pulp scooped out

150 ml (¼ pint) low-fat bio-yogurt, plus 1 tbsp to decorate

8 ice cubes, crushed

4 ripe bananas, about 550 g (1¼ lb), peeled and roughly chopped

225 g (8 oz) seedless white grapes

PASSIONFRUIT, GRAPE AND BANANA SMOOTHIE

SERVES 4 • PREPARATION: 5 MINUTES, PLUS CHILLING

1 Chill 4 tall glasses in the freezer. Reserving 1 tbsp passionfruit pulp for decoration, place the remainder in a blender with the rest of the ingredients; process until smooth. (The passionfruit pips will remain whole but are easy to drink.)

2 Serve the smoothie in the chilled glasses, decorated with 1 tbsp yogurt mixed with the reserved passionfruit pulp.

NUTRITIONAL ANALYSIS (per portion)	
Energy	190 cals
Protein	40.0 g
Carbohydrate	44.0 g
(of which sugars)	41.0 g
Fat	0.8 g
(of which saturates)	0.3 g
Fibre	2.5 g

SUITABLE FOR:
GLUTEN-FREE, LOW-FAT, NUT-FREE, LOW-CHOLESTEROL, LOW-CALORIE AND DIABETIC DIETS.

Yogurt... a versatile dairy product

Yogurt is the ideal low-fat alternative to cream, ranging in type from the rich Greek variety to a version that is fat-free. Bio-yogurt, a mild-tasting live yogurt, contains friendly bacteria which are also present in the gut. These have been shown to help digestion, guard against intestinal upsets and suppress the growth of harmful bacteria and yeasts.

3 large fresh figs,
quartered

1 large ripe mango,
peeled and cut into cubes

1 baby pineapple or 2
thick slices, skin removed
and cut into cubes

1 tbsp dark runny honey

DIP

150 g (5 oz) ready-to-eat
dried pears

juice of 1 orange

1 tsp finely chopped fresh
ginger

½ tsp vanilla extract

50 ml (2 fl oz) very low-fat
natural yogurt

½ tsp ground cinnamon,
plus extra to dust

1 tsp dark runny honey

25 g (1 oz) hazelnuts,
toasted and roughly
chopped

FRUIT KEBABS WITH SPICED PEAR DIP

SERVES 6 • PREPARATION: 20 MINUTES, PLUS SOAKING • COOKING TIME: 8 MINUTES

1 To make the dip, soak the pears in hot water for about 30 minutes, then drain and place in a blender or food processor. Add the orange juice, ginger, vanilla extract, yogurt, cinnamon and 50 ml (2 fl oz) water and process until smooth.

2 Spoon the dip into a bowl, drizzle with the runny honey, sprinkle with the hazelnuts and dust with a little ground cinnamon. Cover and set aside in a cool place.

3 To make the kebabs, thread alternate pieces of fruit on to six 20 cm (8 inch) wooden kebab skewers, using at least 2 pieces of each type of fruit per skewer.

4 Place the skewers on a foil-covered tray and cover the ends of the skewers with strips of foil to prevent them from burning. Drizzle the fruit with honey and cook under a hot grill for about 4 minutes on each side, close to the heat, until lightly charred. Serve warm with the dip.

NUTRITIONAL ANALYSIS (per portion)	
Energy	125 cals
Protein	2.0 g
Carbohydrate	25.0 g
(of which sugars)	25.0 g
Fat	3.0 g
(of which saturates)	0.3 g
Fibre	3.5 g

SUITABLE FOR:
GLUTEN-FREE, LOW-FAT, LOW-CHOLESTEROL, LOW-CALORIE AND DIABETIC DIETS.

2 medium-sized ripe
pineapples

2 tbsp light soft brown
(muscovado) sugar

2 tsp ground ginger

yogurt, to serve

1 tsp runny honey
(optional)

ground ginger, for dusting

GINGER-GLAZED PINEAPPLE

SERVES 8 • PREPARATION: 30 MINUTES • COOKING TIME: 10 MINUTES

1 Cut each of the pineapples into 4 lengthways, keeping the stalk on. Remove the fibrous core and cut along the skin to loosen the flesh, reserving the skin 'shells'. Cut the flesh into pieces and return to the pineapple 'shell'. Wrap the green leaves of the stalk in foil so that they don't burn while grilling. Mix the light soft brown sugar and ground ginger together.

2 Sprinkle each pineapple quarter with the sugar mixture. Place on foil-lined baking sheets and cook under the grill for 10 minutes or until golden and caramelised.

3 Mix the yogurt with the runny honey, if using. Serve the pineapple with the yogurt and dust with ginger.

NUTRITIONAL ANALYSIS (per portion)	
Energy	65 cals
Protein	0.5 g
Carbohydrate	17.0 g
(of which sugars)	17.0 g
Fat	0.3 g
(of which saturates)	0.0 g
Fibre	1.5 g

SUITABLE FOR:
GLUTEN-FREE, LOW-FAT, NUT-FREE, LOW-CHOLESTEROL, DAIRY PRODUCE-FREE AND DIABETIC DIETS.

Right: Fruit Kebabs with Spiced Pear Dip

5 large oranges

5 pink grapefruit

25 g (1 oz) powdered gelatine

8 passionfruit, halved and pulp scooped out

150 g (5 oz) caster sugar

225 g (8 oz) ripe strawberries, hulled and halved

extra strawberries and fresh mint leaves, to decorate

PASSIONFRUIT AND STRAWBERRY TERRINE

SERVES 8 • PREPARATION: 50 MINUTES, PLUS CHILLING • COOKING TIME: 5 MINUTES

1 Squeeze the juice of three oranges. Using a sharp knife, cut the peel and pith from the grapefruit and the two remaining oranges, then cut the grapefruit and orange flesh into segments. Squeeze the juices from the membrane and add to the orange juice. Place the segments in a colander and stand on a plate to drain for 30 minutes.

2 Pour 5 tbsp cold water into a small, heatproof bowl and sprinkle the powdered gelatine over. Leave to soak for 5 minutes.

3 Place the passionfruit pulp and 2 tbsp of the citrus juice in a food processor and pulse for 1 minute. Strain and add enough of the remaining juice to make 600 ml (1 pint).

4 Pour the fruit juice into a pan, then add the caster sugar and bring to the boil. Remove the pan from the heat, add the soaked gelatine and stir until completely dissolved.

5 Line a 1.4 litre (2½ pint) terrine or loaf tin with cling film. Mix the grapefruit and orange segments together with the strawberries and spoon into the mould. Strain over enough warm juice mixture to cover the fruit completely, then gently tap the mould to expel any air bubbles. Cover with cling film and refrigerate for at least 6 hours, preferably overnight, until set.

6 To serve, turn the mould out on to a board or serving platter and remove the cling film. Cut into thick slices with either a hot serrated knife or an electric knife. Decorate with fresh strawberries and mint leaves to serve.

NUTRITIONAL ANALYSIS (per portion)	
Energy	165 cals
Protein	3.0 g
Carbohydrate	40.0 g
(of which sugars)	40.0 g
Fat	0.3 g
(of which saturates)	0.0 g
Fibre	4.0 g

SUITABLE FOR:

GLUTEN-FREE, LOW-FAT, NUT-FREE, LOW-CHOLESTEROL, LOW-CALORIE AND DAIRY PRODUCE-FREE DIETS.

Passionfruit ... exotic and healthy

Underneath the passionfruit's unprepossessing exterior you'll find deliciously perfumed pulpy juice which is rich in vitamin C and beta-carotene. Passionfruit also contain useful amounts of iron and zinc, and, if you eat the seeds, provide plenty of insoluble fibre.

50 g (2 oz) granulated sugar

75 ml (3 fl oz) fruity red wine

2 tbsp ruby port or brandy

1 tbsp balsamic vinegar

juice of 1 orange

pinch of ground mixed spice

225 g (8 oz) strawberries, hulled and halved

225 g (8 oz) cherries, stoned

2 firm ripe nectarines or peaches, stoned and cut into wedges

175 g (6 oz) raspberries

175 g (6 oz) blueberries

125 g (4 oz) blackberries

strawberry leaves or herb sprigs, to decorate

half-fat crème fraîche, to serve

WARM SALAD OF SUMMER FRUIT

SERVES 4 • PREPARATION: 10 MINUTES • COOKING TIME: ABOUT 10 MINUTES

1 Place the sugar in a heavy-based frying-pan over a low heat until melted, then increase the heat and cook, without stirring, to a golden caramel: do not allow it to burn.

2 Meanwhile, in a jug mix together the wine, port, vinegar and orange juice. Stir in the mixed spice. Protecting your hand with an oven glove, pour this mixture into the pan, taking care as the caramel will immediately spit and splatter. (The caramelised sugar may set on impact, but it will melt into the liquid on heating.) Stir over a low heat for 1–2 minutes until the syrup is smooth and thickened slightly.

3 Add all the fruits to the pan. Toss in the hot syrup for 1 minute, until they start to soften, then remove from the heat and leave to cool slightly.

4 To serve, decorate with strawberry leaves and accompany with half-fat crème fraîche.

NUTRITIONAL ANALYSIS (per portion)	
Energy	160 cals
Protein	3.0 g
Carbohydrate	33.0 g
(of which sugars)	33.0 g
Fat	0.5 g
(of which saturates)	0.0 g
Fibre	5.5 g

SUITABLE FOR:

GLUTEN-FREE, LOW-FAT, NUT-FREE, LOW-CHOLESTEROL, LOW-CALORIE AND DAIRY PRODUCE-FREE DIETS.

4 large oranges

50 g (2 oz) light brown (muscovado) sugar

6 whole star anise

2 tbsp brandy or orange juice

150 ml (¼ pint) whipping cream

200 g (7 oz) Greek yogurt

ORANGE AND STAR ANISE SYLLABUB

SERVES 6 • PREPARATION: 10 MINUTES • COOKING TIME: 3 MINUTES

1 Cut away the skins from the oranges, then cut the flesh into segments, cutting away the membranes and discarding any pips. Heat the sugar in a small saucepan with 2 tbsp water until the sugar dissolves. Add the star anise and orange slices and cook until the liquid starts to bubble. Reduce the heat and simmer gently for about 2 minutes until the oranges have softened slightly. Leave to cool in the syrup.

2 Drain the orange slices, reserving the syrup and star anise. Arrange the slices in 6 small, long-stemmed glasses. Remove the star anise from the syrup and reserve for decoration. Add the brandy to the syrup and spoon 2 tsp into each glass.

3 Whisk the cream in a bowl until peaking, then whisk in the yogurt. Gradually whisk in the syrup so the mixture just holds its shape. Spoon over the oranges and chill for several hours until ready to serve. Serve decorated with the star anise.

NUTRITIONAL ANALYSIS (per portion)	
Energy	210 cals
Protein	4.0 g
Carbohydrate	19.0 g
(of which sugars)	19.0 g
Fat	13.0g
(of which saturates)	8.0 g
Fibre	2.0 g

SUITABLE FOR:
GLUTEN-FREE AND NUT-FREE DIETS.

VARIATION:

If you want to reduce the fat content, a simple idea is to mix the oranges with all of the brandy-flavoured syrup, then serve topped with low-fat natural yogurt.

4 passionfruit, halved and flesh scooped out

125 g (4 oz) fresh lychees, peeled and stoned, or 425 g can, drained

1 large mango and 1 medium-sized ripe pineapple, peeled and sliced

2 bananas, peeled and thickly sliced

1 large egg, plus 2 large egg yolks

50 g (2 oz) caster sugar

6 tbsp sweet white wine or orange-flavoured liqueur

WARM TROPICAL FRUITS WITH SABAYON SAUCE

SERVES 4 • PREPARATION: 25 MINUTES • COOKING TIME: 15 MINUTES

1 Place all the fruit in 4 shallow 12 cm (5 inch) diameter dishes. Cover with foil and bake at 200°C (400°F) Mark 6 for 15 minutes.

2 Meanwhile, place the egg and yolks, sugar and sweet white wine in a heatproof ceramic bowl, then whisk until beginning to thicken. Place over a plan of simmering water, with the bowl just touching the water, and whisk for 10–15 minutes until fluffy: do not allow the mixture to become too hot, otherwise it will curdle. The sauce is ready when it is thick enough to leave a ribbon trail.

3 Remove the fruit from the oven and spoon the sauce over. Place under the grill until golden. Serve at once.

NUTRITIONAL ANALYSIS (per portion)	
Energy	250 cals
Protein	5.0 g
Carbohydrate	37.0 g
(of which sugars)	35.0 g
Fat	5.0 g
(of which saturates)	1.5 g
Fibre	2.0 g

SUITABLE FOR:
GLUTEN-FREE, LOW-FAT, NUT-FREE AND DAIRY PRODUCE-FREE DIETS.

NOTE: To save time you can omit the sauce, sprinkle the fruit with icing sugar and brown, reducing the calories to only 135 cals per serving.

75 g (3 oz) caster sugar
1 red chilli, deseeded
juice of 1 lime
1 piece stem ginger from
a jar, finely sliced
1 small ripe Galia melon
1 small ripe Charentais
melon
150 g (5 oz) red or green
grapes, halved and
seeded
low-fat yogurt, to serve

NOTE: *If you like strong,*
spicy flavours, chop the
chilli and sprinkle over the
salad, to give added bite.

MELON AND GRAPE SALAD IN CHILLI SYRUP

SERVES 6 • PREPARATION: 10 MINUTES, PLUS CHILLING • COOKING TIME: 8 MINUTES

1 Put the sugar in a small, heavy-based saucepan with 300 ml (½ pint) water. Heat gently until the sugar dissolves. Add the chilli and bring to the boil. Boil for 6–8 minutes until turning syrupy. Remove from the heat and stir in the lime juice and ginger. Leave to cool.

2 Halve the melons, discard the seeds, then remove the skins. Cut the flesh into small chunks and place in a large dish with the grapes.

3 Remove the chilli from the syrup (see Note), then pour the syrup over the fruit. Toss lightly, then cover and chill for several hours. Serve with yogurt.

NUTRITIONAL ANALYSIS (per portion)	
Energy	116 cals
Protein	1.0 g
Carbohydrate	30.0 g
(of which sugars)	30.0 g
Fat	0.2 g
(of which saturates)	0.0 g
Fibre	1.0 g

SUITABLE FOR:

GLUTEN-FREE, LOW-FAT, NUT-FREE, LOW-CHOLESTEROL, LOW-CALORIE AND DAIRY PRODUCE-FREE DIETS.

75 g (3 oz) dried stoned apricots

75 g (3 oz) dried stoned prunes

75 g (3 oz) dried figs

50 g (2 oz) plump sultanas

1 stick cinnamon

3 oranges

75 g (3 oz) stoned semi-dried dates

125 g (4 oz) kumquats, sliced

1 tsp rosewater

50 g (2 oz) roasted skinned almonds

HONEY GINGER YOGURT

300 ml (½ pint) Greek yogurt

1 tbsp runny orange blossom honey

2 tbsp stem ginger, finely chopped

DRIED FRUIT SALAD WITH HONEY GINGER YOGURT

SERVES 6 • PREPARATION: 15 MINUTES, PLUS SOAKING

1 Put the apricots, prunes, figs and sultanas in a serving bowl, add the cinnamon, cover with water and place in the refrigerator for 24 hours.

2 Peel 2 oranges, then cut into neat segments, removing the membranes and discarding the pips; reserve. Finely grate 1 tsp rind from the remaining orange, then squeeze out the juice.

3 Add the dates, kumquats, orange segments and rosewater to the bowl of soaked fruit. Pour over the orange juice and stir in the grated rind.

4 To make the honey ginger yogurt, mix the yogurt with the honey, then stir in the ginger.

5 To serve, sprinkle the roasted almonds over the compote and top with spoonfuls of honey yogurt.

NUTRITIONAL ANALYSIS (per portion)	
Energy	270 cals
Protein	7.0 g
Carbohydrate	43.0 g
(of which sugars)	43.0 g
Fat	9.0 g
(of which saturates)	3.0 g
Fibre	6.0 g

SUITABLE FOR:
GLUTEN-FREE AND LOW-CHOLESTEROL DIETS.

---

1 tbsp black peppercorns

125 g (4 oz) caster sugar

700 g (1½ lb) strawberries, hulled

2 tbsp balsamic vinegar

sliced strawberries and crushed peppercorns, to decorate

SPICED STRAWBERRY SORBET

SERVES 6 • PREPARATION: 35 MINUTES, PLUS STANDING AND FREEZING • COOKING TIME: 5 MINUTES

1 Using a pestle and mortar, coarsely grind the peppercorns. Place the sugar and 150 ml (¼ pint) water in a small saucepan and bring to the boil, stirring until the sugar has dissolved. Stir in the peppercorns, remove the pan from the heat, cover and allow to stand for 1 hour.

2 Strain the syrup through a fine sieve and discard the peppercorns. Place the syrup and strawberries in a blender or food processor and purée until smooth. Push the mixture through the sieve; discard seeds and bits. Stir in the vinegar.

3 Turn the mixture into a shallow, freezerproof container and freeze for about 2 hours until mushy.

4 Remove from the freezer and beat gently with a fork to break down the ice crystals. Freeze for another hour, then remove and beat again. Return to the freezer and freeze until firm.

5 Transfer the sorbet to the refrigerator for about 30 minutes. Serve, decorated with strawberries and crushed peppercorns.

NOTE: This sorbet has a deliciously tangy flavour and is also fat-free and low in calories.

NUTRITIONAL ANALYSIS (per portion)	
Energy	115 cals
Protein	0.9 g
Carbohydrate	29.0 g
(of which sugars)	29.0 g
Fat	0.1 g
(of which saturates)	0.0 g
Fibre	1.3 g

SUITABLE FOR:
GLUTEN-FREE, LOW-FAT, NUT-FREE, LOW-CHOLESTEROL, LOW-CALORIE, AND DAIRY PRODUCE-FREE DIETS.

2 large ripe mangoes

fresh orange juice, if needed

200 ml (7 fl oz) canned coconut milk

finely grated rind and juice of 2 limes

1 tsp almond essence

200 g (7 oz) Greek yogurt

75 g (3 oz) caster sugar

mango slices and pared lime rind, to serve

NOTE: Use an ice-cream maker for a really creamy, smooth flavour: churn the mixture at the end of step 2, then freeze until ready to use.

COCONUT AND MANGO ICED YOGURT

SERVES 6 • PREPARATION: 10 MINUTES, PLUS FREEZING

1 Halve the mangoes and scoop the flesh into a blender or food processor. Blend until smooth, then measure 500 ml (16 fl oz) into a measuring jug. If there is insufficient purée, add a little fresh orange juice.

2 Return the measured quantity to the food processor. Add the coconut milk, lime rind and juice, almond essence, yogurt and sugar and blend until evenly combined.

3 Pour the mixture into a shallow freezerproof container and put in the freezer until beginning to freeze around the edges. Transfer to a bowl and whisk lightly, then freeze again until frozen around the edges. Whisk and re-freeze once or twice more until the ice-cream is creamy. Re-freeze.

4 Transfer to the refrigerator about 30 minutes before serving. Serve in scoops, with extra mango slices and lime rind, if liked.

NUTRITIONAL ANALYSIS (per portion)	
Energy	230 cals
Protein	3.5 g
Carbohydrate	22.0 g
(of which sugars)	1.0 g
Fat	14.6 g
(of which saturates)	12.0 g
Fibre	1.3 g

SUITABLE FOR:
GLUTEN-FREE DIET.

350 g (12 oz) blackberries

75 g (3 oz) caster sugar

150 ml (¼ pint) red wine

50 ml (2 fl oz) crème de cassis

extra blackberries, to serve

BLACKBERRY GRANITA

SERVES 6 • PREPARATION: 15 MINUTES, PLUS FREEZING • COOKING TIME: 2 MINUTES

1 Place the blackberries in a saucepan with the sugar, wine, cassis and 150 ml (¼ pint) water. Bring to the boil and bubble for 1–2 minutes or until the fruit has softened.

2 Allow the mixture to cool for a few minutes, then strain the blackberries, reserving the juice. Place the blackberries in a blender or food processor and pulse until well broken down.

3 Sieve the cooled fruit and mix the purée with the reserved juice. Pour into a shallow, non-reactive metal container and freeze for at least 2½–3 hours or until the mixture is just firm. Stir after 2 hours to break up the ice crystals. Cover.

4 Place in the refrigerator for 15 minutes before serving. Use a spoon to break down the mixture, then serve in chilled glasses with extra berries.

NUTRITIONAL ANALYSIS (per portion)	
Energy	100 cals
Protein	0.6 g
Carbohydrate	17.0 g
(of which sugars)	17.0 g
Fat	0.1 g
(of which saturates)	0.0 g
Fibre	0.0 g

SUITABLE FOR:
GLUTEN-FREE, LOW-FAT, NUT-FREE, LOW-CHOLESTEROL, LOW-CALORIE AND DAIRY PRODUCE-FREE DIETS.

baking

350 g (12 oz) malted wholemeal flour

125 g (4 oz) strong plain flour

2 tsp salt

25 g (1 oz) fine oatmeal

2 tsp dark brown sugar

7 g sachet easy-blend dried yeast

150 ml (¼ pint) warm water

150 ml (¼ pint) skimmed milk

2 tbsp sunflower oil, plus extra for greasing

TO FINISH
beaten egg

15 g (½ oz) pumpkin seeds

MALTED WHOLEMEAL BLOOMER

MAKES 900 G (2 LB) LOAF • PREPARATION: 30 MINUTES, PLUS RISING • COOKING TIME: 40 MINUTES

1 Sift the flours and salt into a large mixing bowl, adding the bran left in the sieve. Stir in the oatmeal, sugar and yeast.

2 Make a well in the centre of the dry ingredients and add the water, milk and oil. Mix to form a soft dough, turn onto a lightly floured board and knead for 10 minutes, until smooth and elastic.

3 Place the dough in a lightly oiled bowl and cover with oiled cling film. Leave to rise in a warm place for 1½ hours or until doubled in bulk.

4 Knock back the dough for 5 minutes and shape into an oval about 25 cm (10 inches) long and 10 cm (4 inches) wide. Using a sharp knife, make 3 diagonal cuts across the top of the loaf. Place dough on a lightly greased baking sheet and cover with oiled cling film. Leave to rise for 15 minutes.

5 Just before baking, brush the loaf with beaten egg and sprinkle pumpkin seeds over the top.

6 Bake at 220°C (425°F) Mark 7 for 10 minutes. Reduce the oven temperature to 190°C (375°F) Mark 5 and continue to cook for a further 30 minutes. Cool on a wire rack.

NUTRITIONAL ANALYSIS	
(per portion)	
Energy	200 cals
Protein	6.9 g
Carbohydrate	36.0 g
(of which sugars)	2.5 g
Fat	4.0 g
(of which saturates)	0.6 g
Fibre	3.8 g

SUITABLE FOR:
LOW-FAT, NUT-FREE, LOW-CHOLESTEROL AND DIABETIC DIETS.

450 g (1 lb) malted wholemeal flour

450 g (1 lb) plain white flour

2 tsp salt

50 g (2 oz) sunflower seeds

2 tsp bicarbonate of soda

2 tsp cream of tartar

150 ml (¼ pint) buttermilk

1 tbsp runny honey

1 tbsp sunflower oil, plus extra for greasing

600 ml (1 pint) skimmed milk

1 tbsp bran

SUNFLOWER SEED SODA BREAD

MAKES 10 SLICES • PREPARATION: 20 MINUTES • COOKING TIME: 40 MINUTES

1 Sift the flours and salt into a large mixing bowl and stir in the sunflower seeds.

2 Mix the bicarbonate of soda and cream of tartar with a little buttermilk to make a smooth paste. Stir in the rest of the buttermilk with the honey and oil.

3 Make a well in the centre of the flour and pour in the buttermilk mixture and half of the skimmed milk. Gradually stir in the flour, adding more milk to form a soft, but not sticky dough. Do not knead.

4 Tip the dough on to a lightly greased baking sheet. Dust the top with a little extra flour and press the handle of a wooden spoon into the dough to form a cross. Sprinkle the bran over the top and bake at 190°C (375°F) Mark 5 for 35–40 minutes. Cool on a wire rack.

NUTRITIONAL ANALYSIS (per portion)	
Energy	362 cals
Protein	13.0 g
Carbohydrate	69.0 g
(of which sugars)	6.6 g
Fat	5.0 g
(of which saturates)	0.7 g
Fibre	5.8 g

SUITABLE FOR:
LOW-FAT, NUT-FREE, LOW-CHOLESTEROL AND DIABETIC DIETS.

Buttermilk ... low-fat

Buttermilk is very low in fat, containing less vitamin A than whole milk, but almost the same amount of protein.

---

125 g (4 oz) low-sugar muesli

150 ml (¼ pint) warm skimmed milk

75 g (3 oz) rye flour

75 g (3 oz) wholemeal flour

225 g (8 oz) strong white flour

25 g (1 oz) wheatgerm

1 tsp salt

1 tsp easy-blend dried yeast

½ tsp dark brown sugar

300 ml (½ pint) warm water

oil, for greasing

1 small egg, beaten

15 g (½ oz) pumpkin seeds, to finish

MUESLI BREAD

MAKES 6 SLICES • PREPARATION: 30 MINUTES, PLUS RISING • COOKING TIME: 45 MINUTES

1 Mix the muesli and milk together and allow to stand for 10 minutes.

2 Sift the flours, wheat germ and salt into a large mixing bowl. Stir in the yeast and sugar. Make a well in the centre, then add the muesli mixture and three quarters of the water. Mix together to form a soft dough, adding more water if necessary.

3 Turn the dough on to a lightly floured board and knead for 5–7 minutes or until smooth. Put in a lightly oiled bowl, cover with cling film and leave to rise for 1½ hours or until doubled in bulk.

4 Knock back the dough for 2–3 minutes. Divide the dough into 3 pieces and roll each piece into a sausage about 30 cm (12 inches) long, then plait together. Tuck the ends of the plait under and put on a floured baking sheet. Cover the dough with oiled cling film; leave to rise for 20 minutes.

5 Brush the plait with egg and sprinkle with pumpkin seeds. Bake at 200°C (400°F) Mark 6 for 45 minutes until the bread sounds hollow when tapped. Cool on a wire rack.

NUTRITIONAL ANALYSIS (per portion)	
Energy	325 cals
Protein	12.0 g
Carbohydrate	64.0 g
(of which sugars)	6.5 g
Fat	4.0 g
(of which saturates)	0.8 g
Fibre	6.0 g

SUITABLE FOR:
LOW-FAT, NUT-FREE, LOW-CHOLESTEROL AND DIABETIC DIETS.

350 g (12 oz) plain white flour

125 g (4 oz) wholemeal flour

1 tsp salt

1 tsp freshly ground black pepper

2 tsp easy-blend dried yeast

300 ml (½ pint) low-fat natural yogurt, at room temperature

1 tsp runny honey

75 ml (3 fl oz) warm skimmed milk, plus 4-6 tbsp

3 tbsp sunflower oil, plus extra for greasing

1 tbsp poppy seeds

1 tbsp caraway seeds

NOTE: The breads rise slightly during cooking, so do not place too high in the grill, otherwise they might catch the grill and burn.

POPPY SEED NAAN

MAKES 10 NAAN • PREPARATION: 25 MINUTES, PLUS RISING • COOKING TIME: 8 MINUTES

1 Sift the flours, salt and pepper into a large bowl and stir in the yeast. Make a well in the centre and add the yogurt, honey, milk and oil. Mix together to form a dough. Turn on to a lightly floured surface and knead for 3 minutes.

2 Place the dough into a lightly oiled bowl and cover with oiled cling film. Leave to rise in a warm place for 2 hours or until doubled in bulk.

3 Place the poppy and caraway seeds in a large frying pan and shake over a medium heat for 2–3 minutes to toast. Cool completely.

4 Turn the risen dough on to a floured board and add the toasted seeds, knead together until the seeds are well incorporated. Divide the dough into 10 pieces and flatten into ovals, about 18 cm (7 inches) long, with a rolling pin. Arrange on a floured baking sheet, cover with oiled cling film and leave to rise for 10 minutes.

5 Brush the tops of the naan with cold water and grill for 3 minutes on each side until golden brown (see Note). Cool on a wire rack.

NUTRITIONAL ANALYSIS (per portion)	
Energy	210 cals
Protein	7.0 g
Carbohydrate	38.0 g
(of which sugars)	4.0 g
Fat	5.0 g
(of which saturates)	0.8 g
Fibre	2.0 g

SUITABLE FOR:
LOW-FAT, NUT-FREE, LOW-CHOLESTEROL AND DIABETIC DIETS.

1 large egg

200 ml (7 fl oz) Greek yogurt

25 g (1 oz) butter, melted

150 g (5 oz) fine cornmeal

25 g (1 oz) potato flour

1 tbsp gluten-free baking powder

1 tsp salt

pinch of cayenne pepper

1 large red chilli, deseeded and finely chopped

75 g (3 oz) spring onions, trimmed and finely sliced

125 g (4 oz) sweetcorn

50 g (2 oz) freshly grated Parmesan cheese

NOTE: This tasty bread is suitable for anyone on a wheat-free diet.

CHILLI CORNBREAD

MAKES 10 SLICES • PREPARATION: 20 MINUTES, PLUS COOLING • COOKING TIME: 45 MINUTES

1 Base-line a 450 g (1 lb) non-stick loaf tin with non-stick baking parchment. In a large bowl, whisk the egg until frothy, then stir in the yogurt and melted butter.

2 Stir in the cornmeal, potato flour, baking powder, salt and cayenne pepper. Add the remaining ingredients and mix until thoroughly combined.

3 Turn the mixture into the prepared tin and bake at 180°C (350°F) Mark 4 for 45 minutes or until a skewer inserted into the centre comes out clean.

4 Allow the cornbread to cool in the tin for 10 minutes, then turn out on to a cooling rack. When completely cold, cut into slices and serve.

NUTRITIONAL ANALYSIS (per portion)	
Energy	150 cals
Protein	6.0 g
Carbohydrate	16.0 g
(of which sugars)	1.5 g
Fat	6.5 g
(of which saturates)	3.5 g
Fibre	1.0 g

SUITABLE FOR:
GLUTEN-FREE AND DIABETIC DIETS.

VARIATION:

For butternut squash loaf, use 125 g (4 oz) cooked, mashed butternut squash instead of the sweetcorn and Parmesan cheese.

25 g (1 oz) fresh yeast

375 ml (13 fl oz) warm water

500 g (1 lb 2 oz) strong plain flour

1 tsp salt

pinch of cayenne pepper

10 garlic cloves, unpeeled

1 tbsp olive oil, plus extra for greasing and brushing

5 tsp chopped fresh rosemary

½ tsp rock salt

ROAST GARLIC AND ROSEMARY ITALIAN BREAD

SERVES 6 • PREPARATION: 25 MINUTES, PLUS RISING • COOKING TIME: 50 MINUTES

1 Dissolve the yeast in the water. Sift the flour, salt and cayenne pepper into a large bowl, make a well in the centre and add the water. Gradually draw in the flour to form a dough. Turn the mixture on to a lightly floured board and knead for 6 minutes.

2 Put the dough in a lightly oiled bowl, cover with oiled cling film and leave to rise in a warm place for 45 minutes, or until doubled in bulk.

3 Meanwhile, place the garlic in a roasting tin, add the olive oil and toss together. Cook at 180°C (350°F) Mark 4 for 15 minutes, or until soft.

4 Peel the cooked garlic and chop roughly. Mix with 4 tsp rosemary and rock salt; allow to cool. Gently knead the mixture through the risen dough, then shape into a round ball shape. Brush lightly with olive oil; sprinkle over the remaining rosemary.

5 Cover the dough with oiled cling film and leave to rise for a further 5 minutes; remove cling film.

6 Bake at 220°C (425°F) Mark 7 for 10 minutes. Reduce the temperature to 190°C (375°F) Mark 5 and continue to cook for a further 30–40 minutes.

7 Remove the bread from the oven and cool.

NUTRITIONAL ANALYSIS (per portion)	
Energy	300 cals
Protein	8.0 g
Carbohydrate	66.0 g
(of which sugars)	1.5 g
Fat	3.0 g
(of which saturates)	0.5 g
Fibre	2.5 g

SUITABLE FOR:

LOW-FAT, NUT-FREE, LOW-CHOLESTEROL, DAIRY PRODUCE-FREE AND DIABETIC DIETS.

Garlic... high scorer

Garlic gets the highest score of the allium family for health-promoting properties. It contains a significant amount of protein, carbohydrate and dietary fibre. Research suggests garlic may help to prevent coronary heart disease, provided it is eaten raw, regularly and in large amounts.

350 g (12 oz) wholemeal flour

125 g (4 oz) pinhead oatmeal

2 tsp bicarbonate of soda

1 tsp salt

1 tsp runny honey

300 ml (½ pint) buttermilk

2-3 tbsp milk

SODA BREAD

SERVES 6 • PREPARATION: 15 MINUTES • COOKING TIME: 35 MINUTES

1 Combine all the dry ingredients in a large bowl. Make a well in the centre and gradually beat in the honey, buttermilk and enough milk to form a soft dough.

2 Transfer to a lightly floured surface and knead for 5 minutes. Shape the dough into a 20 cm (8 inch) round and place on an oiled baking sheet.

3 Using a sharp knife, cut a deep cross on top of the dough. Brush with a little extra milk and bake at 200°C (400°F) Mark 6 for 30–35 minutes until the bread is slightly risen and sounds hollow when tapped underneath. Cool on a wire rack and serve the same day.

NUTRITIONAL ANALYSIS (per portion)	
Energy	290 cals
Protein	12.0 g
Carbohydrate	56.0 g
(of which sugars)	5.0 g
Fat	3.5 g
(of which saturates)	0.5 g
Fibre	7.0 g

SUITABLE FOR:
LOW-FAT, NUT-FREE, LOW-CHOLESTEROL AND DIABETIC DIETS.

---

125 g (4 oz) hazelnuts

450 g (1 lb) stone ground wholemeal flour

450 g (1 lb) unbleached strong plain flour

2 tsp salt

7 g sachet easy-blend dried yeast

600 ml (1 pint) warm water

1 tbsp hazelnut oil

vegetable oil, for greasing

2 tbsp stoneground wholemeal flour, to finish

HAZELNUT BAPS

MAKES 16 BAPS • PREPARATION: 30 MINUTES, PLUS RISING • COOKING TIME: 25 MINUTES

1 Toast the hazelnuts at 190°C (375°F) Mark 5 for 15 minutes. Remove from the oven and roll in a clean tea-towel to loosen and remove the skins. and roughly chop.

2 Sift the flours and salt into a large warm mixing bowl, adding the bran left in the sieve. Stir in the yeast. Make a well in the centre. Add the water and oil and mix to a soft dough. Turn on to a lightly floured surface and knead for 5–7 minutes, or until the dough is smooth and elastic.

3 Place the dough in a lightly oiled bowl and cover with cling film. Leave to rise in a warm place for 1 hour, or until doubled in bulk.

4 Turn the risen dough on to a lightly floured surface and sprinkle over the nuts. Knead the nuts into the dough, until well incorporated. Divide the dough into 16 pieces. Shape into oval baps and arrange on a floured baking sheet. Cover with lightly oiled cling film and rise for 10 minutes.

5 Sprinkle the top of the baps with wholemeal flour. Bake for 25 minutes at 210°C (425°F) Mark 7 until they are golden and sound hollow when tapped. Remove from the oven and immediately cover with a clean tea-towel. Cool for 20 minutes.

NUTRITIONAL ANALYSIS (per portion)	
Energy	240 cals
Protein	7.0 g
Carbohydrate	40.0 g
(of which sugars)	1.5 g
Fat	6.5 g
(of which saturates)	0.5 g
Fibre	4.0 g

SUITABLE FOR:
LOW-CHOLESTEROL, DAIRY PRODUCE-FREE AND DIABETIC DIETS.

225 g (8 oz) red fleshed
sweet potato, peeled and
cut into chunks

150-200 ml (5-7 fl oz)
skimmed milk

1 tsp runny honey

450 g (1 lb) strong white
plain flour

2 tsp salt

7 g sachet easy-blend
dried yeast

2 eggs, beaten

oil, for greasing

a little beaten egg, to
glaze

poppy seeds, for
sprinkling

SWEET POTATO BREAD ROLLS

MAKES 16 ROLLS • PREPARATION: 35 MINUTES, PLUS RISING • COOKING TIME: 12 MINUTES

1 Cook the sweet potato in boiling salted water for 10 minutes or until tender. Drain well, then mash until smooth. Stir in the milk and honey and leave to cool until tepid.

2 Sift the flour and salt into a large bowl. Stir in the yeast, make a well in the centre of the flour and add the sweet potato mixture and beaten eggs. Mix to form a smooth dough.

3 Turn the dough on to a lightly floured surface. Knead for 10 minutes until the dough is elastic.

4 Place the dough in a lightly oiled bowl and cover with oiled cling film. Set in a warm place to rise for 1 hour or until doubled in bulk.

5 Knock back the risen dough for 5 minutes. Divide into 16 pieces and shape into rolls. Arrange on a floured baking sheet, cover with oiled cling film and leave to rise for 10 minutes.

6 Brush the rolls with a little beaten egg, then sprinkle with poppy seeds. Bake at 200°C (400°F) Mark 6 for 12 minutes. Cool on a wire rack.

NUTRITIONAL ANALYSIS (per portion)	
Energy	128 cals
Protein	4.0 g
Carbohydrate	27.0 g
(of which sugars)	3.0 g
Fat	1.3 g
(of which saturates)	0.3 g
Fibre	1.3 g

SUITABLE FOR:
LOW-FAT, NUT-FREE, AND DIABETIC DIETS.

2 tbsp runny honey

150 ml (¼ pint) warm water

225 g (8 oz) strong plain flour

1 tsp salt

2 tsp easy-blend dried yeast

250 g (9 oz) can cooked chestnuts, finely chopped

oil, for greasing

½ tsp ground cardamom

50 g (2 oz) mixed candied peel, finely chopped

TO FINISH
2 tbsp runny honey

1 tbsp sesame seeds

CHESTNUT BREAD

MAKES 10 SLICES • PREPARATION: 25 MINUTES, PLUS RISING • COOKING TIME: 35 MINUTES

1 Stir the honey into the water. Sift the flour and salt into a large mixing bowl, stir in the yeast and half of the chestnuts. Make a well in the centre and add the honey water. Mix to form a soft dough.

2 Turn the dough on to a lightly floured work surface and knead the dough for 8–10 minutes or until smooth and elastic. Turn into a lightly oiled bowl, cover with cling film and leave to rise in a warm place for 1–1½ hours or until doubled in bulk.

3 Mix the remaining chestnuts with the cardamom and candied peel.

4 Turn the risen dough on to a lightly floured board and knead for 2-3 minutes. Using a floured rolling pin, roll the dough to a 25 cm (10 inch) square. Sprinkle the chestnut mixture over the surface. Roll the dough up like a Swiss roll and transfer to a lightly oiled baking sheet. Cover with oiled cling film and leave to rise for 20 minutes.

5 Bake the bread for 30 minutes at 200°C (400°F) Mark 6. Brush with the honey and sprinkle with sesame seeds. Return to the oven for a further 5 minutes, allowing the seeds to brown.

6 Turn on to a wire rack and allow to cool.

NUTRITIONAL ANALYSIS (per portion)	
Energy	167 cals
Protein	3.0 g
Carbohydrate	37.0 g
(of which sugars)	12.0 g
Fat	2.0 g
(of which saturates)	0.3 g
Fibre	2.1 g

SUITABLE FOR:
LOW-FAT, NUT-FREE, LOW-CHOLESTEROL, DAIRY PRODUCE-FREE AND DIABETIC DIETS.

---

125 g (4 oz) dried apricots, roughly chopped

125 g (4 oz) dried apples, roughly chopped

125 g (4 oz) dried stoned prunes, roughly chopped

about 300 ml (½ pint) strong fruit tea

butter, for greasing

25 g (1 oz) stem ginger, chopped

225 g (8 oz) plain white flour

2 tsp baking powder

125 g (4 oz) soft dark brown (muscovado) sugar

1 egg

GINGER FRUIT TEA BREAD

MAKES 12 SLICES • PREPARATION: 15 MINUTES, PLUS SOAKING • COOKING TIME: 1 HOUR

1 Cover the chopped fruit with the tea. Leave to soak for at least 2 hours, stirring occasionally. Grease and base-line a 900 g (2 lb) loaf tin.

2 Place all the ingredients in a large bowl and mix to combine thoroughly.

3 Turn the mixture into the tin, level the surface and brush lightly with 2 tbsp cold water. Cook at 180°C (350°F) Mark 4 for 1 hour or until cooked through (if necessary, cover after 30 minutes to prevent over-browning).

4 Leave the cake in the tin for 10–15 minutes, then transfer to a wire rack to cool.

NUTRITIONAL ANALYSIS (per portion)	
Energy	165 cals
Protein	3.0 g
Carbohydrate	39.0 g
(of which sugars)	25.0 g
Fat	0.9 g
(of which saturates)	0.2 g
Fibre	3.0 g

SUITABLE FOR:
LOW-FAT, NUT-FREE, LOW-CHOLESTEROL AND DAIRY PRODUCE-FREE DIETS.

NOTE: This moist tea bread is virtually fat-free. The fruit also increases the fibre content.

butter for greasing
(optional)

50 g (2 oz) raisins

grated rind and juice of
1 orange

125 g (4 oz) wholemeal
flour

25 g (1 oz) wheatgerm

3 tbsp caster sugar

2 tsp baking powder

pinch of salt

1 large egg, beaten

50 ml (2 fl oz) milk

50 ml (2 fl oz) sunflower
oil

2 medium-sized ripe
bananas, about 225 g
(8 oz) when peeled,
roughly mashed

TOPPING

5 tbsp orange marmalade

50 g (2 oz) banana chips

50 g (2 oz) roughly
chopped walnuts

*NOTE: These are perfect
for those on cholesterol-
lowering or diabetic diets.*

WHOLEMEAL BANANA MUFFINS

*MAKES 6 MUFFINS • PREPARATION: 15
MINUTES, PLUS SOAKING • COOKING TIME:
25 MINUTES*

1 Line 6 muffin tins with paper muffin cases or grease the tins well. Place the raisins in a bowl, pour the orange juice over, then soak for 1 hour.

2 Place the orange rind in a bowl with the next 5 ingredients and mix together. Make a well in the centre.

3 In a separate bowl, mix the egg, milk and oil, then pour into the flour mixture and stir until just blended. Drain the raisins, reserving 1 tbsp juice, and stir into the mixture with the bananas. Do not over-mix.

4 Fill each muffin case two-thirds full. Bake at 200°C (400°F) Mark 6 for 20–25 minutes or until a skewer inserted into the centre comes out clean. Transfer the muffins to a wire rack to cool slightly.

5 For the topping, gently heat the marmalade with the reserved orange juice until melted. Simmer for 1 minute, then add the banana chips and walnuts. Spoon on top of the muffins. Serve warm.

NUTRITIONAL ANALYSIS (per portion)	
Energy	370 cals
Protein	7.0 g
Carbohydrate	52.0 g
(of which sugars)	34.0 g
Fat	16.0 g
(of which saturates)	2.0 g
Fibre	4.0 g

SUITABLE FOR:
LOW-CHOLESTEROL AND
DIABETIC DIETS.

125 g (4 oz) butter, plus a little extra for greasing

150 g (5 oz) wholemeal flour

125 g (4 oz) soft dark brown (muscovado) sugar

432 g (15 oz) can pineapple in natural juice, drained and roughly chopped

2 eggs

2 tsp baking powder

¼ tsp mixed spice

50 g (2 oz) desiccated coconut

extra desiccated coconut and icing sugar, to decorate

PINEAPPLE AND COCONUT LOAF

MAKES 10 SLICES • PREPARATION: 20 MINUTES • COOKING TIME: 50 MINUTES

1 Grease and base-line a 450 g (1 lb) loaf tin.

2 Place the flour and sugar in a food processor and blend for 1–2 minutes or until well mixed. Add the remaining ingredients and mix until smooth.

3 Turn the mixture into the prepared tin, level the surface and brush lightly with 2 tbsp cold water. Cook at 180°C (350°F) Mark 4 for 50 minutes or until cooked (if necessary, cover after 40 minutes).

4 Allow the cake to cool in the tin for 10 minutes, then transfer to a wire rack to cool. Decorate with a little desiccated coconut and icing sugar.

NUTRITIONAL ANALYSIS (per portion)	
Energy	250 cals
Protein	4.0 g
Carbohydrate	28.0 g
(of which sugars)	19.0 g
Fat	15.0 g
(of which saturates)	10.0 g
Fibre	2.0 g

SUITABLE FOR:
DIABETIC DIET.

---

175 g (6 oz) butter, plus extra for greasing

3 large oranges

225 g (8 oz) caster sugar

2 eggs, beaten

200 g (7 oz) rice flour

2 tsp gluten-free baking powder (see Note)

75 g (3 oz) ground almonds

300 ml (½ pint) orange juice

2 tbsp lemon juice

pared and blanched orange rind, to decorate (optional)

ORANGE SYRUP CAKE

MAKES 10 SLICES • PREPARATION: 30 MINUTES, PLUS COOLING AND SOAKING • COOKING TIME: 45 MINUTES

1 Grease and base-line a 20 cm (8 inch) shallow, round tin. Finely grate the rind of 1 orange and set aside.

2 Cream the butter and 75 g (3 oz) of the sugar, then beat in the eggs gradually. Fold in the rice flour, baking powder and ground almonds. Stir in the grated orange rind and 10 tbsp orange juice (the mixture should be of a soft, dropping consistency).

3 Bake at 190°C (375°F) Mark 5 for 40 minutes or until firm. Cool in the tin for 10 minutes, then transfer to a wire rack.

4 Just before serving, peel the remaining oranges and thickly slice. To make the syrup, combine the remaining sugar and orange juice plus the lemon juice in a small pan. Add the orange slices, bring to the boil and cook for 1–2 minutes. Off the heat, cool for 5 minutes. Remove the orange slices from the syrup and set aside.

5 Place the cake on a serving plate and, with a cocktail stick, prick the cake in a number of places. Drizzle over the syrup and soak for 30 minutes. Serve the cake with the orange slices and decorated with orange rind, if wished.

NOTE: This moist cake is made with rice flour and is a real treat for those on a gluten-free diet! Gluten-free baking powder is available from larger supermarkets.

NUTRITIONAL ANALYSIS (per portion)	
Energy	360 cals
Protein	5.0 g
Carbohydrate	46.0 g
(of which sugars)	30.0 g
Fat	20.0 g
(of which saturates)	10.0 g
Fibre	2.0 g

SUITABLE FOR:
GLUTEN-FREE DIET.

Right: Orange Syrup Cake

125 g (4 oz) butter, plus extra for greasing

125 g (4 oz) gluten-free plain chocolate, broken into pieces (see Notes)

200 g (7 oz) light soft brown (muscovado) sugar

2 eggs

120 ml (4 fl oz) natural yogurt

a drop of vanilla essence

200 g (7 oz) brown rice flour

½ tsp wheat-free baking powder (see Notes)

1 tsp bicarbonate of soda

ICING

300 g (10 oz) gluten-free plain chocolate, broken into pieces

300 ml (½ pint) reduced-fat double cream

CHOCOLATE CAKE

MAKES 10 SLICES • PREPARATION: 40 MINUTES, PLUS COOLING • COOKING TIME: ABOUT 1 HOUR

1 Grease and base-line an 18 cm (7 inch) round, deep cake tin with greaseproof paper.

2 Place the chocolate in a heatproof bowl over a pan of simmering water. Stir occasionally until melted. Allow to cool slightly.

3 Cream the butter and sugar until light and fluffy. Lightly whisk the eggs, then beat into the butter mixture with the melted chocolate, yogurt and vanilla essence. Sift together the flour, baking powder and bicarbonate of soda. Beat into the cake mixture a little at a time.

4 Turn the mixture into the prepared tin and bake at 180°C (350°F) Mark 4 for 45–60 minutes or until a skewer inserted into the centre comes out clean. Leave to cool in the tin for 10 minutes.

5 For the icing, place the chocolate in a heatproof bowl. Heat the cream to boiling point and pour over the chocolate. Leave for 5 minutes, then beat until smooth. Allow to cool, then spread over cake.

NUTRITIONAL ANALYSIS
(per portion)

Energy	550 cals
Protein	6.0 g
Carbohydrate	65.0 g
(of which sugars)	48.0 g
Fat	31.0 g
(of which saturates)	19.0 g
Fibre	1.5 g

SUITABLE FOR:
GLUTEN-FREE AND NUT-FREE DIETS.

NOTES: Bournville Plain Chocolate is gluten free; available from supermarkets and confectioners. Certain large supermarkets stock wheat-free baking powder. Gluten- and wheat-free flours, such as the brown rice flour used here, are available from specialist suppliers.

---

175 g (6 oz) butter, plus extra for greasing

225 g (8 oz) caster sugar

½ tsp vanilla essence

225 g (8 oz) self-raising flour

½ tsp salt

2 tsp baking powder

150-175 ml (5-6 fl oz) milk

3 tbsp Ener-G Egg Replacer (see Note)

50 g (2 oz) chopped walnuts

apricot jam, fresh fruit and whipped cream, to serve

sieved icing sugar, to dust

NOTE: This egg-free cake uses an egg replacer, which is low-protein and cholesterol-free.

WALNUT CAKE

MAKES ABOUT 10 SLICES • PREPARATION: 20 MINUTES • COOKING TIME: 35 MINUTES

1 Grease and base-line two 20 cm (8 inch) Victoria sandwich tins.

2 Cream together the butter, sugar and vanilla essence until fluffy. In another bowl, sift the flour, salt and baking powder. Beat the flour mixture and milk into the creamed mixture, a little at a time.

3 Place the egg replacer and 6 tbsp water in a large bowl and, using an electric whisk, beat until it forms soft peaks. Fold into the cake mixture with the chopped walnuts.

4 Turn the mixture into the tins and bake at 180°C (350°F) Mark 4 for 30–35 minutes or until a skewer inserted into the centre comes out clean.

5 Cool in the tins for 5–10 minutes, then transfer to a wire rack to cool completely. Spread one of the cakes with jam; top with fruit and cream. Top with the second cake and dust with icing sugar.

NUTRITIONAL ANALYSIS
(per portion)

Energy	370 cals
Protein	3.4 g
Carbohydrate	42.0 g
(of which sugars)	24.0 g
Fat	18.0 g
(of which saturates)	10.0 g
Fibre	0.9 g

SUITABLE FOR:
LOW-CHOLESTEROL DIET.

CINNAMON SPONGE WITH BLUEBERRIES

SERVES 6 • PREPARATION: 30 MINUTES, PLUS COOLING • COOKING TIME: 30 MINUTES

3 eggs

75 g (3 oz) caster sugar

1 tbsp tepid water

75 g (3 oz) plain white flour

1 tsp ground cinnamon

FILLING

150 ml (¼ pint) half-fat double cream

1 tbsp icing sugar

4 tbsp Greek yogurt

75 g (3 oz) blueberries, washed and halved

1 tbsp chopped fresh mint

TO FINISH

3 tbsp redcurrant jelly

150 g (5 oz) blueberries, washed and dried

1 tbsp icing sugar

5 sprigs of fresh mint, to decorate

1 Grease two 18 cm (7 inch) sandwich tins and base-line with non-stick baking parchment.

2 Place the eggs, sugar and water in a large heatproof glass bowl and place over a saucepan of hot water. Whisk for 6–7 minutes until very thick and mousse-like. Remove from the heat and continue whisking for 5 minutes or until cool.

3 Sift the flour and cinnamon together and carefully fold into the mousse mixture. Turn into the tins. Bake at 180°C (350°F) Mark 4 for 25 minutes. Allow to stand in the tins for 5 minutes, then turn on to a cooling rack to cool completely.

4 For the filling, whip the cream with the icing sugar to form soft peaks. Fold in yogurt, berries and mint and use to sandwich the cakes together.

5 To finish, warm the redcurrant jelly in a small pan, add the blueberries and coat well. Arrange the blueberries on top of the cake, dust with the icing sugar and decorate with sprigs of mint.

NUTRITIONAL ANALYSIS (per portion)	
Energy	235 cals
Protein	7.0 g
Carbohydrate	34.0 g
(of which sugars)	24.0 g
Fat	9.0 g
(of which saturates)	4.5 g
Fibre	1.5 g

SUITABLE FOR:
NUT-FREE DIET.

50 g (2 oz) plain flour

1 tbsp cornflour

100 g (3½ oz) caster sugar

5 large egg whites

¼ tsp salt

½ tsp cream of tartar

½ tsp vanilla extract

½ tsp rosewater

seeds from 3 large cardamom pods, finely crushed

grated rind of 1 lemon

low-fat fromage frais, berries and sun-dried pineapple slices, to serve

icing sugar, to dust (optional)

LEMON ANGEL CAKES

MAKES 18 TRIANGLES • PREPARATION : 20 MINUTES, PLUS COOLING • COOKING TIME: 35 MINUTES

1 Grease and base-line an 18 cm (7 inch) square cake tin with non-stick baking parchment. Sift the flour, cornflour and 50 g (2 oz) sugar into a bowl.

2 Whisk the egg whites with the salt, cream of tartar, vanilla extract, rosewater and 1 tbsp cold water until stiff and glossy. Sift the flour mixture over the egg white and carefully fold in with the crushed cardamom seeds and grated lemon rind. Spoon into the prepared tin and level the surface.

3 Bake at 170°C (325°F) Mark 3 for 35 minutes or until firm to the touch and the cake has shrunk from the sides of the tin. Loosen round the sides and flip the tin upside down on to a cooling rack, leaving the cake in the tin to cool.

4 Remove the cake and cut into 9 squares, then halve to make 18 triangles. Serve plain or with fromage frais, berries and pineapple.

NUTRITIONAL ANALYSIS	
(per portion)	
Energy	35 cals
Protein	1.0 g
Carbohydrate	9.0 g
(of which sugars)	6.0 g
Fat	0.0 g
(of which saturates)	0.0 g
Fibre	0.1g

SUITABLE FOR:

LOW-FAT, NUT-FREE, LOW-CHOLESTEROL AND DAIRY PRODUCE-FREE DIETS.

50 g (2 oz) plain white flour

50 g (2 oz) plain wholemeal flour

pinch of salt

50 g (2 oz) ground rice

125 g (4 oz) sunflower margarine

50 g (2 oz) golden caster sugar

finely grated rind of 1 orange

50 g (2 oz) walnuts, chopped

WALNUT AND ORANGE SHORTBREAD BISCUITS

MAKES 15 BISCUITS • PREPARATION: 20 MINUTES, PLUS COOLING • COOKING TIME: 15 MINUTES

1 Sift the flours and salt together, adding the bran left in the sieve. Stir in the ground rice.

2 Cream the margarine, sugar and orange rind until light and fluffy. Stir in the dry ingredients with the walnuts and mix to a soft dough. Turn out on to a lightly floured surface and knead for a few seconds until smooth.

3 Shape the dough into a cylinder about 15 cm (6 inches) long. Wrap in cling film and chill in the refrigerator for at least 1 hour.

4 Using a sharp knife, cut the dough into 15 slices and place, slightly apart, on a lightly greased baking sheet.

5 Bake in the oven at 190°C (375°F) Mark 5 for 15 minutes until lightly browned. Leave on the baking sheet for 5 minutes, then transfer to a wire rack to cool.

NUTRITIONAL ANALYSIS (per portion)	
Energy	95 cals
Protein	1.5 g
Carbohydrate	11.0 g
(of which sugars)	4.0 g
Fat	5.0 g
(of which saturates)	0.8 g
Fibre	0.6 g

SUITABLE FOR:
DAIRY PRODUCE-FREE DIET.

50 g (2 oz) butter

2 tbsp runny honey

275 g (10 oz) filo pastry

50 g (2 oz) pistachio nuts, toasted and roughly chopped

1 egg white, lightly beaten

1 tbsp icing sugar

a few extra chopped pistachio nuts, to decorate

NOTE: These unusual little sweet biscuits are surprisingly low in calories, so indulge yourself!

PISTACHIO 'CIGARS'

MAKES 24 BISCUITS• PREPARATION: 30 MINUTES • COOKING TIME:10 MINUTES

1 Melt the butter in a small saucepan with the honey. Lay out the sheets of filo pastry and cut 24 rectangles, each about 12 x 23 cm (5 x 9 inches). Brush the pastry strips with the honey butter and sprinkle with the toasted pistachio nuts. Turn in the edges and then roll up to make long thin 'cigars'.

2 Mix the egg white with the icing sugar and brush over the 'cigars', then sprinkle with a few extra chopped pistachio nuts.

3 Place on a non-stick baking sheet and cook in the oven at 200°C (400°F) Mark 6 for 10 minutes or until they are golden brown and crisp.

NUTRITIONAL ANALYSIS (per portion)	
Energy	55 cals
Protein	0.7 g
Carbohydrate	3.5 g
(of which sugars)	2.0 g
Fat	4.0 g
(of which saturates)	2.0 g
Fibre	0.2 g

SUITABLE FOR:
DAIRY PRODUCE-FREE DIET.

125 g (4 oz) butter, plus a little extra for greasing

350 g (12 oz) porridge oats

125 g (4 oz) unsweetened desiccated coconut

75 g (3 oz) pecans, chopped

100 g (3½ oz) raisins

1 tsp cinnamon

½ tsp allspice

½ tsp freshly grated nutmeg

125 g (4 oz) light brown (muscovado) sugar

175 g (6 oz) honey or maple syrup

3 bananas

juice of 1 lemon

200 g (7 oz) dates, preferably Mejool, stoned and chopped

BANANA AND DATE MUESLI BARS

MAKES 18 BARS • PREPARATION: 15 MINUTES • COOKING TIME: 30 MINUTES

1 Grease a baking tray, measuring 25 x 33 cm (10 x 13 inches) and 2.5 cm (1 inch) deep.

2 Mix the oats, coconut, pecans, raisins and spices together in a bowl. Place the butter, sugar and honey in a small saucepan and heat until the butter has melted and the sugar has dissolved. Pour over the oat mixture in the bowl and mix until well combined.

3 Divide the mixture in half. Press one half of the mixture over the base of the greased tin.

4 Thinly slice the bananas, mix with the lemon juice and chopped dates, then spread over the oat layer. Top with the remaining oat mixture, spreading it evenly. Bake at 180°C (350°F) Mark 4 for 25-30 minutes until golden brown. Leave to cool in the tin.

5 Turn out on to a board and cut into 18 bars.

NUTRITIONAL ANALYSIS (per portion)	
Energy	315 cals
Protein	4.0 g
Carbohydrate	44.0 g
(of which sugars)	29.0 g
Fat	15.0 g
(of which saturates)	8.0 g
Fibre	3.0 g

SUITABLE FOR:
DAIRY PRODUCE-FREE DIET.

NOTE: Full of fibre and very sustaining, these bars are excellent for packed lunches.

150 g (5 oz) butter, plus a little extra for greasing

150 g (5 oz) gluten-free plain chocolate, such as Bournville

1½ tsp instant coffee granules

150 g (5 oz) caster sugar

3 eggs, separated

60 g (2½ oz) ground almonds

75 g (3 oz) walnuts

60 g (2½ oz) cornflour

NOTE: These brownies are gluten-free and will keep for two to three days.

CHOCOLATE BROWNIES

MAKES 9 BROWNIES • PREPARATION: 25 MINUTES, PLUS COOLING • COOKING TIME: 55 MINUTES

1 Grease and line an 18 cm (7 inch) square tin.

2 Melt the chocolate and coffee over a pan of simmering water. Leave to cool slightly.

3 Cream the butter and sugar, then beat in the egg yolks, one at a time. Fold in the almonds, walnuts, cornflour and melted chocolate mixture. Whip the egg whites to a soft peak and fold in gently.

4 Pour the mixture into the prepared tin, then bake at 180°C (350°F) Mark 4 for about 55 minutes. (It is cooked when a skewer inserted into the centre comes out clean.) Cover with greaseproof paper after 30 minutes. Leave in the tin for 10 minutes, then transfer to a wire rack to cool.

NUTRITIONAL ANALYSIS (per portion)	
Energy	425 cals
Protein	6.0 g
Carbohydrate	35.0 g
(of which sugars)	28.0 g
Fat	30.0 g
(of which saturates)	13.0 g
Fibre	0.8 g

SUITABLE FOR:
GLUTEN-FREE DIET.

75 g (3 oz) butter, plus extra for greasing

200 g (7 oz) demerara sugar

175 g (6 oz) ground rice

2 large eggs

pinch of salt

1-2 drops vanilla essence

75 g (3 oz) desiccated coconut

75 g (3 oz) chopped hazelnuts

3 tbsp apricot or raspberry jam, plus extra for brushing

COCONUT SQUARES

MAKES 10 SQUARES • PREPARATION: 10 MINUTES, PLUS COOLING • COOKING TIME: 35 MINUTES

1 Grease a 28 x 18 cm (11 x 7 inch) shallow cake tin.

2 Cream together the butter and 75 g (3 oz) sugar until light and fluffy. Stir in 150 g (5 oz) of the ground rice. Spread the mixture into the prepared tin and bake at 180°C (350°F) Mark 4 for 15 minutes. Leave in the tin to cool for a few minutes.

3 Lightly beat the eggs. Add the remaining sugar, rice, salt, vanilla essence, desiccated coconut and chopped hazelnuts. Mix well. Spread the jam over the base, followed by the egg mixture. Return to the oven for a further 20 minutes.

4 Allow to cool, then brush with a little warmed jam. Cut into squares. Leave in the tin to cool completely before serving.

NUTRITIONAL ANALYSIS (per portion)	
Energy	325 cals
Protein	4.0 g
Carbohydrate	40.0 g
(of which sugars)	25.0 g
Fat	17.0 g
(of which saturates)	9.0 g
Fibre	2.0 g

SUITABLE FOR:
GLUTEN-FREE DIET.

AILMENTS AND DIET

ARTHRITIS

The word arthritis means inflammation of a joint. There are many different forms of arthritis, of which the most common are osteoarthritis (OA) and rheumatoid arthritis (RA). OA is a disease in which joint cartilage cracks and flakes away, while RA is caused by inflammation of the joint lining (synovial membrane).

A LOW-FAT DIET

Because being overweight can increase the risk of arthritis of the knee by as much as seven times, those with arthritis should attempt to lose any excess weight by following a healthy, low-fat diet, and thereby help reduce the strain on painful weight-bearing joints.

REDUCING INFLAMMATION

Plenty of fruit and vegetables providing antioxidant vitamins and minerals which help to mop up free radicals associated with inflammation are recommended. Oily fish (eg salmon, mackerel, herrings, sardines) contains essential fatty acids that reduce inflammation and have been found to be helpful for rheumatoid arthritis.

Another beneficial dietary supplement is glucosamine sulphate, which can help OA by regenerating cartilage and improving the production of synovial fluid – the joint's oil – so it becomes thicker and more protective. Celery is often used to help arthritis and is said to have anti-inflammatory properties. A few patients with rheumatism are sensitive to dairy products, but this is not very common.

CRAMP

Cramp – a painful muscle spasm most often occurring in the legs – is linked with a poor circulation that allows lactic acid and other waste products to build up. This may result from hardening and furring up of the arteries, from immobility at night during sleep, or from lying in an awkward position that reduces blood flow to the lower limbs. Cramp can also occur after eating a heavy meal when blood is diverted away from muscles towards the gut to help the process of digestion – the main reason why swimming is not recommended within an hour of eating.

AVOIDANCE TECHNIQUES

To help avoid cramp, drink plenty of fluids during the day – at least 2 litres. Recurrent night cramps can often be relieved by increasing intakes of calcium in the form of dairy products or sardines, and magnesium, found in nuts and seeds. A poor circulation can be improved by eating foods rich in vitamin E (eg wholegrains, avocado), garlic and oily fish (eg sardines, herrings, mackerel, salmon) three times a week. Supplements that may help include ginkgo extracts, omega-3 fish oils and co-enzyme Q10 which increases oxygen uptake in muscle cells.

GOUT

Gout is a common problem that affects ten times more men than women. It is caused by a fault in the way the body handles a natural chemical, purine, so that blood levels of uric acid increase. Crystals of uric acid then precipitate in the joints, and sometimes the soft tissues, to produce extremely painful swellings. The joint at the base of the big toe is most commonly affected.

ACID FOODS

Drink plenty of fluids but avoid heavy consumption of alcohol which may precipitate an attack. People suffering from gout are advised to steer clear of foods high in uric acid, such as fish roe, shellfish, sardines and liver, and to avoid overly acid foods. Cherries have been found to help lower uric acid and prevent attacks of gout if eaten regularly. Follow a diet rich in green leafy vegetables. Omega-3 fish oil supplements may help.

Eat more...
Cherries; dark green leafy vegetables.

Avoid...
Alcohol, fish roe, shellfish, sardines and liver.

JOINT PROBLEMS

Painful joint problems other than arthritis may be due to sports injuries, frozen shoulder, bursitis (housemaid's knee) or overuse or strain of tendons and ligaments (eg tennis elbow). If you suffer from any of the above, keep body weight within the recommended range for your height to minimise the strain on weight-bearing joints.

TREAT YOURSELF

Adopt a diet rich in antioxidants such as vitamin C, found in citrus fruits, kiwi fruit, blackcurrants and strawberries, vitamin E (wheat germ, avocado, nuts), beta-carotene (orange-green fruit and vegetables) and selenium (Brazil nuts, wholegrains and cereals). Omega-3 fish oils have been proven to reduce joint inflammation and pain.

Eat more...
Foods high in vitamin C (eg citrus and kiwi fruits). Foods high in vitamin E (eg wheat germ, avocado and nuts), plus omega-3 fish oils.

Avoid...
Rich, fatty food or sugary foods that will cause weight gain.

OSTEOPOROSIS

Osteoporosis affects over 3 million people in the UK. It occurs when insufficient new bone is produced to replace that which is naturally broken down and remodelled as part of normal bone metabolism.

Osteoporosis is strongly linked to diet and lifestyle and may also run in families. It is often associated with post-menopausal women, who become more susceptible to the disease when their supplies of oestrogen become depleted. Good intakes of calcium are vital for strong bones throughout life – particularly in childhood and adolescence when bones are still developing. To avoid the condition, eat plenty of calcium-rich foods such as milk, yogurt, cheese, green vegetables and white or brown bread. The easiest way to obtain enough calcium is to drink at least a pint of skimmed or semi-skimmed milk a day. Avoid excessive intakes of alcohol, which reduce absorption of dietary calcium from the gut.

Eat more...
Fresh fruit and vegetables, oily fish, liver, eggs and butter.

Avoid or cut down on...
Salt, red meat and canned fizzy drinks.

IMPORTANT MICRONUTRIENTS

Fruit and vegetables contain important micronutrients that are vital for bone health such as beta-carotene, boron, copper, folic acid, magnesium, manganese, potassium, silica, vitamin C and zinc. Try to eat at least 2–3 servings of oily fish (eg mackerel, herring, salmon, trout, sardines or pilchards) per week as these are rich in vitamin D and essential fatty acids that encourage calcification of bones. Other dietary sources of vitamin D include liver, eggs, butter, fortified milk and fortified margarine/spreads. Beneficial essential fatty acids are also found in evening primrose, sunflower, rapeseed, olive and most nut oils (except peanut). Cut back on table salt as this increases loss of calcium through the kidneys. Heavy consumption of meat seems to reduce absorption of dietary calcium and is also linked with osteoporosis. Avoid canned fizzy drinks that contain phosphoric acid, as high intakes can increase loss of calcium from the bones.

Eat more...
Foods rich in vitamins B,C and E.
Foods rich in manganese, selenium and magnesium.

RHEUMATISM

Rheumatism is an imprecise term used to describe a range of musculoskeletal aches and pains. The term is sometimes used to describe an inflammation of the muscles also known as fibrositis or fibromyalgia which can be a debilitating condition causing widespread aches and pains plus sleep disturbance. Women are five times more likely to suffer than men. The pains tend to move from place to place, vary in severity and are often made worse by cold and stress. Sufferers develop localised areas of tenderness known as trigger points, especially around the lower spine, between the shoulder blades, at the base of the neck, over the sacro-iliac joints, elbows and knees. In some people, these tender spots develop fibrous nodules.

ANTI-INFLAMMATORY FOODS

A diet rich in magnesium (soya beans, nuts, wholewheat flour, brown rice, seafood, dark green leafy vegetables) may help, as can the B-group vitamins (eg wholegrain cereals), manganese (tea, wholegrains, nuts and seeds) and supplements containing co-enzyme Q10. Antioxidants are important to reduce inflammation. These are present in vitamin C-rich foods such as citrus fruits, kiwi fruit, blackcurrants and strawberries, vitamin E-rich foods (eg wheat germ, avocado, nuts, seeds), beta-carotene (eg orange-green fruit and vegetables) and selenium (eg Brazil nuts, wholegrains, cereals).

Instant treatment...

Eating foods laced with the spice turmeric has been shown to reduce inflammation for some rheumatism sufferers.

GASTRO-RELATED PROBLEMS

COELIAC DISEASE

Coeliac disease results from a sensitivity to gluten, a protein found in cereals, including wheat, rye, barley and oats. The condition seems to be a hypersensitivity to gliadin, a polypeptide found in gluten. This may be a direct toxic effect or be triggered by an over-zealous immune system – possibly brought on in susceptible people by exposure to a particular virus.

Gluten sensitivity can start at any age and affects around one person in 130. The condition is most commonly diagnosed in the third to fourth decade and affects more females than males. It often runs in families. If symptoms develop in childhood, growth may be affected due to poor absorption of nutrients from the gut.

SPOTTING THE SYMPTOMS

Symptoms of coeliac disease vary and can include tiredness, feeling unwell, abdominal pain, bloating and wind, diarrhoea, vomiting, weight loss and passing pale, bulky, offensive, fatty stools. These symptoms are due to abnormal changes in the lower part of the small intestine, the jejunum, brought on by exposure to dietary gluten. Following a gluten-free diet (see page 104) produces a rapid improvement within a few weeks, but the diet must be continued for life to keep symptoms at bay. Vitamin and mineral supplements are important to guard against nutrient deficiency.

COLIC

Colic, a severe stomach pain that comes and goes in waves, is most often associated with babies. It is thought to be linked with a build up of wind that triggers painful contractions of the intestinal muscles, but the cause is not fully understood. It often appears around the third or fourth week after birth and usually disappears by the age of four months. Episodes tend to be worse during the night.

A baby with colic will usually be irritable and difficult to console, cry or scream excessively, become tense or rigid and draw their legs up towards the stomach. The baby will otherwise seem well, will not have a fever and will be gaining weight and generally thriving. The baby may have a rumbling, bloated stomach and gain relief after passing wind.

SOME SOLUTIONS

Try giving gripe water containing dill seed extracts, or a little diluted fennel or chamomile tea before feeding. Some bottle-fed babies improve if taken off cow's milk formula – ask your doctor or health visitor for advice. Some breast-fed babies improve if the mother avoids dairy products but it is important to seek nutritional advice before trying this to ensure that enough calcium and other nutrients found in milk are obtained from other sources. Always seek medical advice if a baby seems to be ill, is failing to gain weight or develops diarrhoea, constipation, vomiting or a fever.

Eat more...
Fresh fruit and vegetables.

Avoid...
All foods containing gluten.

Herbal suggestion...
Try giving the baby a little diluted fennel or chamomile tea from a teat pipette before feeding.

Eat more...
Prunes, figs, pears,
rhubarb.
Drink more water.

CONSTIPATION

Constipation is usually defined as passing bowel motions less than twice a week, or straining at stool for more than 25% of the time. It is a common and distressing condition that, in many cases, is linked with a poor dietary intake of fibre or fluids. Fluids help dietary fibre to swell and provide bulk which enables bowel content to be pushed along the intestines more easily. An increased intake of fibre-rich foods (page 102) such as wholegrain cereals, wholemeal bread, pulses, fresh fruit, vegetables, nuts and seeds will help ease constipation, as will drinking one glass of water before each meal, plus another two or three between meals to bulk up a fibre-rich diet.

Natural laxatives include figs, prunes, pears, rhubarb, molasses, linseed and aloe vera juice. A persistent change in bowel habit occurring in someone over the age of 40 should always be reported to a doctor to rule out the possibility of a more serious underlying disorder.

An old-
fashioned
remedy...

Aloe vera juice is said to
help Crohn's disease.

CROHN'S DISEASE

Crohn's disease is an inflammatory disease that can affect any part of the intestines from the mouth to the anus. Swelling and ulceration of the bowel wall causes symptoms that can include pain, fever, diarrhoea and loss of weight. The cause is unknown but it may be linked with a dietary allergy, or an overactive immune response to a viral or bacterial infection. Some people with Crohn's disease find that particular foods such as cereals, dairy products and yeast can make their condition worse.

Research suggests that a sugar-free, unrefined diet containing plenty of oily fish, fruit and vegetables can help, although avoiding fibre may be beneficial during a flare-up of symptoms. Fish oil supplements seem to help damp down inflammation and can improve symptoms. Some specialists recommend a high-vitamin, low-fibre diet.

Eat more...
Live yogurt.
Drink plenty of water to
avoid dehydration.

DIARRHOEA

Diarrhoea causes loose stools and an increased frequency of bowel motions. It may be caused by an infection, an underlying bowel disorder or a food sensitivity. Common dietary causes of diarrhoea are food poisoning and sensitivity to milk proteins (eg casein) or milk sugar (lactose), so it is usual to advise that children with diarrhoea should avoid milk until symptoms have improved.

Yogurt may be given, as bacterial fermentation has already broken the lactose down so it is more easily digested. Live bio-yogurt containing friendly bacteria such as Lactobacillus is especially beneficial. These bacteria help to replenish the healthy bowel bacteria that have been flushed away and can speed recovery where diarrhoea is due to infection.

AVOIDING DEHYDRATION

People with diarrhoea should drink plenty of fluids to avoid dehydration. Electrolyte solutions help to replenish salts that have been flushed away. If a bout of diarrhoea lasts longer than a few days, or if it occurs in a baby, always seek medical advice as infants can quickly become dehydrated and this could be dangerous.

DIVERTICULITIS

Diverticulae are outpouchings that form in the wall of the large bowel due to constipation and straining. When these become infected and inflamed, the condition is known as diverticulitis. Diverticulitis causes symptoms of pain, fever, vomiting and diarrhoea which need medical treatment. The normal contractions of the bowel may be affected and could lead to constipation. If faeces become trapped in the pouches the resulting inflammation may need treatment with antibiotics.

VEGETARIAN ANSWER?

It is important to eat a high-fibre diet and drink plenty of water. A diet high in vegetables and wholegrain cereals may help to prevent diverticular disease as the disorder is around 30% less common in vegetarians, who invariably consume more fibre. Cut back on refined foods and eat more wholegrain products such as wholemeal bread, muesli, porridge and brown rice. Other fibre-rich foods include pulses, vegetables, fresh and dried fruit, nuts and seeds. A high-fibre diet, plenty of fluids and using laxatives to help stop straining will help to relieve the symptoms.

FLATULENCE

Flatulence is caused by a build-up of wind in the intestines which burbles around to cause pain, distension and embarrassing noises (borborygmi) before escaping – sometimes explosively. Most intestinal gas is released during bacterial fermentation of undigested fibre in the large bowel, which releases hydrogen, carbon dioxide, methane and sometimes foul-smelling sulphur-containing gases such as hydrogen sulphide. Small amounts of intestinal gas also come from fizzy drinks and air swallowed with food.

WHAT A GAS!

As much as 1–2.5 litres of gas is expelled through the rectum daily and research suggests that most people pass gas 12–20 times per day. Flatulence is usually caused by abnormal motility of the intestines and disordered passage of wind through the gut, rather than to the production of excess gas. Flatulence can also be a sign of lactose intolerance (see Diarrhoea), and may improve after following a lactose-free diet.

FOODS TO AVOID

If you are prone to flatulence, try avoiding foods that promote bacterial fermentation and gas production such as beans, lentils, cauliflower, cabbage, broccoli, Brussels sprouts and cucumber. Eat meals slowly, chewing each mouthful thoroughly, and avoid fizzy drinks.

Many natural herbs and spices contain substances that calm the bowels, relieve spasm and prevent a build-up of wind. These include aniseed, chamomile, lemon balm, clove, dill, fennel, black pepper, marjoram, parsley, peppermint, rosemary and spearmint. Use them as a garnish on food or as soothing, herbal teas. Live bio-yogurt containing friendly Lactobacillus bacteria can also help.

An old-fashioned remedy...

Taking peppermint, chamomile or ginger tea after meals may help to sooth inflammation and relax intestinal muscles to relieve pain.

Foods to avoid...
Beans, lentils, milk and milk products, onions, beans, celery, carrots, cabbage, broccoli, Brussels sprouts, raisins, bananas, apricots, wheat germ.

FOOD POISONING

Food poisoning is usually caused by eating or drinking contaminated food or liquids. Some cases are due to infection with a virus or bacteria, while others can be put down to the effects of poisons such as those produced by Staphylococcal bacteria, toxic plankton and some types of mushroom. Occasionally, food poisoning is non-infective and due to chemical pollutants. Symptoms usually come on within 30 minutes in the cases of chemical poisoning, between 1 and 12 hours if the illness is due to bacterial toxins, and between 12 and 48 hours if it results from a bacterial or viral infection. Food poisoning after eating shellfish is especially common as viruses, bacteria, toxins or chemicals may be involved.

PREVENTATIVE ACTION

Symptoms of food poisoning include stomach pains, vomiting and diarrhoea. In severe cases, fever or even collapse can occur. Keeping food refrigerated helps to prevent infective food poisoning by slowing bacterial growth. A rise in temperature from just 4–8°C increases bacterial growth by as much as 65%. Reheating cooled dishes, or only partially cooking products also encourages bacterial growth.

Regularly eating garlic and live bio-yogurt containing bowel-friendly bacteria such as Lactobacilli can help to keep food poisoning at bay. Avoid raw and lightly-cooked eggs, especially if pregnant, weak or unwell in any way, very young or elderly. Pregnant women should also avoid pâté, soft-rinded and blue cheeses and undercooked meat to reduce the risk of infection with Listeria and Toxoplasmosis. Mild cases of food poisoning are treated by drinking plenty of fluids and electrolytes (available from chemists) to avoid dehydration. If symptoms are more severe, seek medical advice, especially in the case of children.

Eat more...
Olive oil, globe artichokes and oily fish.

Avoid or cut down on...
Refined carbohydrates, fatty foods; any known triggers.

GALLSTONES

Gallstones are solid collections of material that form in the gall bladder. Most gallstones are made of cholesterol, although some contain high amounts of bile pigments or calcium salts. They are four times more common in women than men, and it is estimated that one in five women develop gallstones at some time in their life. The gallbladder stores bile – a substance made in the liver that helps the digestion and absorption of dietary fats. When eating a fatty meal, the gallbladder contracts to squirt bile into the gut. If the gallbladder contains gallstones these may be pushed into the duct opening leading from the gallbladder, causing severe pain. Eight out of ten people with gallstones do not develop symptoms, however.

LOSE THE FAT

Those with gallstones are usually advised to follow a diet low in saturated fat and to lose any excess weight. Olive oil is a rich source of oleic acid, a monounsaturated fat that has a beneficial effect on blood cholesterol balance. A regular intake may help to prevent gallstones. Some research suggests that avoiding refined (processed) carbohydrate foods may reduce the risk of gallstones, as may cynarin, a substance found in globe artichokes.

GASTROENTERITIS

Gastroenteritis means inflammation of the stomach or intestines and is another term used to describe food poisoning (page 358). It is especially likely when travelling abroad – up to 50% of visitors to tropical regions are affected. A few simple dietary steps can help to reduce the risks:

- For drinking, brushing your teeth, preparing food or cooking, use water from sealed bottles. Carbonated is safer than still water as it's less likely to have been filled from the tap. Alternatively, use freshly boiled and cooled water sterilised with purification tablets.

- Avoid green salads and uncooked vegetables.

- Only eat fruits that can be peeled.

- Avoid ice-cubes, unless made from safe water.

- Avoid ice creams from unreliable sources.

- Avoid unpasteurised milk – boil if unsure.

- Wash hands thoroughly before eating.

- Avoid food exposed to the sun or to flies.

- Avoid snacks bought from roadside vendors.

INDIGESTION

Indigestion and heartburn are common and unpleasant symptoms linked with eating. Indigestion usually describes discomfort or burning felt centrally in the upper abdomen, while heartburn is felt behind the chest bone. One of the commonest causes of heartburn is acid reflux, in which the stomach contents reflux up into the oesophagus. Acid reflux causes hot, burning sensations that usually start within 30 minutes of eating a meal and may be triggered by eating too much, taking exercise too soon after eating, bending or lying down.

COMMON CULPRITS

Meals containing fat, pastry, chocolate, acidic fruit juices, coffee or alcohol are the commonest culprits. To avoid indigestion, follow a healthy, high-fibre diet and eat little and often throughout the day, rather than having three large meals. Avoid hot, acid, spicy or fatty foods and cut down on tea, coffee, acidic fruit juices and alcohol. Try to keep the body upright as much as possible after eating. If you suffer from recurrent indigestion or heartburn, it is important to tell your doctor.

Avoid or cut down on...
Fatty, sugary or acidic foods.
Tea, coffee and alcohol.

Eat more...
Fresh fruit and vegetables, nuts, seeds, figs, prunes, peas and beans.
Unrefined carbohydrates (eg wholegrain breads and breakfast cereal, brown rice and pasta).

Avoid or cut down on...
Red meat and acidic foods (eg oranges, grapefruit, vinegar and tomatoes).

IRRITABLE BOWEL SYNDROME

Irritable bowel syndrome (IBS) is the most common condition to affect the gut. It causes intermittent abdominal discomfort which may be associated with wind, bloating, constipation or diarrhoea. The exact cause is unknown, but it seems to be linked with abnormal or exaggerated bowel movements and muscular spasm. IBS affects at least a third of the population, even if only mildly. Overall, 15% of people are affected badly enough to consult their doctor. Increasing fibre intake will usually help to relieve constipation but may make flatulence or bloating worse. Overall, following a high-fibre diet helps around one-third of people with IBS.

SELF-HELP TIPS

To relieve the symptoms of IBS it is important to eat as many different sources of fibre as possible, as well as more complex, unrefined carbohydrates such as wholegrain bread, wholemeal pasta, brown rice and unsweetened wholegrain breakfast cereals like muesli or porridge. It is also beneficial to increase intakes of fresh fruit and vegetables – especially nuts, seeds, figs, apricots, prunes, peas, sweetcorn and beans. Cutting down on red meat and eating more fish and skinless white meat in its place improves symptoms for some people. Live bio-yogurt containing Lactobacilli often helps. Some people with IBS are sensitive to acid foods such as oranges, tomatoes and vinegar.

JAUNDICE

Jaundice is a yellow pigmentation of the skin and the whites of the eyes caused by a build up of the bile pigment, bilirubin, in the blood. It is quite common in newborn babies as their bodies adjust to life outside the womb, and in these cases it usually disappears without treatment after about a week.

In adults, however, jaundice is often more serious. It may be a sign of a liver disease (eg hepatitis), a blockage of the system which drains bile from the liver (perhaps due to gallstones) or to excess breakdown of the red blood pigment, haemoglobin, from which bilirubin is made (eg haemolytic anaemia). As jaundice is a sign that the liver may be under strain, it is important to avoid alcohol which is broken down in the liver and which can poison liver cells if taken in excess. If jaundice is due to haemolytic anaemia, foods rich in iron and protein such as fish and poultry help. When jaundice is due to severe liver disease such as liver failure, a low-sodium, high-protein diet is advised.

LIVER PROBLEMS

The liver is an important organ that metabolises dietary fats and amino acids, makes bile and blood proteins, maintains blood sugar levels, stores fat-soluble vitamins and removes poisonous chemicals from the blood. Liver cells can be damaged by a diet that is rich in fats, alcohols and sugar which should be avoided. A diet rich in antioxidants such as vitamin C (eg citrus fruits), vitamin E (eg wheat germ, avocado) and beta-carotene (eg yellow-orange fruits) is important for liver health, as are B group vitamins (eg liver, fish, wholegrains) and folic acid-rich green leafy vegetables. Cynarin, a substance found in globe artichokes, may help to improve liver function.

An old-fashioned remedy...
A glass of fresh beetroot juice a day will help improve the flow of bile.

GENERAL AILMENTS

CANCER

Cancer is responsible for 25% of deaths in the industrialised world. Poor diet, low in antioxidant vitamins and fibre and high in saturated fat, is probably to blame for over a third of all cancers. The risk of developing the disease can be significantly reduced by stopping smoking, losing excess weight, taking regular exercise, keeping alcohol intake within safe limits and avoiding sunburn.

To protect against cancer, follow a low-fat, high-fibre diet and eat at least five portions of fruit and vegetables per day. This will provide the recommended amounts of antioxidants such as vitamins C, E and the mineral selenium. Those with the highest blood levels of these agents have the lowest risk of cancer. Reduce your intake of salt-cured, salt-pickled and smoked foods, as these have been linked with an increased risk.

FOODS TO FIGHT CANCER

Protective plant chemicals have been identified in many fruit and vegetables:

■ Broccoli contains sulphoraphane, which has a powerful anti-cancer effect, especially against tumours of the digestive tract, lungs and prostate gland.

■ Cherries, strawberries and grapes contain ellagic acid that helps to protect against cancer by blocking an enzyme needed for growth of the cancer cell.

■ Red and black grapes are especially beneficial as they contain antioxidant pigments that are more powerful than vitamins C or E.

■ Chillies contain antioxidants, including capsaicin, that also protect against coronary heart disease, cancer and premature ageing .

■ Tomatoes contain lycopene, a pigment that is a powerful antioxidant and may protect against cancer.

■ Citrus fruits are an excellent source of vitamin C, while lemons are a rich source of limonene – a phytochemical that protects against cancer.

■ Garlic – studies in China suggest those who regularly eat up to 20 g fresh garlic per day have the lowest rate of stomach cancer.

■ Fish oils have also been shown to halt the growth of some cancer cells, reduce the risk of intestinal polyps and reverse weight loss in cancer patients.

Eat more...
Fresh fruit and vegetables (especially those containing antioxidants), garlic and fish oils.

Avoid or cut down on...
Smoked, pickled or salt-cured foods.

DIABETES

Diabetes is a condition in which blood glucose levels rise due to insufficient production of the hormone insulin. Symptoms include thirst, dry mouth, having to pass increased amounts of urine, and – in younger patients – loss of weight. Older people who get diabetes later in life usually have a milder form that may be associated with being overweight.

People with diabetes no longer need to keep to a special 'diabetic' diet, but are advised to follow the same healthy eating guidelines as everyone else, with a diet that is high in fibre, low in fat, and avoids excess sugar. It is important to eat regular meals, especially if receiving insulin, so that blood sugar levels do not fall too low (see page 116).

Drink more...
Water, fruit and vegetable juices.

FAINTING

Fainting is a temporary loss of full consciousness due to lack of oxygen to the brain. The most common cause is a vaso-vagal attack in which the vagus nerve, which helps to control the heart rate, is overstimulated. This slows the pulse and reduces blood pressure. Warning symptoms include sweating, nausea, dizziness, weakness, loss of vision and ringing in the ears. Vaso-vagal attacks are triggered by a shock, stress, pain, fear, prolonged coughing, dehydration and prolonged standing – especially in a stuffy atmosphere or in a warm, crowded room.

EAT LITTLE AND OFTEN

Fainting is more likely in someone who has missed a meal, thereby causing their blood sugar level to fall. To avoid this, eat little and often during the day and never skip meals, especially if pregnant or when menstruating. Drink plenty of fluids – carrot and other vegetable or fruit juices are excellent for providing potassium salts which help prevent vaso-vagal attacks. Anyone who feels faint should sit down and put their head between their legs so that blood rushes to the brain. If they are unconscious, lie them down, raise their legs above chest level and seek medical assistance.

FATIGUE

Fatigue affects an increasing number of people who admit to feeling tired all the time. When this state occurs after a viral illness, it is known as post viral fatigue syndrome.

If you eat the right types of food, you will gain a natural energy boost from your diet. If you eat the wrong foods, however, you will quickly feel bloated, sluggish and fatigued. The foods that can pep you up are also those that are recommended for healthy eating such as:

■ Crusty wholegrain breads – especially those with added nuts and seeds.

■ Wholegrain cereals such as porridge, brown rice, pearl barley, oatcakes, unsweetened breakfast cereals.

■ Root vegetables, eg carrots, parsnip, turnip, swede, potatoes.

■ Cruciferous plants, eg broccoli, cauliflower, Chinese leaves.

■ Legumes, eg lentils, kidney beans, soya beans.

■ Fresh fruits, eg avocado, banana, melon, plums, grapes, orange, pineapple.

■ Ready-to-eat semi-dried apricots, dates, figs, prunes.

■ Oily fish.

■ Virgin olive oil.

■ Nuts – especially walnuts – and seeds.

■ Honey (in moderation).

Research shows that eating fatty foods for breakfast can leave you feeling tired, sluggish and with poor concentration throughout the morning. If you then have a fatty lunch, you will function below par all day. Foods that can drag you down include:

■ Fatty, sugary snacks, eg doughnuts, pastries.

■ Fatty, salty snacks, eg crisps, pork pies, salami, pizza.

■ Cakes, biscuits and confectionery.

■ Red meat.

■ Alcohol.

■ Caffeine-containing products.

CAFFEINE: THE ENERGY DRAINER

Caffeine is now recognised as one of the great energy drainers. In the short term it gives a quick, alerting boost but in the long term it can lead to caffeine poisoning with symptoms of restlessness, insomnia, headache, anxiety and fatigue. Caffeine mimics the effects of stress in the body and raises blood levels of stress hormones such as adrenaline and cortisol. It is now also known to take away a natural safety valve by blocking the effects of a calming brain chemical, adenosine. Adenosine also has other actions in the body, including regulating blood flow through coronary arteries, transmission of nerve signals, immunity and the storage and production of energy. Overall, adenosine helps to balance the body's response to stress. If its actions are blocked by excess caffeine, you will succumb to the effects of stress more quickly and start to feel drained of energy.

HIGH-ENERGY FOODS

The B-group of vitamins are especially important for energy production. Good sources include yeast extract, wheat germ, wholegrain bread and cereals, brown rice, pulses, nuts, dark green vegetables, meat, dairy products and seafood. Some women experience fatigue because of low iron levels caused by heavy, frequent periods, pregnancy, bad diet or a poor ability to absorb and store iron. Good sources of iron include red meat, seafood – especially sardines – wholemeal bread and green vegetables. Overboiling vegetables decreases their iron yield by up to 20%. An increased intake of vitamin C helps the body to absorb iron, so it is a good idea to drink a glass of fresh orange juice with your breakfast boiled egg. Likewise, iron absorption is blocked by tannin, so never wash down your iron-containing foods or supplements with a mug of tea.

Eat more...
Organic wholefoods.

Avoid or cut down on...
Foods containing artificial colourings, flavourings or preservatives.

Herbal suggestions...
Oil of evening primrose supplements have proved useful. Chamomile tea can also help counteract sleeplessness.

HYPERACTIVITY IN CHILDREN

Hyperactivity – also known as attention deficit hyperactivity disorder (ADHD) – causes children to be continually inattentive, restless and impulsive. The Hyperactive Children's Support Group state that the most important step in helping a child with ADHD is through nutrition – they recommend a wholefood, organic diet which excludes as many artificial colourings, flavourings and preservatives as possible. Any dietary lack of vitamins (A, B complex, C, D, E), minerals (calcium, magnesium manganese, zinc, chromium, selenium and cobalt) and especially essential fatty acids should be corrected.

DIET AND ADHD

Many children with ADHD seem to be lacking in essential fatty acids (EFAs), either because they cannot absorb dietary EFAs normally from their gut, because their EFA requirements are higher than normal, or because their body cannot handle EFAs properly. Over 80% of children given evening primrose oil supplements improve so they are no longer hyperactive. Once the child is following a wholefood diet, the Support Group then recommend gradually cutting out foods containing white flour, sugar and colourings, and replacing these with more nutritious foods. Food should only be sweetened when absolutely necessary. Drinking and cooking water should ideally be filtered to remove all impurities. Foods that seem to upset the child should also be avoided. In one study, when hyperactive children were given a diet excluding common allergens such as wheat, yeast, egg, chocolate, peanuts and artificial colourings and flavours, their hyperactivity ratings dropped by over two-thirds.

However, any parent considering dietary treatment for ADHD should not proceed without consulting a dietician for advice.

INFERTILITY

Infertility is one of the commonest reasons for referral to hospital in adults under 40. As many as one in four women experience difficulty in conceiving at some time – one in eight while trying for their first baby. Both prospective parents should take steps to become as fit and healthy as possible before trying to conceive. A good intake of vitamins and minerals can be built up by following a wholefood and preferably organic diet with plenty of fresh fruit, vegetables, nuts, seeds, cereals and pulses.

PROSPECTIVE FATHERS

Prospective fathers should ensure a good intake of antioxidants such as vitamin C (eg citrus fruits, kiwi fruit, berry fruits), vitamin E (eg wheat germ, avocado, wholegrain cereals) and selenium (eg Brazil nuts, broccoli, mushrooms, wholegrains). Zinc is important for sperm health and fertility and is found in red meat, seafood – especially oysters – wholegrains and pulses.

PROSPECTIVE MOTHERS

Prospective mothers should take a supplement especially designed for the pre-conceptual period which includes folic acid (see Spina bifida, page 381). If you need to lose weight, do so sensibly and slowly and ensure that your diet includes a good intake of vitamins and minerals. Other important lifestyle changes include reducing alcohol consumption, as even a moderate intake is linked with infertility, and stopping smoking, as smokers are only half as fertile as non-smokers. Most important of all, smoking could damage the health of a developing foetus.

KIDNEY DISORDERS

The kidneys help to maintain the body's salt and fluid balance and diet can play an important role in preventing or treating kidney problems. Dehydration, for example, may cause salts to crystallise in the urinary tract to form kidney stones, so it is important to drink 2–3 litres of fluid daily – more in hot weather or if exercising briskly.

Eat more...
Low-protein foods.

Avoid or cut down on...
Dairy products, and foods rich in oxalates, sodium, potassium or phosphorus.

WHAT TO CUT BACK ON

Anyone with a tendency to make kidney stones may benefit from cutting back on foods rich in oxalate such as almonds, beans, beetroot, rhubarb, chocolate, peanuts, spinach and strawberries. They may also be advised to restrict calcium intake by cutting back on dairy foods. People with some types of kidney disorder may be advised to follow a low-protein diet, while others require reduced intakes of sodium, potassium or phosphorus.

MALNUTRITION

Malnutrition is thought of as a Third World problem, yet in the developed world 9 out of 10 people fail to get all the essential fatty acids, vitamins and minerals they need from their diet. While this does not cause severe symptoms of deficiency, it can impair immunity, increase the risk of infections, slow wound healing and lead to fatigue.

Eat more..
Fresh fruit and vegetables, and oily fish.

SOME REASONS FOR MALNUTRITION

Poor intakes of vitamins and minerals may be due to not eating enough fruit and vegetables, to eating produce grown on nutrient-poor soils or produce which has been stored then overcooked, depleting its nutrient content even further. Those following strict slimming diets, elimination diets to treat allergies and elderly people who are living alone may have more serious malnutrition, with insufficient protein and energy intake.

Aim to eat as wide a variety of foods as possible – enough to maintain a healthy body weight – and containing plenty of wholegrains, pulses, fruits, vegetables and salad stuff. While diet should always come first, some people – such as those trying to lose weight – should also consider taking a good multi-nutrient supplement providing around 100% of the RDA for as many vitamins and minerals as possible. Eat oily fish regularly, or take an omega-3 or evening primrose oil supplement.

ME

ME or myalgic encephalomyelitis is also known as post-viral fatigue syndrome or chronic fatigue syndrome. The exact cause is unknown but it is linked with feelings of extreme weakness, fatigue and loss of energy. A diet providing plenty of complex unrefined carbohydrates such as wholemeal bread, wholewheat pasta, porridge oats and brown rice and potatoes can help, as these have a low to moderate glycaemic index and help to maintain steady blood sugar levels over a period of time.

The B-group of vitamins are especially important for energy production. Good sources include yeast extract, wheat germ, wholegrain bread and cereals, brown rice, pulses, nuts, dark green vegetables, meat, dairy products and seafood. Up to 80% of people with ME are helped by taking high doses of evening primrose and fish oils which are rich in essential fatty acids. Some have also benefited from multinutrient supplements containing iron, magnesium, folic acid and zinc. Many also find that it helps to eat a wholefood, additive-free and preferably raw fruit and vegetable diet, while taking care to avoid caffeine, alcohol and smoking.

METABOLIC DEFECTS

Many different congenital metabolic disorders can occur as a result of inheriting a faulty or missing gene needed for making certain enzymes, or for metabolising dietary amino acids, sugars or fatty acids. Some, such as phenylketonuria (PKU), can be controlled by following a strict exclusion diet. PKU for example necessitates following a diet that contains low amounts of the amino acid phenylalanine.

MOUTH ULCERS

Mouth ulcers affect as many as one in five people at any one time. They are most common between the ages of 10 and 40, and seem to affect more women than men. The usual cause is aphthous ulceration – painful sores on the inside of the cheeks, lips or underneath the tongue which are usually oval shaped with a grey centre and red surround.

Most mouth ulcers usually heal within 7–10 days. Their exact cause is unknown, but they have been linked with hypersensitivity to a common mouth bacterium, haemolytic Streptococcus. They may also be a sign of gluten sensitivity, so it may help to follow a gluten-free diet. Soreness and cracking at the corners of the mouth where the lips meet may be due to iron deficiency.

Eat more...
Foods rich in B-group vitamins (eg yeast extract, wheat germ, brown rice and pulses).
Complex unrefined carbohydrates (eg wholemeal bread, wholewheat pasta, porridge oats and potatoes).

Eat more...
Garlic and foods rich in iron (eg offal and red meats), plus dark green leafy vegetables.

BEE PRODUCTS

People suffering from recurrent mouth ulcers should eat more garlic and foods rich in iron. They may also benefit from taking a multinutrient supplement containing vitamins A, B2, B3, B6, B12, folic acid, vitamin C and iron. Colloidal silicic acid may be swirled around the mouth to soothe mouth ulcers and inflamed gums (gingivitis). Propolis – a substance produced by worker bees to keep the hive free from infection – has anti-bacterial and anti-inflammatory properties that can help to keep mouth ulcers at bay. Do not take if you are allergic to bees, bee products or pollen. Any mouth ulcer that lasts for longer than three weeks, or which recurs, should be investigated to exclude a mouth cancer – especially in people who smoke.

STRESS

Stress is a modern term used to describe the effects of an abnormal amount of pressure. A certain amount is essential to cope with life's challenges, but too much pressure can be harmful and lead to unpleasant physical and emotional symptoms. During stress reactions in the body, vitamin C and the vitamin B complex are quickly used up. Vitamin B is further depleted by alcohol and sugary foods, the emotional props often resorted to in difficult times. As vitamin B deficiency in itself can lead to symptoms of anxiety and irritability, a vicious circle is set up that may make anxiety and irritability worse.

Eat more...
Fresh fruit and vegetables, carbohydrates (eg breakfast cereal, wholemeal bread, rice and pasta).

Avoid or cut down on...
Sugar, salt, alcohol, caffeine and saturated fats.

STRESS-BUSTING BREAKFAST

If you are under stress, eat little and often to keep your blood sugar levels up. It is important to start the day with a low-fat, high-carbohydrate breakfast such as cereal every morning as new research shows this not only improves physical performance, but also reduces stress levels. A carbohydrate-rich breakfast provides energy for the brain at a time when biorhythms are just picking up, and is also a rich source of vitamin B1 (thiamine) which has a beneficial effect on mood, so you feel more calm, agreeable, clear-headed, elated and energetic. Eat at least five servings of fresh fruit and vegetables per day for their antioxidant properties, and cut back on sugar, salt, saturated fats and alcohol. Caffeine should be avoided as it mimics some of the effects of stress in the body to make symptoms worse.

THYROID DISORDERS

The thyroid gland produces iodine-containing hormones that help to regulate the body's metabolism. Iodine deficiency is common in the developing world and can result in swelling of the gland to form a goitre. Foods containing iodine include seafood, seaweed, dairy products and iodised salt. Some foods, such as members of the cabbage family, can interfere with iodine metabolism, especially if eaten raw, but this does not usually cause a problem where iodine intakes are adequate.

Eat more...
Iodine-rich foods, including seafood, seaweed, dairy products.

Avoid or cut down on...
Alcohol and caffeinated drinks.

UNDER AND OVERACTIVE

Those with an underactive thyroid will need to follow a healthy low-fat diet and increase levels of exercise to help reduce any weight gained before treatment started. Those with an overactive thyroid need additional B-group vitamins (found in wholegrains and dairy products) as their metabolism is working faster and has a greater need. Caffeinated drinks and alcohol may exacerbate the symptoms of both kinds of disorder.

Avoid or cut down on...
Sweets and fizzy drinks.

TOOTH DECAY

Tooth enamel is the hardest substance in the body but unfortunately it readily dissolves in acid. The bacteria which breaks down dietary carbohydrate in the mouth metabolises some sugars into lactic acid and converts others to a sticky substance that coats bacteria and sticks them to teeth as 'plaque'. If plaque is not removed, infection can penetrate enamel and rot the softer dentine beneath. A cavity forms and the weakened enamel overhead collapses away. The two ways of fighting tooth decay are to control carbohydrate intake and remove dental plaque.

CONTROLLING CARBOHYDRATES

It is not the quantity of carbohydrate eaten that is important, but the frequency with which it's consumed. Snacking on crisps, fizzy drinks and sweets between meals bathes the teeth in rich, sugary solutions that rapidly become more acid. Eating fresh fruit or cheese after a meal is much better for dental health than eating a sweet dessert. Never allow a child to fall asleep with a bottle containing milk formula, fruit juice or sweetened liquid as this will quickly destroy their first teeth. Brushing should start as soon as the first teeth show. Brush along the gum margin, not up and down. This loosens and flicks out food debris in pockets between the gums and teeth. Brushing should be done after breakfast, last thing at night and, if possible, after meals and snacks too. Older children (over 10 years) should be shown how to gently floss with dental tape. This cleans pockets between teeth but will cause damage if not done properly. Ask your dentist to demonstrate.

TRAVEL SICKNESS

Travel sickness is caused by excessive and repetitive stimulation of motion-detecting hair cells in the inner ear. When the brain receives conflicting messages from the eyes that do not match the degree of movement detected by the inner ears, this triggers motion sickness. The sickness is especially likely when travelling in a closed space such as a car, where the eyes tend to focus on a nearby object. The eyes tell the brain that the environment is stationary, while the balance organs say it is not. If there is good visual evidence of the head's position – as in cycling or skiing for example – motion does not trigger travel sickness.

An old-fashioned remedy...
Ginger is an effective traditional treatment to relieve the nausea of travel sickness. It can be drunk as an infusion (tea), or taken as capsules or tincture. For travelling, ginger tea can be carried in a flask (sweetened with honey to taste) – or crystallised ginger may be chewed.

HOW TO AVOID IT

Avoid reading when travelling. Try to sit in a position where plenty of fresh air is circulating and take regular breaks to stretch your legs. Only eat light meals just before and during travel, and avoid alcohol. Drink plenty of fluids to prevent dehydration. Try nibbling a ginger biscuit while you travel, or sucking a peppermint – both are effective natural remedies.

HEART AND BLOOD DISORDERS

ANAEMIA

Anaemia literally means 'lack of blood' and occurs when the concentration of the red blood pigment, haemoglobin, falls below normal levels. This can cause symptoms of paleness, dizziness, tiredness, lack of energy, headache and shortness of breath.

The commonest form of anaemia is due to lack of iron which is needed to produce haemoglobin in the body. Iron deficiency can result from excessive loss of blood which may need investigation, bad diet (an unbalanced vegetarian diet, for example) or poor absorption of iron from the gut. Similarly, lack of folic acid or vitamin B12 may be due to poor diet – especially an unsupplemented vegan diet – or to a condition known as pernicious anaemia in which the bowel loses its ability to absorb vitamin B12.

AN INTAKE OF IRON

A healthy intake of iron helps to prevent iron-deficiency anaemia. Foods rich in iron include seafood, especially molluscs, red meat, poultry, nuts, wholegrains, egg yolk, green vegetables and parsley. The form of iron found in red meat (haem iron) is up to ten times more easily absorbed than non-heam iron in vegetables. Meat-eaters are therefore less prone to iron-deficiency anaemia than non meat-eaters. Vitamin C helps to ensure optimum absorption of dietary iron in the gut. Oily fish – especially sardines – are a good source of vitamin B12, along with meat and dairy products. Beetroot juice is an excellent source of folic acid, as are green leafy vegetables, wholegrains, beans and nuts.

CIRCULATION PROBLEMS

A poor circulation is usually linked with hardening and furring up of the arteries. This may be caused by following a high-fat, low-fibre diet lacking fruit and vegetables rich in protective antioxidants over a long period of time. This type of diet is often also associated with obesity and lack of exercise, both of which exacerbate circulatory problems. Following a low-fat, high-fibre diet and taking regular exercise will aid weight loss and may improve circulation.

Eating more oily fish containing essential fatty acids will reduce blood stickiness so that circulation is improved. Olive oil, garlic and onions are also beneficial. Research shows that garlic powder tablets are helpful.

HEART DISEASE

It is estimated that one in three deaths from coronary heart disease (CHD) are due to an unhealthy diet. Losing excess weight by following a low-fat, low-calorie diet can reduce the risk of coronary heart disease by as much as half for those who are obese.

Aim to eat oily fish (eg salmon, herrings, sardines, mackerel) two or three times per week, as research shows this significantly reduces the risk of dying after a heart attack or stroke. Try to eat at least five servings of fruit and vegetables per day as these contain fibre, vitamins, minerals and important

Eat more...
Iron-rich foods (eg red meat, offal, seafood, poultry and dark green leafy vegetables).
Oily fish, especially sardines.
Drink more beetroot juice.

Herbal suggestion...
A dietary supplement containing extracts from the leaves of the ginkgo biloba tree has also been shown to improve circulation to the peripheries. It can improve poor memory, reduced circulation in the legs and even help erectile problems which are due to blocked arteries.

Eat more...
Fresh fruit and
vegetables, and oily fish.
Drink more tea.

Avoid or cut down on...
Alcohol and salt.

antioxidants which can lower the risk of CHD considerably.

Reduce salt intake by avoiding obviously salty foods and adding less salt during cooking or at the table. Research shows that cutting back on salt helps to reduce the risk of CHD and you can always obtain flavour from herbs, spices and black pepper instead of salt – it's just a matter of getting used to the idea.

Interesting new research also shows that those who drink tea are 50% less likely to develop coronary heart disease or have a fatal heart attack than non tea-drinkers. Tea is a rich source of protective antioxidant flavonoids – the other main dietary sources are onions and apples. Taking high dose vitamin E supplements (400 i.u. daily) was recently shown to reduce the risk of coronary heart disease by 75%.

Those who have a high intake of vitamin C (including the use of supplements) also have up to a 40% lower risk of CHD, while taking garlic tablets can reduce the risk of CHD by up to 25%. It is also important to exercise regularly, keep alcohol intake within safe limits and stop smoking.

Eat more...
Oatmeal, garlic and oily
fish.

HIGH CHOLESTEROL

Most of the cholesterol in the circulation is made by the liver – cholesterol in foods such as egg yolk actually has little effect on circulating blood cholesterol levels. There are two types of cholesterol in the bloodstream. Low-density lipoprotein (LDL) cholesterol is linked with hardening and furring up of artery walls (atherosclerosis), high blood pressure and coronary heart disease (CHD). High-density lipoprotein (HDL) cholesterol protects against atherosclerosis and CHD by transporting LDL cholesterol away from the arteries and back towards the liver for metabolism.

Research shows that as HDL cholesterol levels rise by 1%, the risk of CHD falls by 2%. If the level of LDL cholesterol is increased however, this increases the risk of CHD. Until recently, eating too much saturated fat was thought to be the sole culprit in raising blood cholesterol levels and triggering atherosclerosis. Researchers now increasingly believe that it is eating too much omega-6 polyunsaturated fatty acids (mainly found in vegetable oils) and not enough omega-3 polyunsaturated fatty acids (mainly found in fish oils) that increases the risk of atherosclerosis. This is especially true if your intake of antioxidants (eg vitamins C, E, beta-carotene and mineral selenium) is low.

A HIGH-FIBRE DIET

People with high cholesterol levels are advised to increase the amount of exercise they take, to follow a diet that is relatively low in fat but which supplies good amounts of omega-3 fatty acids (eg oily fish, walnuts) and monounsaturated fatty acids (eg olive and rapeseed oils). It is also important to increase fibre intake and to eat at least five servings of fruit and vegetables per day. Foods rich in soluble fibre such as oatmeal help to reduce absorption of fat from the gut. Garlic contains a substance, allicin, that has been shown to reduce harmful LDL cholesterol by as much as 12%. It has such a powerful effect that in Germany, garlic tablets containing the equivalent of 4 grams of fresh cloves are available on prescription to treat high blood cholesterol levels and high blood pressure.

NERVOUS SYSTEM DISORDERS

DEPRESSION

Depression is a low mood brought on by an imbalance of various chemicals in the brain. In some cases, this imbalance may be related to diet.

When carbohydrate is eaten, it triggers the release of a brain chemical called serotonin, which lifts mood and also helps to signal that you have eaten enough. In people with a low-carbohydrate, high-fat diet, serotonin levels may be lower than normal so their mood is naturally depressed.

CHOCOLATE CRAVINGS

Interestingly, chocolate contains tryptophan, a chemical which is converted to serotonin in the body, so cravings for chocolate that can occur during times of stress and when mood is low may, in fact, be a form of self medication.

To reduce depression, follow a low-fat, high-carbohydrate diet. Try increasing your intake of:

- Wholegrain bread.

- Wholegrain cereals such as porridge, brown rice, pearl barley, oatcakes, unsweetened breakfast cereals.

- Root vegetables such as carrots, parsnips, turnip, swede, potatoes.

- Cruciferous plants such as broccoli, cauliflower, Chinese leaves.

- Legumes such as lentils, kidney beans, soya.

- Fresh fruit.

- Ready to eat semi-dried fruit (apricots, dates, figs, prunes).

- Oily fish and cheese which contain tryptophan.

- Foods rich in vitamin B6 (which helps production of serotonin) such as yeast extract, wholegrains, soya, walnuts, oily fish, green leafy vegetables, avocado, bananas, walnuts.

- Foods rich in vitamin C, which also helps production of serotonin (citrus fruits, kiwi fruit, blackcurrants, strawberries, sweet peppers).

Eat more...
Fresh fruit and vegetables. Food high in carbohydrate (eg bread, potatoes).

Avoid or cut down on...
Alcohol, fatty foods and sugary foods.

Herbal suggestion...
St John's wort is an effective remedy for mild to moderate depression.

Try limiting your intake of fatty foods, as well as foods that are both fatty and stodgy (eg doughnuts, cream buns) and confectionery. It is also important to keep your alcohol, salt and caffeine intake to a minimum and to increase levels of exercise to at least 20 minutes, three times per week and preferably every day. This will reduce feelings of stress and tension and promote feelings of overall wellbeing. If, after several months, there is no improvement, see your doctor or try discussing your feelings with a family member or friend.

FOOD CRAVINGS

Cravings for certain foods may be linked with stress and depression. Cravings for non-food substances – known as pica – can also occur, especially during pregnancy. Some people believe that these cravings are the body's way of obtaining a nutrient that is in short supply. Pica, for example, is often linked with iron deficiency. Cravings for chocolate and stodgy foods may help to lift depression by triggering production of the brain chemical, serotonin. Certainly, low levels of serotonin in the hypothalamus have been linked experimentally to overeating brought on by carbohydrate craving.

SNACK ATTACK

Unfortunately, what usually happens when we experience a craving for carbohydrate is that we snack on foods that are also high in fat, such as doughnuts, sausage rolls, cream cakes or crisps, which leads to an unhealthy diet and excess weight gain.

Try to limit the bad effects of food cravings by eating non-fatty carbohydrate-rich foods such as rice, wholegrain bread, muesli, pasta and potatoes. It also helps to take brisk exercise which stimulates production of brain chemicals that reduce cravings.

TENSION HEADACHES

Tension headaches are common and feel like a severe, continuous pressure on both sides of the head which may seem to centre over the top of the skull, over the back of the head or above both eyes. Some tension headaches feel like a tight, constricting band, while others are more like a non-specific ache.

Tension headaches are linked to changes in blood flow within the brain as well as stress or tension in the neck and scalp muscles. They can be brought on by feelings of excess pressure, physical fatigue, lack of sleep, stressful emotions such as anger or frustration, and even missed meals. Eating little and often throughout the day helps to maintain blood sugar levels so tension headaches are less likely. Cut back on excessive intakes of caffeine, salt and alcohol and avoid dehydration by drinking plenty of fluids – especially in hot weather and after exercise.

BETTER POSTURE

Better posture will help to alleviate tension. Try not to stoop when standing or sitting, and concentrate on keeping the back straight, shoulders square and abdomen lightly pulled in. This reduces stress by helping you to breathe correctly. Avoid folding your arms tightly and shake arms and hands regularly to

Eat more...
Brown rice, pasta, wholegrain bread.

Eat more...
Fresh fruit and vegetables.
Drink plenty of water.

Avoid or cut down on...
Caffeine, salt and alcohol.

An old-fashioned remedy...

To banish tension headaches, add 4 drops of chamomile or lavender essential oils to running bathwater, lie back, close your eyes, and relax! If possible, do away with the glare of overhead electric light.

relieve tension in the upper limbs and shoulders. Avoid clenching or grinding your teeth as this tenses jaw muscles. Relaxing exercises will also help to relieve symptoms.

INSOMNIA

Insomnia is one of the commonest disorders there is. Sufferers either have difficulty in falling asleep, or maintaining sleep, or both, and when they do manage to nod off, the quality of sleep is not restorative. Most people have suffered from insomnia at some stage of their life – usually when they are worried about something or suffering from stress. Hunger can also be the cause – it is a primitive alerting response and so the more hungry you are, the more difficult it is to ignore it and fall asleep. Avoid hunger pangs – even when on a weight-loss diet – by filling up with healthy wholefoods with plenty of unrefined complex carbohydrates (eg cereals, bread, pasta), fruit and vegetables. Eat your evening meal before 7 pm and resist late-night snacks, especially of rich food.

A WARM, MILKY DRINK

Also avoid over-indulgence in substances that interfere with sleep such as caffeine (found in coffee, tea, chocolate, cola drinks) nicotine and alcohol – although alcohol may help you fall asleep, you are likely to have a disturbed sleep once the drugged effect has worn off. A warm, milky drink just before going to bed will help you to relax – hot milk with cinnamon or nutmeg is better than shop-bought chocolate drinks that may contain some caffeine.

Soothing herbal teas can also help you sleep – try infusions of limeflower, lemon balm, fennel, rosehips, passionflower, nutmeg, cinnamon or chamomile. Don't drink too much fluid in the evening however – a full bladder is guaranteed to disturb your rest.

MIGRAINE

As any migraine-sufferers will tell you, a migraine is far worse than a headache. The pain is generally much worse on one side of the head and often centres around one eye. Abdominal symptoms such as loss of appetite, nausea, vomiting, dislike of food, constipation or diarrhoea may also occur. One in ten migraine sufferers also experience visual disturbances.

CHEMICAL CHANGES

The exact cause of migraine is not fully understood. Attacks seem to be linked to chemical changes in the blood vessel walls and nerve cells within the skull.

Eat more...
Cereals, bread and pasta.
Fresh fruit and vegetables.
Have a warm, milky drink before bed.

Avoid...
Rich food and late-night snacks.
Too much alcohol.

Herbal suggestions...
Try taking St John's wort or valerian supplements daily to treat your insomnia.
Sprinkle a couple of drops of lavender oil on your pillow last thing at night.

Eat more...
Citrus fruit.

Avoid...
Any well-known triggers, such as cheese or chocolate.

Migraine is often triggered by dietary factors such as:

■ Tyramine (found in bananas, beans, avocado, cheese, chicken livers, yogurt, sour cream, nuts).

■ Phenylethylamine (found in chocolate, some cheeses, red wine).

■ Sodium nitrite (found in food colourings, preservatives, processed meats and fish).

■ Monosodium glutamate (found in Chinese food, processed meats, frozen dinners, canned soups, soy sauce, seasonings).

■ Alcohol.

■ Caffeine.

■ Artificial sweeteners.

■ Hunger, fasting, delayed or insufficient food.

Keeping a food and migraine diary can help to pinpoint the dietary causes of migraine so that the culprits can be avoided. The success rate of migraine management through diet is disappointing however, as dietary factors are important in less than 20% of sufferers.

Eat more...
Fresh fruit and vegetables, nuts, seeds, oily fish and carbohydrate-rich foods.

Avoid or cut down on
Fatty foods, alcohol.

MULTIPLE SCLEROSIS

Multiple sclerosis (MS) is a neurological disease in which the fatty, myelin sheaths surrounding and protecting nerve fibres in the brain and spinal cord become inflamed and degenerate. The exact cause is unknown, although lack of the mineral selenium has been suggested. One study found that those with MS had low levels of an important antioxidant enzyme, glutathione peroxidase. When their intakes of vitamins C, E and selenium were increased the activity of this enzyme increased five-fold.

LOW-FAT, HIGH-CARB DIET
It is important to eat a low-fat, carbohydrate-rich diet to help overcome the fatigue that can accompany MS, and keep alcohol intake to within recommended limits. Omega-3 fish oils may be beneficial.

RESPIRATORY COMPLAINTS

ASTHMA

Asthma is a long-term, inflammatory disease of the lungs. It is becoming increasingly common in the western world, with the number of people affected rising by 5% each year, probably due to chemical pollutants in the air we breathe. An asthma attack is precipitated when the lining of the airways becomes red and swollen and produces increased amounts of mucus. This triggers a spasm, producing symptoms of coughing, wheezing and shortness of breath. Some people find that certain foods trigger their asthma, especially those containing artificial additives. Peanuts can also trigger a serious attack in those with a nut allergy.

DIETARY IMBALANCE?

Some researchers believe that the increased incidence of chronic inflammatory diseases such as asthma is linked with an imbalance of dietary fats. Dietary polyunsaturated fatty acids are of two main types: omega-3, derived from fish oils and omega-6, derived from vegetable oils. Ideally, we need a balanced intake of the two types, but the average diet now contains seven times more omega-6s than omega-3s.

Fish oils contain anti-inflammatory substances and seem to protect against asthma. Aim to eat oily fish (eg salmon, mackerel, herrings, sardines) two or three times per week or take an omega-3 fish oil supplement. Asthma has also been linked with low dietary levels of selenium, magnesium or B6 in some studies, while those with high intakes of antioxidants such as vitamin C (eg citrus fruits, kiwi fruit, berry fruits) and vitamin E (eg wheatgerm, avocado, nuts and seeds) seem to have the lowest risk.

CATARRH

Catarrh – or excess mucus – is a thick, sticky secretion produced by the lining of the nose and sinuses. Mucus lubricates the respiratory tract, moistens inhaled air and traps smoke and other foreign particles to keep them from reaching the lungs. A certain amount of mucus is therefore desirable. If excess is produced however, it can lead to a constant irritating cough as secretions drip down behind the nose, a blocked or runny nose, chestiness, bringing up thick phlegm and sensations of heaviness around the sinuses – all of which are very uncomfortable.

DIETARY POINTERS

In some cases, catarrh may be linked with sensitivity to dairy and wheat products. Foods which may help the condition include onions and garlic, as they act as natural decongestants. Spices, such as chili, ginger, horseradish, mustard and black pepper, stimulate watery secretions that help to clear catarrh away and aid clear breathing.

Drink plenty of fluids and increase your intake of vitamin C (eg citrus fruits, kiwi fruit, berry fruits) to help damp down inflammation.

Eat more...
Oily fish, including salmon, mackerel, herring and sardines.
Food high in vitamins C and E.

Eat more...
Vitamin C-rich foods (eg citrus fruits), onions and garlic.

An old-fashioned remedy...

Steam inhalation can help to liquefy catarrh secretions. Add essential oils of menthol, eucalyptus, cinnamon, or pine to your bowl to provide additional decongestant qualities.

Eat more...
Brazil nuts, garlic, breakfast cereals, oily fish and fresh fruit and vegetables.

COLDS

As many as 200 different viruses can infect the upper respiratory tract to cause symptoms of the common cold such as sore throat, headache, runny nose, coughing, sneezing and mild fever. To boost immunity and reduce the risk of developing symptoms on exposure to a cold virus, eat at least five servings of fresh fruit, vegetables or salad stuff per day. Symptomatic viral infections are more likely in those lacking selenium, as high selenium levels seem to interfere with viral reproduction. The richest dietary source of selenium is Brazil nuts. Oily fish (eg salmon, mackerel, herring, sardines) contain essential fatty acids important for good immune function. For those who don't like eating fish, consider taking an omega-3 or evening primrose oil supplement.

ANTIVIRAL FOODS

Garlic has a natural antiviral action, as does extracts of the herb Echinacea. A high intake of vitamin C damps down inflammation and may reduce symptoms if a cold appears. Drink plenty of fluids and increase your intake of zinc, which may help to shorten the duration of a cold. Good dietary sources of zinc include red meat, eggs and oysters. Recent research has found that only one in six of those eating a cereal breakfast every day developed a cold over the 10-week study period, compared with one in three of those who ate a cereal breakfast less than once a week.

Eat more...
Vitamin C-rich foods (eg citrus fruits), oily fish, monounsaturated fats (eg olive oil) and garlic.

Avoid or cut back on...
Saturated fat.

EAR PROBLEMS

The ears are the organs of hearing and balance. Each is divided into three parts: the outer ear, middle ear and inner ear, all of which can become infected. Infection of the middle ear (otitis media) is common in childhood and may result from excess mucus that can lead to glue ear and impaired hearing. Breastfeeding helps to protect against glue ear as the sucking action involved strengthens the mechanism that allows the middle ear to drain properly.

CUT BACK ON FAT

In later life, some forms of deafness are due to hardening and furring up of the arteries which is linked with dietary intakes of fat. To guard against this, follow a low-fat diet, cut back on saturated (animal) fats, but ensure a good intake of omega-3 essential fatty acids (eg fish oils) and monounsaturated fats (eg olive and rapeseed oils) which help to maintain healthy cholesterol balance in the circulation. Garlic also helps to lower levels of harmful cholesterol. Hearing problems should always be taken seriously and medical advice sought.

Eat more...
Foods rich in the B-group vitamins and vitamin C.

HAYFEVER

Hayfever is an allergic response triggered by a sensitivity to plant pollens or fungal spores. Symptoms include itchy, red, streaming eyes, runny nose, sneezing and stuffiness. In some people, hayfever can bring on allergic asthma or eczema – especially where skin has come into direct contact with pollen. A diet rich in B-group vitamins may help to reduce symptoms. Vitamin C (eg citrus fruits, berry fruits, kiwi fruit) also acts as a natural antihistamine and damps down inflammation.

PROTECTION AGAINST POLLEN

Some practitioners also recommend chewing lumps of honeycomb as a chewing gum throughout winter and late spring as a preventative. Alternatively, eating honey produced from local bees can help to desensitise sufferers. The simplest thing you can do to protect against hayfever symptoms is to avoid heavy exposure to pollen. Try to stay indoors when pollen counts are highest, between 7–9 am and 3–7 pm. Avoid city streets during the afternoon as hayfever symptoms worsen on exposure to traffic fumes. Use a negative ioniser indoors to remove airborne particles such as pollen and dust. Put a small dab of petroleum jelly just inside your nostrils to trap pollen. Keep bedroom windows shut to avoid sleeping in a pollen trap at night.

INFLUENZA

Eat more...
Fresh fruit and vegetables, garlic, oily fish and wholefoods.

Influenza is a viral disease that attacks the upper respiratory system and sometimes the lungs as well. Symptoms are initially similar to those of a cold with dry cough, sore throat and runny nose. These symptoms then get significantly worse and are accompanied by chills, fever, headache, loss of appetite, fatigue and widespread muscle aches and pains. Immunisation helps to protect against infection for those at risk of complications, such as the elderly. A wholefood diet also helps boost immune function to protect against viral diseases such as influenza. Fresh fruit and vegetables supply vitamins, minerals, antioxidants and certain non-nutrient substances (phytochemicals) important for immune function.

RESEARCH RESULTS

Research involving elderly people showed that those taking multivitamins for one year had better immune function, mounted a better response to influenza vaccination, and had half as many days ill with infections (23 days in the year) compared with those not taking multivitamin supplements (48 days illness).

It is best to follow a low-fat diet with less omega-6 polyunsaturated fatty acids derived from vegetable oils and more omega-3 polyunsaturated fatty acids derived from oily fish. Ideally, the body needs a balanced intake of omega-3s and omega-6s. Those who don't like eating fish should consider taking an omega-3 supplement. Evening primrose oil capsules also supply important essential fatty acids. If you develop influenza, drink plenty of warm fluids and try to eat simple, soothing foods such as soup, yogurt or scrambled eggs on toast made from wholemeal bread. Sucking ice cubes will help you feel cool and relieve a sore throat. Garlic has antiviral and decongestant properties that may help.

SKIN PROBLEMS

Eat more...
Fresh fruit and vegetables, pulses, nuts, seeds and wholegrain cereals.

Drink plenty of...
Water.

Avoid or cut down on...
Tea, coffee and alcohol; sweet, rich or fatty foods.

An old-fashioned remedy...

To give blocked pores a deep cleanse, try mixing a little dried lavender, yarrow and elderflowers in a large bowl and adding boiling water. With a towel over your head, lower your face over the steam for about 5 minutes at a time.

ACNE

Acne is a well-known and immediately recognisable skin problem normally associated with teenagers, eight out of ten of whom are affected by it to some extent. It mainly affects the oily (sebaceous) glands within the hair follicles of skin on the face, outer ear canal, back, chest and groin, resulting in an outbreak of angry-looking pustules (spots). Severe outbreaks can be uncomfortable, as well as distressing.

EXCESS GREASE

The onset of acne is linked with excess production of skin grease and the consequent blockage of oil-gland ducts. These secretions increase the risk of infection with bacteria, and cause inflammation as enzymes produced by the bacteria break the grease down into fatty acids and inflammatory chemicals. The oily glands respond to hormone changes occurring at puberty. Most cases are short-lived and improve within a year or two, but in 1% of men and 5% of women, symptoms still occur over the age of 40.

ACNE AND DIET

There is no evidence that acne is solely caused by bad diet, although poor nutrition can certainly make symptoms worse. In some people, acne is exacerbated by drinking excess tea, coffee or alcohol. Lack of zinc, selenium, or vitamins A, B or E has been linked with acne in some cases, as has lack of essential fatty acids which are found in nuts, seeds and wholegrain cereals. Premenstrual acne has been helped by increasing intake of vitamin B6. A healthy, wholefood diet full of fresh fruit and vegetables, pulses, seeds and wholegrain cereals helps to supply vitamins and minerals needed to damp down inflammation and fight infection.

Eat more...
Oily fish.

Avoid or cut down on...
Any foods that trigger your eczema, such as milk, cheese and eggs.

Herbal suggestion...
Evening primrose oil contains gammalinolenic acid, an essential fatty acid that may help to reduce itching and dryness in those whose eczema is linked with essential fatty acid deficiency.

ECZEMA

An estimated one in 10 people suffer from eczema. Symptoms vary from mild to severe and can include dry, scaly, thickened skin, redness, itching, blisters, weeping sores, crusting and flaky scalp. Eczema commonly affects skin on the hands, inside the elbows or behind the knees but may be found anywhere on the body.

DAIRY LINK?

Some people with eczema find their symptoms are brought on, or made worse, by certain foods such as eggs and milk or dairy products. Not all sufferers can link their symptoms to food allergy, however. Eczema is most common in babies between the ages of two to eighteen months who are not being breast fed. This may be linked to an allergy to cow's milk proteins or to lack of certain essential fatty acids, although many formula milks are now supplemented with these. Fish oils have also been shown to help damp down inflammatory conditions such as eczema.

HIVES

Hives is an allergic skin condition sometimes also known as nettle rash or urticaria. Raised white or yellow lumps appear on the skin, surrounded by red inflammation. These burn at first, and then become intensely itchy. If the intestinal tract is affected, vomiting and diarrhoea may also occur. Symptoms usually last for a few hours but occasionally persist for longer.

THE CAUSES OF HIVES

Hives is caused by a release of histamine in the skin – a chemical that triggers a powerful inflammatory response with dilatation of blood vessels and leakage of fluid from the circulation into the tissues. It is often triggered by allergic food reactions (eg to shellfish, strawberries, peanuts), sensitivity to insect venom (eg wasp or bee stings) or to drugs (eg penicillin). It can also be caused by exposure to heat, cold, sunlight or severe stress. Recurrent hives may be associated with a tooth abscess or other bacterial infection. If the symptoms are accompanied by facial swelling, collapse or difficulty breathing, seek emergency medical treatment. Vitamin C has an antihistamine action and may help to reduce symptoms. Evening primrose oil also has an anti-inflammatory effect.

Avoid...
Any foods that trigger hives, such as shellfish, strawberries or peanuts.

Herbal suggestion...
A tea made from 3 tsp agrimony, 2 tsp meadowsweet and 1 tsp wood betony may help the condition if it is food-related. Simply mix the herbs, make an infusion and sip before meals.

Instant treatment...

Eat vitamin C-rich foods such as citrus fruit, kiwi fruit, chilli peppers, red and yellow peppers, cabbage and oranges.

PSORIASIS

Psoriasis is a long-term scaling disease of the skin which affects around 2% of the population. At its worst, it can be severely debilitating. The condition occurs when new skin cells start producing around ten times faster than normal, and consequently push up to the surface before the old ones have naturally worn away. The result is characteristic raised, red patches that are often covered with dead cells forming fine, silvery scales.

DIFFERENT FORMS

There are several different forms of psoriasis. The most common, plaque psoriasis, affects nine out of ten sufferers. Patches appear on the trunk and limbs, especially on the elbows, knees, hands, umbilicus, over the sacrum and on the scalp. Fingernails may become pitted, thickened or separate from their nail beds. Between 10–20% of people with psoriasis also develop inflamed joints, known as psoriatic arthropathy. Some evidence suggests that eating a healthy diet can help. A high intake of carrots, tomatoes, fresh fruit and foods rich in beta-carotene appears to protect against psoriasis, and a diet rich in fish oils has been shown to reduce the risk of similar inflammatory diseases by up to 50%. Drinking excess alcohol can make psoriasis worse in some people.

Eat more...
Fresh fruit, carrots, tomatoes and foods rich in beta-carotene.

Avoid or cut down on...
Alcohol.

Herbal suggestion...
For a scalp rinse, an infusion of rosemary applied to the scalp after shampooing will help ease itchiness.

WOMEN'S ISSUES

Drink more...
Cranberry juice.

Herbal suggestions...
Take herbal supplements containing extracts of dandelion, bearberry and peppermint.

CYSTITIS

Cystitis is an inflammation or infection of the bladder. Symptoms vary in severity and can include a burning sensation on passing urine, an increase in the frequency or urgency with which you need to pass urine, low abdominal pain, backache and urine that may be cloudy, blood-stained or smell unpleasant.

FLUSH WITH FLUIDS

As soon as symptoms start, drink 600 ml of water. Then drink 300 ml every 20 minutes for the next three hours, if you can. It's best to drink water but chamomile tea, yarrow infusion, milk or other bland substances will do. Avoid normal tea, coffee, fruit juice and alcohol as these can irritate inflamed tissues. Fluids help to flush the urinary system through and you will soon start passing urine regularly. This may sting at first but will improve as you continue to empty your bladder.

Seek medical advice if symptoms last longer than a day or keep recurring, if you are pregnant, your urine is cloudy or stained with blood or you develop a fever or uncontrollable shakes. Drinking 300 ml cranberry juice per day has been shown to almost halve the risk of cystitis by preventing bacteria from sticking to the walls of the urinary tract. Herbal supplements containing extracts of dandelion, bearberry and peppermint may also prevent recurrent cystitis.

Eat more...
Soya bean products, celery, fennel, Chinese leaves and other green or yellow vegetables, nuts, seeds, wholegrain cereals and fish.

Avoid or cut down on...
Sugar, salt, tea, coffee and caffeinated fizzy drinks.

Herbal suggestion...
Evening primrose oil contains essential fatty acids that act as building blocks for making sex hormones.

MENOPAUSE

The menopause signals the end of a woman's fertility and her monthly menstrual cycle. It is triggered when the ovaries start to run out of eggs so that oestrogen levels fall. This produces symptoms of oestrogen withdrawal, which may include hot flushes, night sweats, vaginal dryness, urinary problems and mood swings. The three main ways through which diet and nutrition affects hormone balance are:

■ The types of fat and fibre eaten.

■ The natural plant hormones present in food.

■ The amount of vitamins, minerals and trace elements obtained.

Researchers have found that a high-fat, low-fibre diet is associated with relatively high levels of circulating oestrogen. Women who have followed a lifelong high-fat, low-fibre diet are more likely to have menopausal symptoms of oestrogen withdrawal – their tissues are used to a relatively high level of circulating hormones, and they therefore seem less able to tolerate the menopausal drop. Suddenly switching to a healthier, low-fat, high-fibre diet around the time of the menopause may make symptoms of oestrogen withdrawal worse however, by lowering the oestrogen levels even further, unless the daily diet is rich in natural plant hormones.

GOOD AND BAD FOODS

To combat the adverse effects of the menopause, aim to increase intakes of soya bean products, celery, fennel, Chinese leaves and other green or yellow vegetables. Eat more nuts and seeds, wholegrain cereals and fish. Cut back on sugar, salt, tea, coffee and caffeinated fizzy drinks. If hot flushes are a problem, steer clear of spicy foods and convenience foods. Avoid alcohol and cigarettes which lower oestrogen levels further.

PREGNANCY GUIDE

PICA

Pica is a type of craving in which a person – often a pregnant woman – feels a strong urge to eat non-food substances such as clay, chalk, earth or coal. Some people believe that these cravings are the body's way of signalling that certain important nutrients are in short supply. Certainly, pica is often a symptom of iron deficiency, and if it occurs in pregnancy iron supplements are prescribed. The urge to eat non-food substances should always be resisted, as they may cause harm to the developing baby. If pica occurs, seek advice from your midwife, family doctor or obstetrician.

Avoid...
All non-food substances, even if the cravings are very strong!

SPINA BIFIDA

Spina bifida is a congenital abnormality known as a neural tube defect. Research shows that in many cases, neural tube defects may be prevented if a woman increases her intake of folic acid just before the time of conception and for at least the first 12 weeks of pregnancy. Folic acid is routinely given to pregnant women as a supplement because of its important benefits when a cell divides in two, and its genetic material is duplicated. If folate levels are low, dividing cells become larger than normal and are therefore more likely to contain abnormal chromosomes which may lead to conditions such as spina bifida. Women planning a baby should increase their intake of folic acid before trying to conceive. The recommended dose is a daily supplement of 400 µg daily. Women who have previously conceived a child with a neural tube defect should take at least ten times more folic acid (4–5 mg).

Eat more...
Fortified foods (eg cereals and bread).
Naturally folate-rich foods (eg green leafy vegetables).
Oily fish – especially sardines.

Where to find folate

Good sources of folic acid include fortified foods such as cereals and breads, dark green leafy vegetables (eg spinach, broccoli, kale, spring greens), green beans, cooked black-eye beans and baked beans. There are also useful amounts in cauliflower, potatoes, wholemeal bread and citrus fruits such as oranges. Don't boil vegetables for too long. Eat them crisp – or even raw – as prolonged boiling destroys much of the folic acid in green leaves.

Vitamin B12

Mothers with low blood levels of vitamin B12 also have a greater risk of conceiving a baby with spina bifida, whether or not they have a good folic acid intake. Foods rich in vitamin B12 include oily fish – especially sardines – meats, eggs and dairy products.

Eat more...
Of the things you fancy, little and often. Peppermint tea, ginger and fennel, to settle the stomach.

Avoid...
Strong-smelling foods and fatty foods.

MORNING SICKNESS

Many women suffer feelings of nausea and dizziness in the first months of pregnancy, especially on getting up in the morning. The hormonal changes taking place in the body are thought to be the cause. Nibbling a dry cracker or a ginger biscuit before getting out of bed might help with morning sickness. If you feel nauseous at other times of the day, try these suggestions:

■ Wear comfortable clothes with loose waistbands.

■ Eat little and often, rather than the normal three meals a day.

■ Avoid any foods and smells that bring on the nausea.

■ Remember, the feelings of nausea won't last forever – they normally disappear around week 12–14.

Eat more...
Wholefoods, fish, wholegrain cereals, nuts and seeds.

Avoid or cut down on...
Salt, alcohol, caffeine.

Herbal suggestion...
Try taking 3 g oil of evening primrose every day for at least three months.

PREMENSTRUAL SYNDROME

Premenstrual syndrome (PMS) is a common and distressing problem affecting as many as one in two women. Emotional and physical symptoms begin up to two weeks before a period and usually stop quickly once bleeding occurs. Common symptoms include depression, anxiety, irritability, poor concentration, tiredness, bingeing, bloating, breast tenderness, headache and backache.

HORMONE IMBALANCE?

PMS is thought to be caused by a relative imbalance between the two female hormones, oestrogen and progesterone. Some research suggests that progesterone can't work properly when blood sugar levels are low, so nibbling regular carbohydrate snacks every 3 hours may help to reduce symptoms. Evening primrose oil contains hormone building blocks and will help to even out hormonal imbalances, but needs to be taken at doses of up to 3 g a day for at least three months before an effect may be noticed. Foods containing calcium, magnesium, iron, folic acid, vitamin E and the B-group vitamins, especially vitamin B6, are important. Eating more fish, wholegrain cereals, nuts and seeds may be helpful, as will cutting down on intakes of salt, alcohol and caffeine.

recipes suitable for special diets

HIGH-FIBRE DIET

GLUTEN-FREE DIET

LOW-FAT DIET

NUT-FREE DIET

LOW-CHOLESTEROL DIET

LOW-CALORIE DIET

DAIRY PRODUCE-FREE DIET

DIABETIC DIET

index